W9-BCN-407

The Fossil Book

Books by
CARROLL LANE FENTON *and* MILDRED ADAMS FENTON

THE FOSSIL BOOK

GIANTS OF GEOLOGY

THE ROCK BOOK

MOUNTAINS

ROCKS AND THEIR STORIES

THE LAND WE LIVE ON

OUR CHANGING WEATHER

Books by
CARROLL LANE FENTON

OUR AMAZING EARTH

OUR LIVING WORLD

Diplodocus, a plant-eating dinosaur 87 feet long, had a slender neck and tail. This restoration of the reptile as it looked during life is based on skeletons found in northeastern Utah.

46802

THE
FOSSIL BOOK

A Record of Prehistoric Life

CARROLL LANE FENTON

and

MILDRED ADAMS FENTON

discarded

Garden City, New York

DOUBLEDAY & COMPANY, INC.

560
F367f

Merner - Pfeiffer Library
enne Lee Wesleyan
Athens, Tennessee

LIBRARY OF CONGRESS CATALOG CARD NUMBER 58-13278

COPYRIGHT © 1958 BY CARROLL LANE FENTON AND MILDRED ADAMS FENTON

ALL RIGHTS RESERVED

PRINTED IN THE UNITED STATES OF AMERICA

JUL 27 58

Acknowledgments

This book surveys the realm of fossils from the earliest plantlike organisms to beasts and birds that lived a few centuries ago. Only man is omitted, not because his story is unimportant, but because it is already told in excellent books mentioned in Chapter XXXIV.

A survey as extensive as this goes far beyond the firsthand knowledge of authors whose research has been limited to algae and early invertebrates. We therefore have drawn material from a wide array of technical articles and monographs, as well as from textbooks and reference works. Few of these can be mentioned in Chapter XXXIV, but we want to acknowledge our debt.

Chapters and parts of chapters have been discussed with many paleontologists. Those who have read and criticized actual manuscript include Drs. Erling Dorf (plants), Kenneth E. Caster (all invertebrates), Bobb Schaeffer (agnaths and fish), Edwin E. Colbert (amphibians and reptiles), and Glenn L. Jepsen (birds and mammals). Mrs. Rachel Nichols guided us to many important books and papers in the Osborn Library of the American Museum of Natural History.

Most of our photographs of invertebrate fossils—and some vertebrates—were made at the United States National Museum, where we were helped by Drs. Ray S. Bassler, G. Arthur Cooper, C. Lewis Gazin, David Dunkle, John B. Reeside, and Roland W. Brown. Dr. Ellis Yochelson provided a Permian snail with coloration preserved, and Dr. A. R. Palmer provided photographs and information about the remarkably preserved insects of the Mojave Desert. Drs. Samuel Welles, R. A. Stirton, and R. W. Chaney selected specimens for photography at the University of California; Drs. Erling Dorf and B. F. Howell did the same at Princeton. Dr. Henry A. Andrews, of Washington University, provided negatives of sections through Pennsylvanian plants. Dr. Frank M. Carpenter, of Harvard, lent negatives showing fossil insects and sent data on specimens. Color photographs of restorations (dioramas) in the Exhibit Museum of the University of Michigan were furnished by Irving G. Reimann, the museum's director.

Drawings of actual fossils were made from specimens, photographs, and published figures. Most of the drawings themselves are new, but some are borrowed. The latter include figures of brachiopods from Volume VIII of the *Palaeontology of New York,* and of echinoids from *Mesozoic and Cenozoic Echinodermata of the United States,* by W. B. Clark and M. W. Twitchell, published as Monograph 54 of the U. S. Geological Survey.

Restorations of invertebrates are based chiefly upon our own studies. Those of vertebrates embody the work of Knight, Horsfall, Price, Germann, and other artists, and of such paleontologists as Osborn, Matthew, Scott, Case, Williston, Merriam, Stock, Simpson, and Romer. Restorations of plants reveal our debt to Seward, Wieland, Goldring, and other authorities.

CARROLL LANE FENTON
MILDRED ADAMS FENTON

February, 1958

ABOUT ILLUSTRATIONS AND THEIR CAPTIONS

The illustrations in this book portray the progress of life upon our planet. They also enable readers to recognize and understand fossils they find or see in museums. For both purposes, the caption above or below each picture is as important as the drawing or photograph itself.

Captions like those in Chapter I require little comment. They tell what each fossil shows and may or may not give its age and the region in which it was found. Most of them do not mention size, though it is indicated by the magnification of spores, fungi, and cells in stems. Geologic and geographic data are included only when the fossils are characteristic of certain formations or regions.

Most of the remaining captions are more concerned with detail and include the following information:

1. The name of the genus or species to which the specimen belongs. If the specific name is given, it is followed by the name or initials of its author; e.g., *Caryocrinites ornatus* Say or *Cribrillina verrucosa* C. and B.
2. Geologic age, as Silurian or late Ordovician. In many captions, this is followed (in parentheses) by the name of the series, group, or formation in which the particular species is found. Thus *Caryocrinites ornatus* Say is of Silurian age and is found in rocks of the Niagaran group.
3. Geographic range. Some fossils have been found at only one place, such as Burgess Pass, British Columbia, or Florissant, in Colorado. Others are found at many places in extensive regions—New York, the Atlantic Coastal Plain, and so on. These regions are mentioned in captions unless precise localities are important.
4. Size. This is given when it seems helpful but omitted when it is not. Thus the reader probably will want to know that *Stylonurus* was 54 inches long, and that *Brontops* stood 8 feet 4 inches high, but he does not need to be reminded that each drawing of a brachiopod is natural size.

   Most dimensions are given in feet and inches, but some are expressed in millimeters. (A millimeter is about one twenty-fifth of an inch.) Some illustrations are merely marked "enlarged," but for others the scale of enlargement is given. A drawing marked x 4, for example, has dimensions four times those of the actual specimen.

Paleontologists may wonder why *early, middle* (or *mid-*) and *late* are used to subdivide periods, rather than *lower, middle,* and *upper.* The reason is that we are more concerned with the history of life than with stratigraphy. In other words, we tell when a given organism dwelt upon earth, not where its remains are found in a sequence of beds or formations. Thus a certain fossil may be found in *lower* Devonian rocks, but it lived during *early* Devonian times and is of *early* Devonian age. To use *early* in our text but *lower* in our caption would be needlessly confusing, and to use *lower* in both might obscure the historical sequence we want to emphasize.

Contents

Contents

Color Plates

CHAPTER I

Tales Told by the Dead

A<small>S AGE GOES</small> in earth history, hills west of Rockford, Iowa, are young. Barely 12,000 years have passed since the prairie of which they are part was laid bare by the melting of glacial ice. The hills themselves took shape still later under the wear of rain and rills that ran to the nearby Shellrock River.

Though both rounded heights and depressions are young, the rocks beneath them are ancient. They began as plastic or limy mud that settled in a shallow sea some 270,000,000 years ago. For a long time the sea floor was almost barren; later it teemed with seaweeds, corals, and other organisms. Diminutive clams plowed through the mud; snails crept over it; sea lilies waved to and fro above it. There were hordes of brachiopods, or lamp-shells, some lying free on the bottom, though others fastened themselves to it or to other shells. Distant relatives of the nautilus swam or crawled about, sea urchins devoured scumlike plants, and animals called bryozoans built colonies that looked like corals. Fish swam lazily above them, some breathing with lungs instead of gills.

These creatures give a glimpse into the long story of life on our planet. That story has been one of change—change that led from jellylike blobs to great oaks and redwoods; from very simple wormlike creatures to snails, elephants, and dinosaurs. It produced the two million or so species that are living today, as well as many more millions that are now extinct. Some of those extinct types vanished utterly, leaving only gaps—real missing links—as evidence of their existence. Others, like inhabitants of the ancient Iowa sea, died but became fossils. They enable us to reconstruct the story of life during past ages.

WHAT FOSSILS ARE

Here we pause for a definition. In everyday language fossils are prehistoric animals and plants that have been petrified, or "turned into stone." Cartoons

1

and comic strips have clothed some of them in flesh, producing herbivorous dinosaurs that served as steeds for Stone Age men who pursued hairy mammoths or fled from *Tyrannosaurus rex.*

These comic strips, though entertaining, have little connection with fact. At least 40,000,000 years divided the "tyrant" dinosaur from the great long-necked herbivores, and the last dinosaur died 60,000,000 years before mammoths ranged from Europe to South America, or before man learned to wield stone weapons. These varied creatures associate only when their bones are displayed in museums of natural history. Even there they generally stand in widely separated halls.

The concept of fossils as petrified remains of prehistoric organisms also is inadequate. It is true that countless fossils have been "turned into stone," but others are footprints, charred wood, tar-soaked bones, and frozen or dried flesh. These things also vary greatly in age, from some 1,500,000,000 years for very ancient fossils to a few centuries for the latest moas (giant birds) of New Zealand. Though all are literally *prehistoric,* that term acquires much greater meaning than it had when prehistory was restricted to the half million years or so before man learned to write.

The everyday concept of fossils, therefore, fails; it lumps too much together, ignores too much, and tells much too little. We replace it with a definition which says that *fossils are remains or traces of organisms that lived during ancient geologic times and were buried in rocks that accumulated in the earth's outer por-*

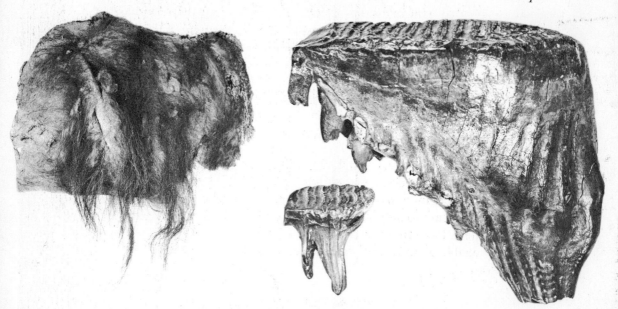

These fossils of Mammuthus primigenius Blumenbach, the woolly mammoth, have undergone little change. At the right are adult and milk molars. At the left is some skin, with wool and hair. The skin was preserved in ground ice of Siberia.

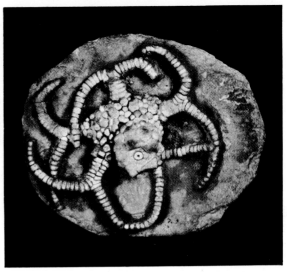

This wood has been replaced by silica, preserving cells, growth rings, wood rays, and distortion produced by disease. Colors are due to iron minerals and are not those of the original wood. (*U.S. National Museum*)

This permineralized crinoid contains some of its original calcite. It also shows the shape and structure of plates in the calyx and arms. Mississippian, Burlington, Iowa. (*U.S. National Museum*)

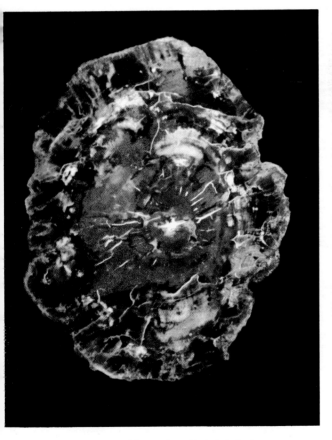

Wood replaced by silica, colored brightly by iron compounds. It preserves none of the original woody structure. Triassic, Petrified Forest, Arizona. (*U.S.N.M.*)

Impression of a spicebush leaf (Lindera), showing its shape and its veins; the color is due to mineral matter. Oligocene, Republic, Washington. (*U.S. National Museum*)

FOSSILS PRESERVED IN VARIOUS WAYS

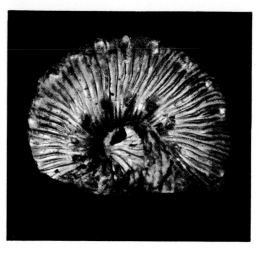

Scaphites quadrangularis nodosus Meek. This ammonoid shows the shape of the shell and its nacreous, or pearly, structure. Cretaceous Pierre shale, Cheyenne River, South Dakota. (*U.S. National Museum*)

(*Above*) Baculites compressus Say, Pierre shale of Pennington County, South Dakota. (*Below*) B. eliasi Cobban, Bearpaw shale, Valley County, Montana. Both specimens preserve the nacreous structure and show the sutures made by septa dividing the shell into chambers. (*United States National Museum*)

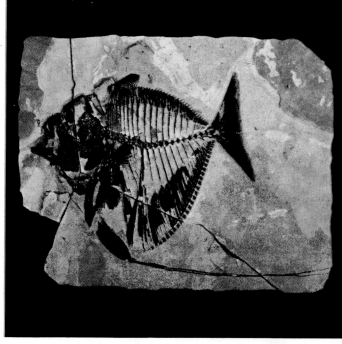

Pinus florissanti Lesq., a pine cone from Oligocene deposits of Florissant, Colorado. It shows both the shape of the cone and the scales that enclosed its seeds. (*Princeton University*)

Mene rhombeus (*Volta*), a deep-bodied fish related to the modern pompano. Hundreds of petrified bones make up this fossil, which shows the shape and structure of the fish and its strange hind, or pelvic, fins. They have moved far forward and have degenerated into bony spines. (*United States National Museum*)

FOSSILS SHOWING BOTH FORM AND STRUCTURE

tion, or crust. This covers the ground if we bear in mind two amplifications:

First, the term "ancient geologic times" embraces all earth history from the earliest ages recorded in rocks to the epoch that immediately followed the last Ice Age—a range exceeding 3,000,000,000 years. Second, the word *rock* need not and often does not mean "stone." To the geologist, a rock is any considerable deposit that makes up part of the earth's outer portion, its so-called crust. In this sense, gravel beds and clay are rocks; so are the ground ice, or permafrost, of Siberia and Alaska, natural paraffin beds of Poland, and asphalt that oozes to the surface in southern California. Remains found in such deposits are fossils, quite as truly as any embedded in stone.

HOW FOSSILS HAVE BEEN PRESERVED

We have said that fossils range from footprints to frozen bodies; from petrified bones and shells to wood and desiccated skin. Suppose we now review the methods of preservation to make sure of their significance:

Freezing. The ideal fossil is one that has been kept in cold storage since death, undergoing a minimum of change. Such ideal remains are rare, however, and they never are very old. Among animals, they are restricted to hairy elephants and rhinoceroses of the last great Ice Age, which fell into pits or crevasses in ground ice and remained there for thousands of years. Such remains preserve bone, muscles, skin, and hair, as well as internal organs. Dried blood fills arteries and veins; partly digested food still lies in the stomach. The famous frozen mammoths of Siberia and Alaska are examples of such preservation. One from Alaska has been displayed, still safely frozen, in an American museum.

Drying, or Desiccation. Next to frozen fossils in quality are those that have been thoroughly dried. Such remains of camels, ground sloths, and a few other animals have been found in caves of our semiarid Southwest and South America. Cave-dwelling sloths also are represented by their dried dung. Sloths of one Patagonian cavern were penned in by ancient Indians who apparently kept the animals until they were needed for food.

Wax and Asphalt. Natural paraffin is almost as good a preservative as ice. In 1907 the head, forelegs, and a large part of the skin of a woolly rhinoceros were dug from a paraffin mine in eastern Poland. Asphalt, however, preserves only hard parts, such as bones, teeth, and the shells of insects. Vast numbers of these have been found in asphalt deposits of California, especially those now enclosed by Hancock Park in Los Angeles. There an exhibit enables visitors to walk into a pit and examine fossil bones as they still lie in the tar.

Simple Burial. Plant remains and limy shells often lie for long periods without much change. Postglacial peat, for example, contains cones, stems, and pollen grains that accumulated in bogs. Buried forests of Norfolk, England, are famous for their logs, stumps, and masses of fern roots. Logs buried in

External molds of shells in porous dolomite

Internal molds of clamshells in shale

This snail shell is crumbling, leaving only the internal mold

This coprolite is fossilized excrement

Under side of a sandstone slab showing internal molds of shells where they were attached to the sea bottom

Impression of a leaf in coarse sandstone

Impression of a fernlike leaf in a shale nodule, Mazon Creek, Illinois

Paramphibius, tracks left by otherwise unknown xiphosurans

Fossils that are impressions or traces

German lignite about 40,000,000 years old are discolored and slightly decayed, but the texture and grain of their wood show little alteration. Sand dollars, sea urchins, and mollusk shells whose ages range from a few thousand to at least 75,000,000 years generally have lost their colors, but their hard, limy substance has suffered little change.

Carbonization. This is a process of incomplete decay which gets rid of volatile substances but leaves carbon behind. "Charred" plant remains of peat bogs reveal an early stage of carbonization; a more advanced one appears in the crumbly woods of many lignite deposits. At its extreme, carbonization reduces plants and animals to shiny black films that are finer than tissue paper. They reveal the appearance of ferns and other leaves, as well as the fleshy forms of ancient aquatic reptiles, and internal organs of some marine invertebrates and fish.

Petrification. This process, which results in stony fossils, takes place in two related ways. The simpler, termed *permineralization,* takes place when fat and other organic substances decay while water containing dissolved mineral matter soaks into every cavity and pore of hard—especially limy—structures. There the minerals are deposited, producing stony fossils that still contain a good deal of their original solid material. Most marine fossils were preserved in this way, as were the bones and teeth of varied vertebrates.

Replacement takes place when water dissolves original hard parts and replaces them with mineral matter. This may happen very slowly—so slowly that the new mineral matter duplicates microscopic structures of shell, coral, bone, or wood. Replacement also may take place with such speed that no trace of original structure remains. The difference may be seen by contrasting massively agatized and structureless wood with plant remains from so-called coal balls, which retain every microscopic cell. Many replaced bones and shells show equal detail, but others have lost all trace of their original structure.

Such replacement is primary; it takes place when organic remains first become petrified. Secondary replacement, on the other hand, destroys microscopic structure long after it was preserved. This often happens when limy fossils are dissolved and replaced by such minerals as silica. On the other hand, many petrifactions formed of silica in the first place are among our best-preserved fossils.

Molds and Casts. Shells, stumps, and other remains often lie in sediment until it becomes firm. Later the dead objects decay or dissolve, leaving a cavity known as a natural mold. This may be collected and studied as it is, or it may be filled with plaster of paris, wax, or some other compound. This filling, which duplicates the shape and surface of the fossil, is termed a cast or squeeze.

Casts and internal molds also are produced by nature. The former develop when grains of sand, clay, or finer materials fill natural molds, but internal molds consist of material that fills such things as empty shells. Internal molds (sometimes miscalled casts) of mussel and snail shells are common. Natural

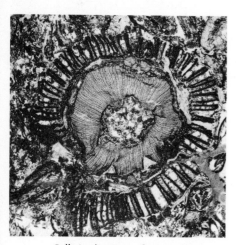

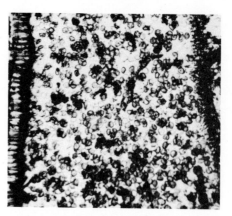

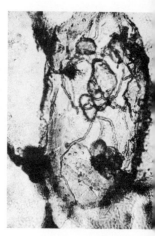

Cells in the stem of Lyginopteris,
a seed-fern

Spores in the cone of Lepidocarpon,
a lycopod related to Lepidodendron.
Enlarged 73 times

Mycelia of a fungus that grew
in a fern stem, x 210

*Examples of the remarkably preserved plants found in coal balls. Photographs by
Dr. Henry Andrews*

molds of shells and trees are plentiful, too, especially in beds of sandstone.
The finest of all molds, however, are fossil insects in northern European amber. The amber began as resin that oozed from ancient trees, often trapping
insects. Since that time the resin has hardened and the insects have dried to
almost nothing. In spite of this, their forms remain as cavities showing heads,
antennae, bodies, and legs. With a microscope one may examine scales on the
wings or count bristles on the bodies of these almost nonexistent creatures.

Imprints. These are little more than external molds of very thin objects, such
as leaves. They are found in sandstone, shale, and layers of tuff formed by
volcanic ash. Vast numbers of plant imprints lie in strata of the Coal Age, especially in Illinois. There the finest are enclosed in concretions, which must
be split in order to reveal their fossils.

Tracks, Trails, and Burrows. These, even more than casts and molds, explain
why we say that fossils are either remains or traces of ancient organisms. The
most famous fossil tracks are those left by dinosaurs that walked upon moist
mud banks or plastic swamp bottoms which later solidified. Other reptile tracks
have also been found, as well as footprints of amphibians, birds, elephants,
ground sloths, and even Stone Age men. A great variety of trails also was left
by creeping and crawling invertebrates. Others burrowed in sand, mud, or
soil, or bored into hard organisms. Many sponges, sea anemones, snails, and
crabs are known from their burrows or borings, as well as from petrified remains. Structures called *Cruziana* seem to be filled pits that once held eggs
laid by the trilobite *Olenellus;* and *Daemonelix,* the "devil's corkscrew," apparently was the home of a land-dwelling beaver whose bones are named

A carbonized marine animal showing internal organs. Mid-Cambrian, British Columbia

This scallop shell still contains much of its original material.

Carbonized leaves and bark in Pennsylvanian shale. Illinois

Permineralized corals that preserve both shape and structure

Wood completely replaced by silica still shows its original grain. Yuma County, Arizona

These silicified fossils preserve the shapes of corals but not their structure.

Details of grain, cell structure, and injury are preserved in this silicified wood from Lincoln County, Idaho.

This coral from the "silex" beds at Tampa, Florida, is a hollow chalcedony geode. Only the shape of the coral remains.

Fossils preserved in various ways

Steneofiber. The animal dug a spiral hole 6 to 8 feet deep, followed by a tunnel that sloped upward, growing larger as it went. Freshets sometimes filled these odd burrows with sand, which now forms spectacular fossils in buttes and banks of western Nebraska.

Castings and Coprolites. Castings are indigestible remnants of meals swallowed by burrowing invertebrates. Lugworms, for example, swallow sand in order to eat small organisms. Once this food has been extracted, the sediment is regurgitated in the form of contorted castings. Ancient worms doubtless had similar habits, and fossil castings are common in some marine formations. Other castings may have been made by burrowing sea cucumbers, which now feed as if they were worms.

The term *coprolite* ("dung-stone") is applied to feces preserved by petrifaction or as molds or casts. Some show grooves made by the spiral valve found in sharks' intestines; their origin is obvious. Others seem to be hardened droppings of amphibians, and some probably came from reptiles. Still others can only be attributed to unknown vertebrates.

Gastroliths, or Gizzard Stones. Everyone who has seen a fowl being prepared for cooking knows that the birds swallow stones. They come to rest in the muscular stomach, or gizzard, where they help grind food to pieces as it is squeezed to and fro.

Many ancient reptiles shared this habit of grinding food with gizzard stones. Formally called gastroliths, they may be recognized by their rounded edges and smooth—even polished—surfaces, *provided they are associated with reptilian remains.* Those seven words are important, for pebbles may be rounded and smoothed by running water or wind-blown dust as well as by churning against each other in the stomach of a reptile. The surest proof, of course, is to find gastroliths among fossil bones, in the place once occupied by a stomach. Lacking that, bones should lie near the pebbles, with no hint that the latter might have been polished by water or wind. Smoothed pebbles that merely lie in beds that may hold reptilian remains should not be called gastroliths.

HOW MUCH DO FOSSILS TELL?

We now come to a critical question: How much do these varied types of fossils tell about life in the past?

Answers depend upon the fossils found in particular places and upon the questioner. If the former are only trails or burrows in rocks such as sandstone, they may tell us what ancient creatures did but reveal almost nothing about those organisms themselves. In New Jersey and southern New England, for example, footprints show that dinosaurs walked, ran, and rested on muddy sandbanks, but there are few petrified bones to tell what those ancient reptiles were like. Some of the oldest fossil snails are mere furrows made as the ani-

This sandstone cast of skin on the chest of Anatosaurus, a duck-billed dinosaur, shows thousands of small, bony plates. (Photograph from the American Museum of Natural History.) Plates in the skin of Glyptosaurus, an Oligocene lizard, are petrified, as are the jaws and teeth.

mals crawled in mud. Such traces are welcome when nothing else can be found, but they are disappointing to anyone who wants to know what these early Cambrian snails looked like and the group to which they belonged.

Even the best and most plentiful fossils disappoint people who want to know as much about ancient faunas and floras as they might—but seldom do—learn about modern ones. Fossils are remains or traces that have been preserved; but most ancient organisms decayed, were eaten, or were weathered a short time after they died. Bones were crushed by carnivores and gnawed by rodents; logs and dead leaves rotted; shells were ground to bits by waves. Tracks and trails were washed away; beds of sand containing burrows were stirred up and reworked before they finally became stone. Only a small part of the things that actually lived, left traces, and then died escaped these varied forces of destruction and finally became fossils. To restore life's past from such records, say some critics, is like trying to reconstruct a city from a few of its cemeteries.

This comparison holds a measure of truth, but it also is exaggerated. Though fossils do not record all the things that lived during past ages, they include a vast variety of organisms, many of which are well preserved and show the ways in which they lived. Such fossils do more than tell a general story; for many epochs and in many places they provide an amazing amount of detail.

This becomes clear when we reconsider the fossils found near Rockford, Iowa. There seaweeds are not much more than impressions; small floating and scumlike plants have vanished; so, we may confidently assume, have small animals without shells or similar hard parts. But other creatures, from one-celled protists to vertebrates, remain, and their hard parts were neither worn nor broken before fossilization. Their very excellence shows that most of them lie where they lived and died. Few were mixed and worn by waves and currents, or carried long distances before they came to rest and were buried in slowly settling mud.

As the restoration shows, these fossils present a general picture of sessile and crawling animal life, as well as a few swimmers—a general picture that is filled out by facts about structure and anatomy. Stony corals, for instance, contain complex systems of plates built by and as supports for the body. The halves of a brachiopod fall apart, revealing notches and teeth that held them together, scars to which muscles were fastened, and channels for watery blood. Some shells have bands and blotches of color, while broken ones show fibrous structure that could not be seen while the creatures were alive.

Many petrified fossils equal those from Iowa, but few show as much detail as those from Miocene concretions in the Mojave Desert. The specimens are secured by dissolving the concretions from what are popularly known as "button beds." Finds include silicified spiders, insects, and fairy shrimps that once lived in or near a lake which resembled Soap Lake in the Grand Coulee region of present-day Washington. Brood pouches of female fairy shrimps contain eggs; some insects still lie in their pupal cases; others died and were preserved in the act of emerging. Jointed antennae as well as spines on legs are seen on some specimens. Especially fine fossils preserved in calcium carbonate show muscles as well as tubes that took air through the insects' bodies.

Such fossils are surpassed only by rare insects and spiders whose soft parts, as well as shapes, are preserved in amber. One amber spider contains the abdominal organs and muscles of the legs; another shows the structures of cells in the abdominal wall. Spider's silk is almost common, and in one specimen the individual threads can be traced to separate spinning tubes.

Countless specimens that are inferior to these still provide information which is often overlooked by critics who dwell on "imperfections in the fossil record." Thus many petrified trees preserve what once were woody cell walls, as do stems, roots, and cones found in chert or limy coal balls. Palmlike cycads still bear organs that served the purpose of flowers, and plants that falsely resemble ferns contain seeds in pods at the tips of their leaves. Fossil spores are abundant in cannel coal, and some reveal nuclei that once were the centers of life in their gelatinous cells. Nuclei even contain chromosomes, those complex though tiny structures whose elements, called genes, control heredity. Cones and roots are common fossils, and flowers are not as rare as they once seemed to be. A cactus some 50,000,000 years old bears both flowers and fruit. Carbonized marine invertebrates of vastly greater age show internal organs as well as bristles, scales, and other external structures.

Fossil vertebrates are often called perfect if they contain all important bones and if most of their teeth remain in the jaws. But fish found in a suburb of Cleveland, Ohio, also possess carbonized flesh and fins, and so do some aquatic reptiles. Dinosaurs buried in fine-grained sandstone have impressions of skin around their bones. Frozen elephants preserve almost as many details as do those shot, but seldom studied, by hunters in Africa.

Muscles, Brains, and Senses. Even bones devoid of flesh may tell a great deal about soft anatomy. The key parts of any body are its muscles, for they both give it shape and determine its movements. Muscles, in turn, are fastened to bones, leaving marks that indicate sizes, shapes, and functions of these varied organs.

Brains and nerves determine intelligence and behavior, and their principal features can be determined from cavities and channels in skulls. Thanks to

At the left are tracks of a small amphibian from the Permian Coconino sandstone of the Grand Canyon, Arizona. Footprints at the right were made by Triassic dinosaurs in what is now New Jersey.

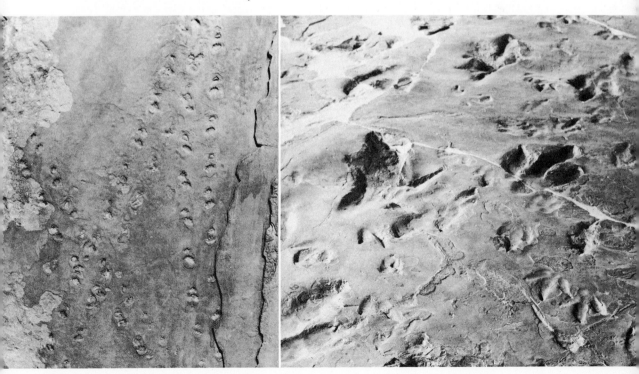

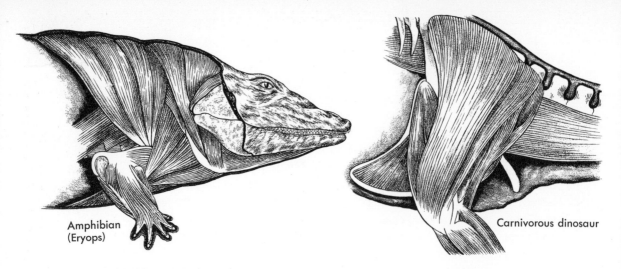

Muscles in the shoulder and head of the amphibian Eryops (left) *and the hip of a carnivorous dinosaur* (right). *Both are restored from marks on the petrified bones.*

them, we know the mental and sensory equipment of many fossil vertebrates, from jawless pre-fish to mammals. Thus flying reptiles and birds saw well but smelled very poorly; both obviously hunted by sight. Early mammals, however, reversed this order and found their food by smell. The largest dinosaurs had such small, weak brains that most of their actions were regulated by swellings, or ganglia, in the spinal cord. Brain casts of dinosaurs and some fossil mammals are shown in Chapters XXVI, XXVII, and XXX.

Growth, Injury, and Disease. Living things now change as they grow up and age, and that rule also holds for organisms of the past. Fossils 300,000,000 to 500,000,000 years old show that the jointed invertebrates called trilobites developed from minute oval larvae into adults as much as 30 inches in length. Many mollusks and brachiopods changed shape and ornamentation from the time they first developed shells until they were ready to die. Dinosaur eggs contain bones of unhatched young, and small skeletons have been identified as the young of much larger species.

Some petrified logs bear scars made by fire, apparently while the trees were alive. Other fossil plants reveal pathologic burls, spot fungi, and insect galls. Tumors, rheumatic disorders, arthritis, and abscesses are shown by the bones of ancient vertebrates. Some skeletons are distorted by what seem to be muscular spasms that ended in death.

Activities and Instincts. Enlarged areas in brains tell us that some animals hunted by sight though others relied on smell. Mastodons often waded into swamps so far that they mired in mud which still contains their bones. Large size and skeletal structure prove that ground sloths were terrestrial, though their modern relatives climb trees. A crab found in an ancient worm burrow lived there, just as its modern relatives dwell in burrows made by similar worms. Tusks of so-called giant pigs, or entelodonts, are deeply notched—a feature that became significant when someone discovered that the notches were worn by dirty roots which the animals dug for food.

Plants and animals of a late Devonian sea in what is now northern Iowa

AMMONOID   STROMATOPOROID   LUNGFISH   NAUTILOID

RUGOSE CORALS,   SNAIL   COLONIAL AND RUGOSE CORALS
BRYOZOANS, AND BRACHIOPODS

                                                                    CLAMS AND BRACHIOPODS

                                RUGOSE CORALS AND SEVERAL BRACHIOPODS

Miocene insects and a spider from the Mojave Desert. **1.** *Under surface of a spider, x 20.* **2.** *Under surface of a leaf hopper, x 10.* **3.** *An adult male midge, x 10.* **4.** *Female of the same species of midge, still in her pupal case, x 50.* **5.** *A larval water beetle, x 10.* **6.** *A larval dragonfly, x 5. Photographs by N. W. Shupe.*

Fossil burrows called Daemonelix, in Miocene rocks of western Nebraska, and a restoration of Steneofiber, the small land beaver that apparently dug the spiral burrows, which are now filled with rock.

The habits of invertebrates are sometimes shown by their shapes, sometimes by their relationships, and sometimes by the positions in which they are found. Ancient oysters, for instance, were attached to other shells or to rocks; belemnites (Chapter XV) swam like the squids which they resemble; some snails bored holes in other shells and devoured the animals inside. Other snails crawled to the top of sea lilies (crinoids) and there fed upon waste materials from meals eaten by their hosts. The snails moved so little and clung so tightly that their shells grew to fit the plated sea-lily body. A few starfish adopted the same sort of life, but instead of growing to fit they coiled tightly around their hosts' jointed arms.

Several modern snails bore holes into other mollusks, insert a rough, tonguelike structure, and devour flesh inside the shells of their victims. Bored fossils show that this method of feeding was practiced during ancient ages as remote as the Ordovician. Many fish and reptiles, on the other hand, swallow active victims whole. Fossil marine reptiles from Germany contain the undigested remains of such meals, and so do some American fish. In one the predator seemingly choked to death, for its victim is only partly swallowed. Another, the 14-foot "bulldog tarpon" (*Portheus molossus*), swallowed a 5-foot 7-inch meal in one piece but died soon afterward. The victim's death struggles probably caused fatal internal injuries.

Some marine reptiles were swift, strong swimmers, and gastroliths sometimes show the range, though not the speed, of their travels. One mosasaur swallowed lumps of a special pink quartzite in western Iowa or Minnesota but died in Kansas, some 400 airline miles away. Since the reptile did not

This snail clung to a crinoid so persistently that the shell grew to fit its resting place

These brachiopod shells show marks left by muscles, blood vessels, and other organs, as well as the structure of the shells themselves

Here sand filled pits, preserving marks that match legs and spines of trilobites. The pits may have contained eggs

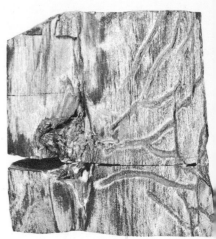

Larval beetles, called Paleoscolythus, gnawed tunnels in this ancient wood. Triassic, Petrified Forest, Arizona

Gastroliths, or "gizzard stones," of dinosaurs. One stone contains petrified corals

These brachiopod shells were distorted after injury to their mantles

Snails bored through these brachiopod shells and ate the animals inside

Burrowlike trail of a snail, called Olivellites, in Pennsylvanian sandstone from west-central Texas. The actual snail shell is unknown

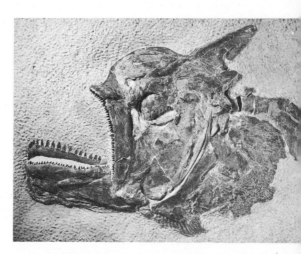

Teeth of this fish, Ichthyodectes, show that it was a predaceous carnivore. Late Cretaceous (Niobrara), western Kansas

Fossils that reveal habits of ancient animals

travel by air, it doubtless roamed much farther than this minimum of 400 miles.

Still more remarkable, as a record of behavior, is the devil's corkscrew, *Daemonelix,* with its helical shaft and upward-slanting tunnel. Such a burrow demanded more than mere digging; it meant digging by an inherited pattern as precise as the one that leads a goldfinch or robin to build its distinctive nest. Since we call nest-building instinctive, this term may also be applied to the actions of that ancient beaver. By only a moderate stretching of terms, *Daemonelix* becomes a fossilized instinct about 15,000,000 years old.

ENVIRONMENTS AND TEMPERATURES

Fossils also tell a great deal about their surroundings and the conditions under which they lived. Trees obviously grew on land, but seaweeds inhabited salt water. So, we may safely assume, did corals, oysters, and squidlike creatures, all of whose living relatives are found in seas today. But snails, mussels, and fish belonging to groups now found only in fresh water may be assigned to that environment. Animals such as horses and camels surely lived on dry land, while animals built like the hippopotamus made their homes in swamps.

Protists, plants, and animals also give clues to ancient climates. Palms, for example, live in warm regions; spruces thrive where weather grows cold. Ferns require a great deal of moisture, but grasses and most cacti get along with much less. Small reptiles are plentiful in deserts, but big dinosaurs could have lived only in humid regions. Reindeer are evidence of cold weather, and so are woolly mammoths whose remains have been found in frozen ground.

Facts such as these have been refined until they provide remarkably exact pictures of ancient lands, waters, and climates. Not until 1950, however, did fossils provide data on temperature in actual degrees. In that year Dr. H. C. Urey analyzed a Jurassic belemnite (Chapter XV) roughly 150,000,000 years old. From the isotopes of oxygen in this fossil, Dr. Urey found that the animal hatched in the summer, lived almost four years, and died early in its fourth spring. During the animal's life, summer temperatures ranged between 20 and 21 degrees Centigrade, or 68 to almost 70 degrees Fahrenheit. The highest winter average was 64 degrees Fahrenheit and the lowest 59.

Several people have applied Urey's method to fossils of other kinds and ages, with equally convincing results. One series of data shows how temperatures changed during the latter part of the Mesozoic, or era of reptiles; near the end of Chapter XXVII these changes are related to the rise and fall of Cretaceous dinosaurs. A general discussion of temperature measurements may be found in an article on "Ancient Temperatures," by Cesare Emiliani, in the *Scientific American,* volume 198, pages 54–63, for February 1958.

CHAPTER II

Rocks, Fossils, and Ages

W<small>E HAVE SAID</small> that fossils are remains or traces of once-living things buried in rocks of the earth's so-called crust. But we did not say that all such rocks contain fossils. Which do and which do not? How can we arrange them in order, and how—by means other than guessing—can we tell their age?

ROCKS AND THEIR FOSSILS

Rocks, which vary greatly in hardness, also differ in origin. Origins, in turn, determine our chance of finding fossils in them.

Igneous Rocks. The word *igneous* means "fiery"; though rocks of this class did not really burn, all once were intensely hot. They include lavas that came to the surface in eruptions, as well as related deposits that cooled and hardened underground. Most lavas were fluid when they came from cracks or volcanoes and flowed out upon the surface. Subterranean masses were much stiffer; before cooling they are termed *magma,* a Greek word for "dough." Upon cooling they form granite and similar rocks, which lack the bubbles and traces of flowage that are characteristic of lava.

Igneous rocks that hardened underground contain no fossils, for nothing can live in great heat or far below the surface. Fossils are very rare in lavas, most of which destroyed all plants and animals over which they flowed. Exceptions are the baked stromatolites described in Chapter IV and tree trunks that left molds in rapidly cooling flows. A lava mold of a dead and bloated rhinoceros was found near the southern shore of Blue Lake, near the Grand Coulee, Washington.

Lavas often are blown to pieces and shot into the air, where they cool rapidly. Falling to the ground, they form deposits called agglomerate if the

Silicified cones of an araucarian "pine," one cut to show its structure. Triassic of Argentina. (*Princeton University*)

A snail, Euconospira, that preserves its color pattern. Pennsylvanian, near Alamogordo, New Mexico. (*U.S.N.M.*)

Leaf of Platanus, a sycamore. This impression shows shape and venation; colors are due to minerals. Late Miocene, Faraday Dam, Washington. (*U.S.N.M.*)

Uintacyon, a small carnivore whose bones and teeth are petrified. Eocene (Bridger) of south-central Wyoming. (*U.S.N.M.*)

An external mold showing one valve of Derbyia keokuk Hall, a brachiopod. Mississippian, Galena, Kan. (*U.S.N.M.*)

Coenites crassus (Rom.), a silicified tabulate coral that shows only the surface of the colony. Silurian (Niagaran), Louisville, Kentucky. (*U.S.N.M.*)

FOSSILS SHOWING SHAPES, COLORS, AND STRUCTURES

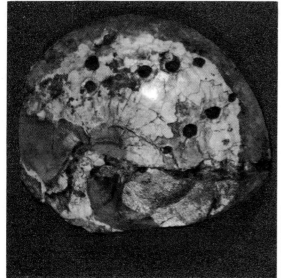

(*Left*) Placenticeras, a large ammonoid from the Cretaceous Pierre shale of South Dakota. Holes in this shell show that it was bitten by a hungry mosasaur, or marine lizard. (*Univ. of Michigan*)

FOSSIL CEPHALOPODS AND CORALS

(*Right*) Restoration of Cooperoceras, a spiny nautiloid, among corals, glass sponges, and other animals of a Permian sea bottom in the region that now is southwestern Texas. (*University of Michigan*)

(*Below*) Emmonsia, Coenites, and other corals in a piece of weathered limestone stained by hematite. Middle Devonian (Onondagan) near Louisville, Kentucky. (*U.S.N.M.*)

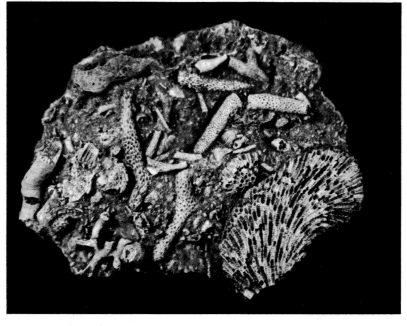

At the left are two petrified redwoods (Sequoia affinis) in tuff, a soft rock composed of volcanic ash. Pliocene, near Calistoga, California. At the right is a mold of a charred pine tree preserved in solidified lava of Recent age. Craters of the Moon, near Arco, Idaho

fragments are coarse, and tuff if they are very fine. Both bridge the gap between igneous and sedimentary rocks, since their particles settle upon the earth's surface although they once were hot.

Agglomerate covers many fossil trees, some of which were dead logs at the time of burial. The most famous are in Yellowstone National Park, where as many as eighteen successive forests of redwoods, pines, sycamores, and oaks were buried under showers of volcanic rock. Hills west of Vantage, Washington, also contain petrified logs covered by agglomerate and lava flows.

Redwood logs, excellently preserved, are found in light-colored tuff a few miles from Calistoga, California. Ash mixed with mud settled in lakes near Florissant, Colorado, forming light gray shale. It contains enormous numbers of leaves, as well as eleven hundred species of butterflies, crickets, grasshoppers, flies, beetles, and other insects. The butterflies still preserve their original stripes and spots.

Sedimentary Rocks and Their Fossils. Though fossils are exceptional in igneous rocks, they are the rule in sedimentary deposits.

Sediment literally means "something that settles"; sedimentary rocks consist of dust, sand, mud, and other materials that settled under water or on land. As they did so they built up deposits called strata or beds, layers, and laminae, depending upon their thickness. No sedimentary rocks were hot when they accumulated, and many consist largely of shells, corals, plants, and other remains. Coal is a well-known sedimentary rock that is made up almost wholly of plants.

Still, not all sedimentary rocks contain fossils. Most conglomerates, for instance, lack them, for organisms that lived among coarse sands and shifting pebbles were ground to pieces soon after they died. Fine-grained limestones may be equally barren, since they consist of material that once was dissolved in water. Shells and corals are rare in most marine sandstones—corals because they could not live amid sand; shells because they were destroyed by acids in beds of sand or by water seeping through the rock after it solidified. Where fossils do remain they seldom are more than external molds.

In contrast to these barren deposits are others in which fossils are abundant or actually form most of the rock. The Iowa clay-shale described in Chapter I contains so many remains that a collector who takes small ones with large may get ten thousand specimens in a day. Slabs of limestone from Missouri are covered with crinoids, while limy shales from the Cincinnati region and southeastern Indiana are crowded with shells. The chalk of England and northern France is little more than a mass of tiny shells through which larger ones are scattered. Other limestones consist of mollusk shells, corals, or the puzzling creatures called stromatoporoids, held together by matrix worn from

Collecting fossil fish from fresh-water shale of Triassic age at Princeton, New Jersey

similar remains. Reefs described in Chapter IV consist almost entirely of unworn algal masses.

Even coarse sandstones may enclose bones of large dinosaurs, while fine-grained beds containing clay and mica often abound in tracks and burrows. Other fine-grained sandstones that settled on land are rich in fossil mammals. In the famous Agate bone bed of Nebraska (Chapter XXXI), fine sandstone merely fills spaces between closely packed skulls and bones.

Metamorphic Rocks. These are typified by slate, true marble, and contorted crystalline rocks often called granite, though the proper terms are gneiss and schist. Some began as sediments; others were igneous. All have been changed by heat, by steam from buried magmas, or by pressure that bent and squeezed rocks into mountains. The process often went so far that we no longer can tell whether a given deposit began as magma, lava, or sediment.

Intensely metamorphosed rocks contain no fossils; any that may have been present were utterly destroyed. But stromatolites are abundant in some slightly changed marbles, and shells of various kinds have been found in slate, which is mildly metamorphosed shale. Such fossils were flattened and squeezed side-wise or stretched as the rocks were forced into mountain ranges. Though such remains can be recognized, their shapes may be quite different from those the creatures had when alive.

WHERE ARE FOSSILS FOUND?

We now are ready to answer the question of where and how fossils can be found. The first step, of course, is to rule out igneous and metamorphic formations in which fossils are almost sure to be lacking. Then, unless the collector is interested in special problems such as stromatolites (Chapter IV) or animals of ancient rocky shores, he eliminates formations and beds in which remains are likely to be rare and poor. This still leaves him a vast range of formations in which fossils are fairly common to abundant, and good in quality to superb.

About many of these deposits there is no question; experts have combed them again and again and have published reports describing their finds and the best localities for collecting. Other formations are judged to be promising because of their appearance, because they are related to known fossil-bearing deposits, or because specimens found in them appear on curio stands or in museums. Following such leads, the determined collector examines every exposure he can find, until he either brings home an array of specimens or proves that they are not to be found.

Here the collector who deals with invertebrates has a great advantage over the one who seeks vertebrate fossils. Although a few beds are filled with teeth and bones, fossil vertebrates are much less common than shells or corals and much harder to identify. Most snails, after all, can be recognized as snails, but a skull or even a skeleton may appear as little more than a light- or dark-colored bump on a rock. In the hands of an unskilled collector it also may be easily destroyed, though many invertebrates (by no means all!) are easily removed from the rocks in which they were fossilized.

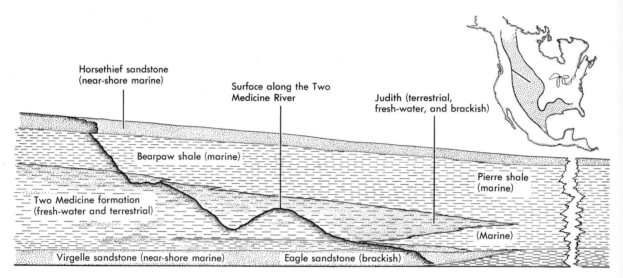

Diagram of late Cretaceous formations from northern Montana (left) *to South Dakota* (right). *Position of the section is shown by the line on the map. Shading shows the general extent of late Cretaceous seas in the South and West.*

FOSSILS AND FORMATIONS

Every collector soon notices that fossils of certain types are found in particular kinds of rocks. Marsh plants, for example, are most abundant in shales and sandstones between beds of coal. The colonial animals called graptolites (Chapter XX) are generally found in dark, fine-grained shales that split into thin layers and sometimes are miscalled slate. Both reptile tracks and invertebrate trails characterize fine-grained sandstone, especially where it is interbedded with shale. Corals are found in limy shales and massive limestones, many of which are ancient reefs.

Records of Change. Equally obvious is the fact that fossils are similar throughout some series of strata although they differ in others. These similarities and differences show what beds should be grouped together and what should be separated, while the fossils themselves may reveal the conditions under which rocks were deposited.

These related aspects of fossils may be observed along the course of the Two Medicine River in Pondera and Glacier counties, Montana. At first we find ledges of gray to buff standstone whose beds bear traces of shifting currents and waves, as well as impressions of shells related to some that now live near sandy seashores. Next come greenish-gray clays and soft sandstones with oyster shells and basket clams, which now are found in the brackish water of bays where rivers empty into the sea. Above these are clays and sandstones that contain fresh-water mussels and snails, as well as plants and dinosaur bones. Some of the dinosaurs look as if they walked on dry land, but others were web-footed reptiles that often swam in swampy rivers or lakes. Near its middle the series is interrupted by a thin deposit containing sea shells. Evidently the lowland was submerged but soon became land again.

These rocks are some 1,750 feet thick, and we follow them for miles. Then we come to dark gray, rather limy shale with petrified shells of mollusks whose nearest relatives now are marine. The shale is capped by more coarse sandstone with oysters, basket clams, and jingle shells, all relatives of mollusks that now inhabit brackish water.

Different fossils thus enable us to distinguish five separate formations, although some of their strata are almost identical in appearance. We also trace a series of changes in physical conditions. Putting all these facts together in conventional form, we get this stratigraphic section, which should be read from bottom to top:

Horsethief sandstone. Slabby to massive sandstone, brackish water
    and marine. . . . .   360 feet
Bearpaw shale. Dark gray clay-shale with marine fossils. . . . .   490 feet
Two Medicine formation. Gray to greenish clay and soft sandstone,
    with some red clay and nodular limestone. Terrestrial and fresh
    water, with one marine horizon. . . . . 1,750 feet
Eagle sandstone. Greenish-gray clay and sandstone with brackish-
    water fossils. To the north and west this becomes part of the Two
    Medicine formation. . . . .   200 feet
Virgelle sandstone. Gray to buff sandstone with littoral fossils. . . . . . .   220 feet

These formations change from one place to another; witness the fact that the brackish-water Eagle sandstone gives way to fresh-water and terrestrial deposits which add a basal 200 feet to the Two Medicine formation. Still greater changes appear if we travel southeastward toward the Black Hills. First the lower sandstones and the Two Medicine formation vanish and the Bearpaw becomes a thick formation of shale, called the Pierre, which tells of a sea that changed very little while land and salt water repeatedly shifted in what is now western Montana and Alberta. At last, however, the sea shallowed, and sandstone was deposited. Although called the Fox Hills, it once was continuous with the Horsethief sandstone which caps ridges near the Two Medicine River.

If we take the time—several geologists have done so—we can trace the formations in our section, making sure how they come to an end, intergrade, or overlie one another. We also can trace deposits at the bottom or top of the series to places where they lie upon or are covered by older and younger beds. By repeating this process several times, we expand our first section into a greater one that shows formations and events in the West during 35,000,000 years of late Cretaceous time.

Index Fossils. Still, we cannot always trace one deposit to the next or find thick series that overlap like shingles on a roof. When this happens reliance must be placed upon index fossils.

An index fossil is found in rocks that formed in one limited part of earth history. *Inoceramus barabina,* for example, is common in late Cretaceous shales that extend from Minnesota to Alberta, and formations containing this shell settled at about the same time. The snail called *Maclurites magnus* is equally characteristic of certain much older (Ordovician) formations throughout eastern North America. The attractive coral known as *Pachyphyllum* means that rocks formed late in Devonian times, whether they occur in Iowa, Nevada, Arizona, or northern Canada.

A really good index fossil has three outstanding characteristics. First, it is easily recognized, which means that it cannot be confused with fossils that lived at other times. A good index fossil also spread rapidly and widely, becoming common during one small division of time, or epoch, after which it became extinct. Finally, it was easily preserved, leaving a large number of fos-

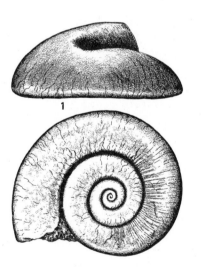
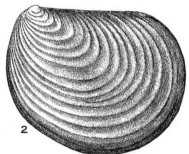
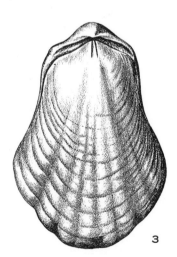

1. Maclurites magnus Lesueur. Early Ordovician (Chazy)
2. Inoceramus barabina Morton. Late Cretaceous (Montana)
3. Pentamerus laevis Sowerby. Middle Silurian

Three index fossils

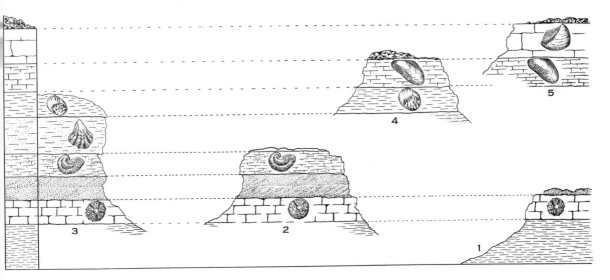

How index fossils are used to match, or correlate, beds of similar ages. The complete section of these varied strata is shown at the left.

sils. Rare species may have index value when we find them, but they are much less useful than others that are plentiful.

Correlation. To make sure how index fossils are used, let us picture three isolated hills and two quarries. All contain strata in orderly sequence, but no two sequences match. Does this mean that different sediments settled in different places, as they did in Montana, Alberta, and South Dakota? Or do these beds form one continuous series, with the oldest at the bottom and the youngest at the top?

These questions cannot be answered by following strata, for they are hidden in the stretches between our quarries and cliffs. Instead, we collect fossils from each place and then correlate, or match, them. At the top of Hill 1 we find some sea urchins, identical with others collected at the bottom of Hill 2. High up in that hill is an oysterlike shell called *Gryphaea,* which also appears in Quarry 3. A plump snail links Quarry 3 with Hill 4, and a mussel shows that a bed near the crest of the hill is found at the bottom of Quarry 5. By matching strata that contain these index fossils, we arrange our exposures in one continuous series, or section.

DIVIDING EARTH'S HISTORY

This method of correlating beds and formations by their fossils was discovered during the 1790's by an English engineer, William Smith. He also used differences between fossils to divide thick series of strata into related groups,

GEOLOGIC TIME SCALE

FORMATION NAMES IN *italics* ARE EUROPEAN; OTHERS ARE AMERICAN

	PERIODS AND EPOCHS AND THEIR LENGTHS	SOME IMPORTANT DIVISIONS AND FORMATIONS	IMPORTANT CHANGES AND EVENTS	SOME TYPICAL DATES
Cenozoic Era 60 million years — Quaternary Per. 1 million years	Recent Epoch 5,000–20,000 yrs.		Continents remained high, glaciers melted, and climates became milder and more arid. Many mammals became extinct.	8,000 11,000 12,000
	Pleistocene, or "Ice Age" 1 million yrs.	Wisconsin *Würm* Illinoisan *Riss* Kansan *Mindel* Nebraskan *Günz*	Sierras uplifted again. Four great glacial advances in North America and Europe, interrupted by stages of warmth and melting. Sea levels shifted repeatedly and animals migrated before the ice.	17,000 370,000 700,000
Tertiary Period 59 million years	Pliocene Epoch 11 million yrs.	Citronelle Blanco Waccamaw Hemphill Alachua Clarendon Caloosahatchee	Uplift, eruptions, and mountain building continued, especially in the Americas. Climates became cooler and more varied; sea covered much of the Pacific coastal region. Mammals reached their zenith in variety and size, and probably in abundance.	13,000,000
	Miocene Epoch 16 million yrs.	Barstow Loup Fork Pawnee Creek Deep River Hemingford Harrison Arikaree	The Sierra Nevada and modern Rocky Mountains were uplifted; eruptions built the Cascades and the Columbia-Snake River lava plateaus. Seas covered Atlantic, Pacific, and Gulf coastal belts, as well as northern South America. Climates grew cooler late in this period.	15,500,000 16,000,000 18,000,000
	Oligocene Epoch 12 million yrs.	Brulé John Day Chadron	Lands were worn down to low plains; volcanoes erupted in the central Rockies; the Alps and Himalayas began to rise. Early in the period, a sea covered northern Europe. Climates generally mild, equable.	36,000,000 38,000,000
	Eocene Epoch 10 million yrs.	Jackson Duchesne Claiborne Uinta Wilcox Green Bridger River Wasatch	Mountains were eroded, sending great thicknesses of sediment into basins; extensive lakes formed in the West. Seas covered southern Europe and northern Africa. Modern types of mammals became common.	48,000,000 55,000,000
	Paleocene Epoch 10 million yrs.	Clark Fork Fort Tiffany Union Torrejon Dragon Puerco	Mountains became and remained high, though erosion was rapid. Climates ranged from mild to cool. Archaic mammals spread widely and others of modern types appeared.	60,000,000
Mesozoic Era 125 million years	Cretaceous, or "Chalk Age" 70 million yrs.	Laramie Ripley Montana Selma Colorado Eutaw Dakota Raritan Tuscaloosa Washita Fredericksburg Potomac Trinity	Lands were extensive but low; climates were mild and uniform over most of the earth. Shallow seas spread widely for the last time, especially in the West; the Sierras were uplifted again and mountains formed in Mexico. The period was closed by the Laramide revolution, with extensive mountain building and cooling of climates.	85,000,000 105,000,000 110,000,000
	Jurassic 25 million yrs.	Morrison *Kimmeridge* Navajo *Oxford* Wingate *Dogger* *Lias*	Lands were low and climates mild; shallow seas covered much of Europe and invaded other continents. Great eruptions and intrusions in the Northwest; mountains began to rise from Mexico to Alaska.	131,000,000
	Triassic 30 million yrs.	Newark *Keuper* Chinle *Muschelkalk* Shinarump *Bunter* Moenkopi	Continents were relatively high, with mountains and arid regions. A shallow sea invaded the West, and eruptions were common in the East, southern Africa, and New Zealand. Seas covered much of Europe.	170,000,000 180,000,000

560
F367f

Era	Period	Subdivisions		Events	Years
Paleozoic Era 330-335 million years	Permian 25 million yrs.	Ocho, Guadalupe, Leonard, Wolfcamp	Coconino, Clear Fork, Wichita	Seas invaded the Southwest, Europe, and Asia; coal swamps were still extensive; climates at first were mild. The period closed with the culmination of the Appalachian revolution, which built extensive mountains and was accompanied by world-wide glaciation and cooling.	207,000,000 230,000,000
	Carboniferous — Pennsylvanian 25 million yrs.	Lr. Dunkard, Monongahela, Conemaugh, Allegheny, Kanawha, Lee	Virgil, Missouri, Des Moines, Atoka, Morrow, Springer	At first lands were low and were often invaded by seas or were covered by extensive coal swamps. Lands then became higher as the Appalachian revolution got under way; climates became less uniform. Amphibians and reptiles first reached large size.	232,000,000(?)
	Carboniferous — Mississippian 30 million yrs.	Chester, Meramec, Osage, Kinderhook	Mauch Chunk, Greenbrier, Madison, Pocono and Price	Seas spread widely early in the period, but retreated as mountains were built in the East, Texas, and Colorado. Dry conditions alternated with swamps in the East. Echinoderms became very abundant.	250,000,000
	Devonian 50-55 million yrs.	Chautauquan, Senecan, Erian, Ulsterian, Oriskany, Helderberg		Europe remained rugged, with mountains and seasonally arid basins. North America was low and flat and was invaded by seas. Later there were eruptions and mountain building in New England and eastern Canada. Fish and agnaths became common; amphibians evolved.	255,000,000 278,000,000 300,000,000 316,000,000
	Silurian 40 million yrs.	Cayugan, Niagaran, Medinan and Alexandrian		At first North America was low and flat; shallow seas spread widely. Later there were great eruptions in eastern Canada and New England, salt was deposited, and mountains were built in Europe.	365,000,000 380,000,000
	Ordovician 80 million yrs.	Cincinnatian (Richmond, Marysville, Eden), Mohawkian (Trenton, Black River, Chazy), Canadian		Shifting seas covered almost two thirds of North America, though the continent emerged twice. The period closed with mountain building in Europe and eastern North America, accompanied by great eruptions and intrusions. Before that, climates were mild and uniform.	388,000,000 400,000,000
	Cambrian 80 million yrs.	Croixan, Albertan, Waucoban	Acadian	Most of North America was low; it was invaded by long, narrow seas. Seas also were extensive in Europe, Asia, and Africa. In Europe the period closed with mountain building, eruptions, and erosion.	425,000,000 445,000,000 531,000,000
Eozoic Era 670 m.y.	Lipalian	Windermere, Grenville (?)	Hector	Period closed with mountain building and erosion in the West.	620,000,000 820,000,000
	Beltian	Keweenawan	Belt	Seas narrow. Great eruptions and intrusions in Lake Superior region.	1,030,000,000± 1,190,000,000
Proterozoic Era	Animikie			Thick delta deposits formed in Canada and more iron deposits settled in the Lake Superior region. Later uplift and intrusion.	1,260,000,000 1,440,000,000
	Huronian	Cobalt, Bruce	Gunflint, Uncompahgran	Shallow seas spread widely; iron ores settled in the Lake Superior region. During Cobalt times glaciers spread over eastern Canada.	1,620,000,000 1,900,000,000
	Timiskaming	Knife Lake, Doré, Sudbury		Seas were widespread at first; they were followed by extensive mountain building, especially in eastern Canada.	2,500,000,000
Archeozoic Era	Laurentian period or epoch of mountain building			Uplift, erosion, and intrusion in Canada and nearby regions.	
	Keewatin	Soudan, Keewatin, Coutchiching		Great intrusions and eruptions, especially in Canada. Mountain building was extensive. Important deposits of iron ore formed.	3,000,000,000 3,300,000,000
Azoic, or Formative, Era				No divisions have been made, and events are theoretical.	

Merner - Pfeiffer Library
Tennessee Wesleyan College
Athens, Tennessee

or formations. Both devices appealed to geologists who were trying to escape from an outworn dogma which held that all fossil-bearing rocks had formed during one brief epoch that came soon after creation. Within forty years after Smith announced his ideas, his followers produced a classification of formations and larger units extending from the earliest Cambrian through the "newer Pilocene." Though terms differed and many details were lacking, this series included deposits from the last three eras of earth history—the only ones in which fossils other than stromatolites are common and well defined.

This classification made fossils more important than they really were. A formation became the rocks deposited while certain species existed; when they vanished a new formation began. This also was true of epochs, ages, and periods, the time divisions during which related beds were deposited. Thus the Chalk—now called the Cretaceous—was a system of rocks and a period in which a special array of corals, sea urchins, and oysterlike and squidlike mollusks lived in seas where extinct reptiles swam. The Tertiary period, which followed, was marked by the appearance of still-living species among its mollusks. Two authorities even divided the period into epochs based on the increasing percentage of living species found among Tertiary fossils.

AN EARLY DIVISION OF THE TERTIARY PERIOD

Formation and Epoch	Meaning of Name	Percentage of Species Still Living
Newer Pliocene	Newer More Recent	90–95
Older Pliocene	More Recent	35–50
Miocene	Less Recent	17
Eocene	Dawn of the Recent	3.5

From Fossils to Changes in the Earth. This did well enough so long as geologists knew more about fossils than they knew about rocks and the earth. In time, however, they discovered that this method of dividing earth history put effects in place of causes. The Cretaceous period did not begin because certain mollusks and reptiles came into existence, nor did it end because they died out. It was a time when lands were low and seas spread widely, though there were progressive upheavals in the West. Similarly, the Pennsylvanian was more than a time of fernlike plants and primitive trees; it was one in which seas often spread and withdrew, turning their basins into swamps where the raw material of coal could settle. The Pleistocene, or Ice Age, on the other hand, was distinguished by high lands, changing climates, and glaciers that repeatedly spread in the Northern Hemisphere. These events are merely reflected by fossils, which adjusted themselves to the world in which they lived.

The number of time divisions has grown as knowledge of earth's history increased. When Charles Lyell published his *Elements of Geology* in 1839, he described sixteen epochs and formations distributed among three larger units, the Primary (or Transition), Secondary, and Tertiary. Today we recognize at least seven eras, fifteen or sixteen periods, and a still larger number of epochs. Only the most recent epochs are listed in the accompanying Table of Earth History, in which names, events, and dates are correlated with outstanding developments in life.

The terms *period, epoch,* and *age* apply to divisions of earth history; others are needed for rocks. In general, the rocks that formed during a period make up a system; those deposited during an epoch are a series or group. Since age is a popular term for either a period or an epoch, it has no stratigraphic equivalent.

As the number of periods and epochs increased, groups and formations grew smaller and smaller. Lyell's Cretaceous "group" is now a system; his Lias "formation" has become a series. Modern formations generally are limited to strata that settled during one compact portion of earth history, under essentially uniform conditions, and in one limited region. Many formations, therefore, contain one dominant kind of rock and take names from localities in which they are well developed. Others comprise rocks of two or more kinds, so intimately linked that they plainly belong together. These differences are reflected in names such as Brunswick shale, Selma chalk, St. Peter sandstone, and Green River formation. The last is a complex sequence of shales, sandstones, limestones, and marls deposited in two large, shallow lakes. Strata as varied as those along the Two Medicine River may be either a formation or a group.

AGES OF FOSSILS AND ROCKS

With this we come to a distinction that puzzles many people; the difference between geologic age and age determined in years. We give the geologic age of a rock or a fossil when we assign it to a division of earth history, or to a group or formation. The geologic age of *Inoceramus barabina,* for example, is late Cretaceous or Montanan; a particular specimen may come from the Bearpaw shale. *Maclurites magnus* belongs in the Chazy subepoch of the Ordovician period.

So far all is clear though not always simple; confusion comes when we translate geologic dates into years. Here index fossils reveal nothing, and strata from which they come tell no more. We therefore put both aside and hunt lavas or other igneous rocks whose relationships show that they hardened at well-known *geologic* dates. Some of these will also be useless, but others will contain uranium, the element that can be made to yield plutonium. Left to itself, however, uranium turns into lead that is a little lighter than the ordinary kind. This happens at an unvarying rate, so slow that only half of any amount of uranium becomes lead in 4,500,000,000 years. In technical terms, this period is the half-life of uranium.

The earth does not seem to be 4,500,000,000 years old, and no rock has been found in which the ratio of lead to uranium shows that the latter has been decomposing for anything near that period. But dates of 60,000,000 to 2,300,-000,000 years have been determined, and a good many between. Igneous rocks that hardened while *Maclurites magnus* was living give a date of 400,-000,000 years.

Helium can be used in much the same manner as lead, since it is also produced as uranium disintegrates. Other promising substances include radioactive isotopes of rubidium, calcium, and zircon. Their ages, which can be determined from very tiny amounts, range up to 3,300,000,000 years. That figure supports other estimates which indicate that the earth's crust has been solid for at least 3,700,000,000 years.

These methods serve well for very old formations but cannot be applied to young ones, such as deposits of the Pleistocene Ice Age. Many geologists have tried to date these by estimating rates of weathering and erosion, or from changes in the earth's orbit which affect the amount of sunshine that falls upon any selected region. Though these methods give some general ideas, they are too uncertain to mean much in terms of calendar years.

Marine sediments contain radium and other radioactive elements which decrease in quantity for about 400,000 years. The age of samples no older than that can be told by matching their radium content against a curve representing this known decrease. Since marine deposits can be correlated with many on land, this method gives some excellent dates for the last third or more of the Ice Age.

Much more recent deposits and fossils can be dated by means of Carbon 14. This radioactive substance is produced when cosmic rays from outer space bombard nitrogen atoms high up in the atmosphere. Carbon 14 is absorbed in known amounts by plants and animals; when they die it is lost at a regular rate which destroys half in about 5,600 years, three fourths in 11,200, and so on. Dates are found by determining the concentration of Carbon 14 in wood, horns, dung, and other substances. They give dates ranging from A.D. 550 to more than 20,000 B.C. A number of late Ice Age fossils range from 11,000 to 21,000 years old. Since there is always a chance of error in these computations, it is always given along with the actual date. Thus Ice Age sloth dung from South America shows an age of 10,832 ± 400 years. In other words, the sloth may have lived as few as 10,432 years ago or as many as 11,232. Spruce trees in Manitowoc County, Wisconsin, were pushed over by ice of the last great glacier that reached the Mississippi Valley. They died at least 10,668 years ago, and perhaps 13,668.

Still another method of determining age relies upon dark and light layers of clay and silt that settled in lakes of glaciated regions and in some others besides. Each pair of layers, or varve, represents a year; to learn how much time one deposit represents, we count layers and divide by two. Longer series are secured by matching overlapping sections and estimating gaps where they do not overlap. By this method one authority found that 13,500 years have passed since ice melted from the southern tip of Sweden. Another worker counted 6,500,000 varves in deposits of the great Green River lakes of ancient Colorado and Wyoming (Chapter XXI). Those lakes, therefore, lasted 6,500,-000 years, an amazingly long time for inland waters whose basins were not very deep.

CHAPTER III

Groups, Names, and Relationships

FOSSILS once were alive, and most textbooks divide living things among two kingdoms, plant and animal. The former contains organisms that generally are green, do not move about, and make food from two lifeless materials, carbon dioxide and water. Typical animals, on the other hand, are not green beneath their skins, commonly move freely, and feed upon other animals or plants.

This division is respectably old, for it goes back some 2,500 years. During most of them, however, it has required alterations and repairs. As early as 345 B.C. the Greek philosopher Aristotle added mushrooms and red seaweeds to plants, but transferred the sessile corals and sponges to the animal kingdom. Since Aristotle's time the plant kingdom has grown into a bewildering array of organisms that range from tiny and simple to large and complex; that may be green, purple, or other colors; that grow in one spot or move about; that make their own food or devour living and dead organisms. Animals have become equally varied, and many forms are assigned to both kingdoms. Others shift from plants to animals and back again as their activities change.

FROM TWO KINGDOMS TO FOUR

These difficulties have convinced a growing number of biologists that the two traditional kingdoms are relics far removed from reality. To keep them is to squeeze here and stretch there; to put unlike things together while separating others that are related. The result is worse than confusing, for it gives an unnatural structure to the world of life.

Still, it has been easier to pronounce old kingdoms obsolete than to de-

32

scribe new ones. Everyone is accustomed to plants and animals, and all except a few puzzling groups have received places among them. But when other kingdoms are set up the old rules must go, and experts do not agree on the new ones to be followed. Some authorities are content to add one new kingdom for the bacteria and their kin; others would do so for free-swimming "plants"; a few would make still a third new kingdom for fungi and their relatives. One expert divided the so-called algae into six groups, each of which he regarded as a kingdom. Then, "as a matter of convenience," he left all six, plus a few others, in the domain of plants.

We shall not be so cautious as he, yet we need not make such sweeping changes as those he thought desirable. Many organisms that seem to form separate kingdoms did not become fossils. The others apparently can be accommodated in four kingdoms: monerans, protists, plants, and animals. The third and fourth of these are the "standard" kingdoms, redefined and restricted. The first and second were named by a German biologist, Ernst Haeckel, in 1866. Though Haeckel made monerans part of his kingdom Protista, later authors have separated them and have clarified both groups. The definitions accepted here were published by H. F. Copeland in 1938.

Monerans, the Simplest Kingdom. Though some of Haeckel's monerans were results of faulty observation, this kingdom is now made to include two groups of very simple creatures, the blue-green algae (or cyanophytes) and bacteria. Both agree in being very small and in consisting of a single cell. Although some monerans are specialized in habits, shapes, and structures such as lashes for swimming, the basic plan of their cells remains simple. They are not divided, like cells of animals or plants, into one part of relatively minor importance and another (called the nucleus) which is essential for reproduction. The nuclear structures of monerans apparently are scattered through the cell, which seems merely to pinch in two when the time for reproduction arrives. This type of division is reflected in the term *schizophytes* ("fission plants") which is used in many books that retain the two traditional kingdoms and put monerans among the plants.

Blue-green algae, as their name implies, contain both blue and green material, the latter being chlorophyll. No one knows what the blue material does, but chlorophyll makes sweetish food by combining water with carbon dioxide, a gas now plentiful in the air and dissolved in seas, lakes, and streams. The process uses energy from sunshine, and part of that energy is stored in the end product, which is a simple form of sugar.

Most living things now depend upon food made by chlorophyll, though it may be secured in roundabout ways. This fact, plus the simple structure of blue-green algae, was once supposed to mean that they were the earth's first organisms, making food that was eaten later by "degenerate" bacteria. We now reverse this theoretical order, for it seems that bacteria came first and fed on almost-living material that accumulated before they evolved. In time,

Two Recent purple bacteria of types that may have evolved into plants

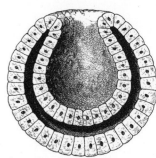

Section through a gastrula, the two-layered stage that is characteristic of animals

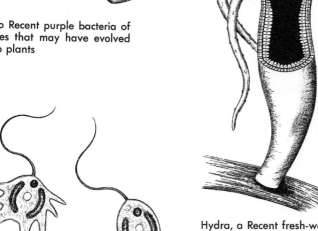

Hydra, a Recent fresh-water animal belonging to the coelenterates. It still has only two layers of cells

Chrysamoeba, a Recent protist, sends out "feet" when it feeds (left) but withdraws them when resting (right)

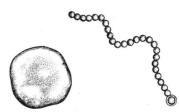

A chain of Nostoc, a blue-green alga (right) and its coating of jelly (left)

Bacteria and blue-green algae are monerans. Chrysamoeba is a protist, and the hydra is a simple animal.

some of the original grayish or whitish bacteria produced dull purple descendants whose color came from a mixture of red and green substances that made food much as chlorophyll does. Cyanophytes were born when this coloring matter became chlorophyll and the puzzling blue stuff was added. The swimming lash disappeared, too, for blue-greens get along without that useful structure.

This sequence is inferred from things living today, not from the fossils. If it is correct, blue-greens followed bacteria, yet the former are very old. Cyanophytes almost certainly helped build stromatolites, for their cells have been identified in Eozoic fossils. Both blue-greens and bacteria have been found in Huronian rocks of northern Michigan, the identifications having been made by experienced biologists. Bacteria apparently are common in coal and petrified plants of Devonian and later ages and have been found in coprolites. The commonest types are spheres and rods that may be joined end to end in short chains.

Protists Are Abundant Fossils. Protists are commonly called protozoans ("first animals") and are placed in the animal kingdom, though a few also appear as green algae. This confusion comes from the fact that some protists contain chlorophyll. One, *Chrysamoeba,* even alternates between the traditional kingdoms. Part of the time it is egg-shaped, swims with a lash, and makes its own food, like a plant. At other times it loses its lash, sends out armlike "false feet," or pseudopods, and eats in the manner of animals.

The kingdom of protists is hard to define, for its members belong to various groups that differ enormously. All are one-celled, all have nuclei, and many build shells or other hard parts that readily become fossils. In fact, remains of certain protists make up beds of limestone, while others are equally plentiful in chert or are common in quartzite and diatomaceous earth. Paleontologists generally are content to determine the lesser groups to which these fossils belong and let biologists find the characters that bring them together in a single kingdom.

Plants, Another Complex Kingdom. Plants are better defined by what they have been than by what they are. They probably began as one-celled descendants of green protists that swam with two lashes, not one. They combined carbon dioxide and water into sugary food, using some of it to cover their cells with the woody stuff called cellulose. That characteristic persisted as plants evolved into a variety of one-celled groups as well as multicellular

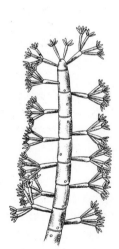

Clavator
Jurassic-Cretaceous

Perimneste
Jurassic-Cretaceous

Three fossil charaphytes

Trochiliscus
Devonian-
Mississippian

Vertical section

Transverse section

Oldhamia, perhaps
the imprint of a red
alga. Cambrian, New York

Surface and section of
Cylindroporella, a green
alga. Cretaceous

Primicorallina, a green
alga from the Ordovi-
cian of New York

Macroporella, a
green alga of
Permian age

Fossil algae and charaphytes. All enlarged

forms ranging from pond scums to trees. Cellulose even survived the loss of chlorophyll, which happened several times in the complex array of plants called fungi—mushrooms, molds, rusts, and so on. Many modern fungi are parasites or live on dead plants, and both habits are very ancient. Tubes and spores have been found in plants more than 300,000,000 years old, as well as in less ancient trees. Ball fungi appear on Carboniferous leaves, and other parasitic types have been found in later formations. Some resemble modern rusts, which do great damage to grain and fruit.

If red algae are true plants, this kingdom seems to appear with the stromatolite *Hadrophycus* of Precambrian age. Land plants arose during mid-Silurian times and became common near the end of the Devonian. Except for stony algae, most fossil plants come from Devonian and later formations.

The chlorophytes, or grass-green algae, are sometimes placed among the plants and sometimes in the protists. The group contains three families that are important as fossils. One of these families, the codiaceans, contains stony algae made up of small tubes that branch repeatedly. The dasyclads consist of short stems with tufts of leaflike structures; the fossils are short tubes or bulbs that are important in reef limestones. Charas are bushy plants as much as 2 feet high that now grow in fresh waters and cover themselves with crusts of lime. Fossils include twisted stems and rootlike structures, as well as bulblike organs that once contained spores. Because they are very small, these fossils must be examined by means of a microscope. Many fossil charas are marine.

Animals, the Simple Kingdom. The bodies of animals become vastly more complex than those of plants, yet the kingdom they form is much simpler and more closely knit. The first animals also were offspring of lash-bearing protists, but their ancestors had lost their chlorophyll and had grown into hollow, many-celled balls that formed co-ordinated colonies. In animals those balls collapsed and lengthened, so that each colony became one organism made up of two layers of cells. All animals still go through this stage unless they simplify the process of reproduction by starting from swellings or buds in the bodies of their parents. Most animals, however, add many cells to the two original layers and develop a third that is still more complex. The results may be traced in shells and bones produced by these layers, as well as in carbonized, dried, or frozen remains of actual ancient flesh. This versatile layer is the mesoderm, or "middle skin."

Sponges—Animals or Protists? Our statement that the animal kingdom is unified takes no account of sponges. They are usually called animals, yet their early development seems quite unlike that of other members of this kingdom. Moreover, cells that line the digestive cavity of sponges seem to be inherited from protists with collarlike structures around their lashes. These protists, however, were hardly the ones that gave rise to typical animals. We therefore face these alternatives: If sponges are animals, this kingdom is a composite made up of two separate stocks which are only very remotely related. But if sponges should not be put into the animal kingdom, we must give them one of their own or call them many-celled protists. Since fossils cannot solve this problem, this book leaves the sponges as doubtful animals.

WHYS AND HOWS OF CLASSIFICATION

We have been engaged in classification, which separates unlike organisms and groups like ones together. This practice is far from novel, for it was used by the first human being who recognized his kinship with other men or gave different deer one general name because they had branching antlers. Ever since that time people have tried to distinguish different living things and put them together in larger and larger groups. In doing so, men were able to talk with one another about plants and animals. At the same time they organized their knowledge of the animate world.

The Linnaean System. There have been many systems of classification, both rule-of-thumb and scientific. The one now used took form during the 1700's in the books of a Swedish explorer-doctor-professor named Carl (or Carolus) Linnaeus. He based classification upon the kind, or species, which for him was a unit that could be clearly defined. Species that resembled each other in structure or appearance were grouped together in genera, each group being a genus. Similar genera formed orders, and orders made up classes. Linnaeus recognized six classes of animals and several more of plants.

Linnaeus assumed that species were divinely created and described them without pausing to explain how or why they had come into existence. Later naturalists and theologians abandoned his example, especially when skeptics began to suggest that species might vary, or that they might produce other species, and so on through genera, orders, and classes. To combat these here-

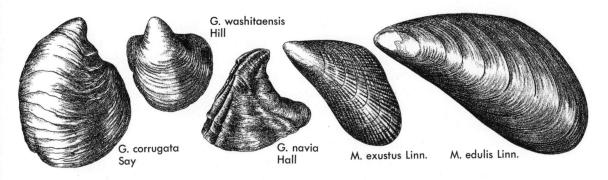

G. washitaensis
Hill

G. corrugata
Say

G. navia
Hall

M. exustus Linn.

M. edulis Linn.

Examples of related but distinct species of Gryphaea and Mytilus

sies, clerics built up a dogma of divinely established classification, while natural philosophers explained that it revealed the "power, wisdom, and good- ness of God as manifested in His creatures." Others invented a long series of catastrophes to get rid of fossil plants and animals, following each disaster by a new creation in which divine wisdom progressed enough to permit the crea- tion of more and more advanced organisms. The culmination of this process supposedly took place in early November of 4004 B.C., when man was created as an improvement of a plan already tried, with limited success, in the anthropoid apes.

This sort of thinking prevailed until 1859, when Charles Darwin declared that species could and did produce other species by processes which also accounted for larger groups and the general sequence of life that was revealed by fossils. Darwin's theory aroused bitter opposition but reoriented paleontology and gave new meaning to classification. Scientists began to study fossils in order to learn how they had varied and how they had changed, or evolved, as age succeeded age. Classification, besides distinguishing and naming the spe- cies and lesser groups produced by evolution, began to show how these groups were related in genera, families, orders, and so on. Revising their sequence, to go from great to small, we may illustrate the system thus developed with the common Atlantic coast oyster as an example:

KINGDOM: Animalia (all animals, either as they are restricted in this book or in- cluding the so-called protozoans)
  PHYLUM: Mollusca (the mollusks, most of which have limy shells)
    CLASS: Pelecypoda (the pelecypods—clams, oysters, mussels, etc., whose shells contain two parts, or valves)
      ORDER: Dysodonta (jingle shells, scallops, oysters, marine mussels, etc.)
        FAMILY: Ostreidae (oysters and their close relatives)
          GENUS: *Ostrea* (true oysters)
            SPECIES: *virginica* (the common eastern or American oyster, a fos- sil as well as a living species)

These are the basic groups used for all organisms. Modern scientists have added such divisions as subphyla, subclasses, and superorders, as well as sub- genera, subspecies, races, and varieties. Since these are recognized in some groups but not in others, we need not give examples of them.

Names and What They Tell. Every group of organisms needs a name, which is chosen according to methods established by Linnaeus but elaborated by later workers. With a few exceptions, Linnaeus gave one-word names to groups larger than species—*Ostrea* for all oysters, *Aves* for the whole class of birds, and so on. But a species requires two words, the first to place it in its genus and the second to distinguish it from related species. Thus the dark blue edible mussel was called *Mytilus edulis,* while another species tinted with buff and brown became *Mytilus exustus.* The name of the genus always comes first, just as John Smith becomes Smith, John in an index or directory. To avoid tiresome repetition, however, the generic name may be indicated by its initial after it has been given in full.

Two types of additions have been made to the names employed by Linnaeus. The first type recognizes divisions and includes them. If a genus is divided, the appropriate subgeneric name is inserted in parentheses, *Mytilus (Hormomya) adamsianus* being a convenient example. When a species is divided, the varietal or subspecific name is added, as in *Theodossia auritus pterotus.* If an effort is made to distinguish between various types of subspecific divisions, the appropriate term or abbreviation may be inserted, as *Mucrospirifer mucronatus* mut. *profundus,* "mut." being an abbreviation for "mutant." Paleontologists tend to avoid triple names, or trinomials, by raising subspecies to the rank of species. This shortens labels and saves breath in discussion, but it obscures close relationships and so limits the value of classification.

The second type of addition comes from the fact that different people sometimes name the same genus or species, or give the same name to different groups. To show who named what, the author's name is added—*Mytilus* Linnaeus, for instance, or *Strophomena neglecta* James. If a species first named in one genus is moved to another, the author's name goes into parentheses. Thus *Atrypa reticularis* (Linnaeus) was first called *Anomites* but later was transferred to *Atrypa.* Paleobotanists go still further, putting the original author's name in parentheses and adding that of the authority who gave the species its present generic assignment. Thus *Metasequoia occidentalis* (Newberry) Chaney 1951 was described as *Taxodium occidentale* by Newberry but was transferred to *Metasequoia* by Chaney in 1951.

Names in "Dead" Languages. Linnaeus wrote his books in Latin and chose names from that language or from Latinized Greek. Other scientists followed his example, Latinizing words from modern tongues when the classics became inadequate, and combining words of varied origins when that suited the author's purpose. The results have often been useful, even helpful, but they also include such bizarre or puzzling names as *Agassizocrinus, Chicagocrinus* (should it be pronounced Chi ca″ go cri′ nus?), and *Hesperopithecus haroldcooki.* Moreover, the whole practice of using "dead" languages has brought endless complaints from people who want things to bear familiar names. Why use polysyllables borrowed from or turned into ancient languages?

The best reason for doing so is the fact that familiar names do not exist. Most species, genera, and other groups were unrecognized, unknown, or unnamed until scientists described them; English, for instance, has no original, everyday names for fossils or the study of them, for such great groups as mammals, amphibians, vertebrates, or mollusks, or for the horde of families, genera, and species which are recognized today. Names, therefore, had to be invented, and the simplest way to do that was to take them from Latin and

Spyroceras bilin-
eatum (Hall).
Middle Ordovician

Michelinoceras sociale
(Hall). Middle to late
Ordovician

Striaoceras typum
(Saemann). Middle
Devonian

Protocycloceras
lamarcki (Billings).
Early Ordovician

Protocameroceras
brainerdi (Whitfield).
Early Ordovician

How names change. All these fossils were once called Orthoceras.

Greek. Just how would one make a familiar and truly English name for reptiles, protists, or *Astylospongia praemorsa?* And why are these names more
"outlandish" than telephone, torque converter, or high-fidelity phonograph?

Another good reason for Latinized names is the fact that they can be used
round the world, in accordance with recognized rules. But "familiar" names
are parts of everyday language, which varies from place to place. Thus the
creatures we call sea urchins are *poundstones* in one part of England, *oursins*
to the French, *Seeigeln* in German, and *erizos de mar* in Spanish-speaking
countries. Even if these terms could be turned into names for genera and species, they would differ in every language and mean nothing to all who did not
speak it. And if only one of the terms were used, it would be "outlandish" in
all other tongues. Just suppose an English-speaking collector had to use the
Japanese sounds and symbol in place of echinoid!

No, the demand for "familiar" names is futile; most of them do not exist
or would not work if we tried to use them. The most we can do is employ the
few that are available and make a limited number of new ones by translating
some technical names and by giving others familiar forms. The first method
turns *Hyalospongea,* for instance, into "glass sponges"; the second writes
Reptilia as "reptiles" and transforms *Mollusca* into "mollusks." It also takes
the capitals from a few generic names, producing new English words such as
eohippus and hydra. Little would be gained by translating the former into
"dawn horse." Not only is the term unfamiliar; the creature itself fell so far
short of being or even resembling a horse that such a name would be deceptive to all who do not understand its evolutionary significance.

Why Names Change. The Linnaean method allows names to be used round
the world, but it cannot keep them from changing.

Many names change because new discoveries show that old groups were so loosely defined that they included various things. In 1758, for example, Linnaeus named the fossil shell now called *Atrypa reticularis*. He did not illustrate his species, however, nor did he describe it in detail. During the next 160 years, therefore, paleontologists applied *reticularis* to a great variety of shells from Silurian and Devonian formations in many parts of the world. Other names were ignored or neglected, and the "species" became a catchall for shells of one general type that lived during periods that amounted to 90,000,000 years.

This went on until the 1920's, when paleontologists began to re-examine this supposedly long-lived species. Looking closely and following modern standards, they recognized forgotten species and described several new ones. Thus fossils once called *reticularis* now bear names such as *nuntia, devoniana,* and *nevada*. Similar refinement has turned *Platystrophia lynx* Eichwald into *ponderosa, moritura, biforata,* and other species or subspecies.

Genera also are subject to refinement and renaming, a good example being *Spirifer*. It too became a catchall that ranged from Silurian to Pennsylvanian, with a vast variety of species. Then it was divided into subgenera and genera —*Delthyris, Eospirifer, Syringothyris,* and so on. More than twenty of these groups are so common that some of their species are recognized as index fossils. The genus *Orthis,* named in 1828, has been divided even more thoroughly.

Other names change because of a rule which says that the first name given a genus or species must hold, even though a later one may be more appropriate or better known. In 1839, for example, bones and teeth of a fossil whale were called *Zeuglodon* ("yoke-tooth"). This name was used for many years, till an expert on whales found that identical bones had been named *Basilosaurus* in 1835. Though *Basilosaurus* means "king of reptiles" it now is the technical name of these whales, leaving zeuglodon—without a capital Z—only in popular usage.

Orthoceras illustrates another rule which says that when the same name is given to more than one genus or species the first usage shall be kept. For more than a century *Orthoceras* was applied to straight-shelled cephalopods (Chapter XIV) found in Ordovician to Triassic formations. Then, in 1936, two authorities showed that this name has been given to clams and several other creatures before it was used for cephalopods. A clam, therefore, has become *Orthoceras,* and many American fossils once given that name are now called *Michelinoceras.*

Large groups, from orders to kingdoms, are exempt from rules, and their names vary with the habits and opinions of authors. Thus the kingdom Protista of this book appears (with a few omissions) as the phylum Protozoa in most older volumes. Corals are Anthozoa or Actinozoa, and the technical name of graptolites (Chapter XX) may be Graptolithina, Graptolitoidea, or Graptozoa. Even duplication is permitted, for both lampreys and a class of bryozoans are called Cyclostomata.

FAMILY TREES OF PHYLA AND CLASSES

In the old, simple days of special creation, biologists often arranged organisms in what was called an "ascending order." This meant that the simplest group was put at the bottom of a series. The one that seemed to rank next in complexity went above it, and so on through the living world. Everyone agreed that plants such as algae (bacteria were virtually unknown) belonged at or near the bottom of this sequence, and animals with backbones at the top. Between these extremes there was some variation, depending on how experts understood complexity.

Then came Darwin and the effort to make classification reflect relationships. But chapters in books follow each other, and so do printed lines on a page. To overcome this disadvantage, biologists began to draw "family trees" for the major groups of organisms. Such trees indicated descent and kinship among these organic groups, just as similar trees had traced kinships in human families.

If this book sought to describe phyla and classes in the order of their relationships, it would begin with monerans, progress with protists, and continue through plants and animals with never a backward glance to tell what members of one great group lived with or upon those of another. Such a plan would serve very well in a textbook, but it would obscure important factors in life's progress, such as the dependence of land-dwelling vertebrates upon complex terrestrial plants. Even then the order of chapters alone would not give relationships clearly unless the text itself went far afield into subjects such as embryology, which is seldom recorded by fossils.

We have chosen to avoid such digressions and to arrange chapters in an order that tells significant stories. Since the relationships of kingdoms have been discussed we make no further effort to trace them. We also do not try to show connections within the kingdom of protists, which may contain several phyla commonly referred to as plants. This leaves relationships within two kingdoms, plants and animals, to be represented by so-called family trees.

The plant kingdom begins with green algae, whose ancestors apparently were green, lash-bearing protists. Some living green algae have only one cell; others, such as sea lettuce, are multicellular. Some of the most remarkable green algae cover themselves with plates or continuous deposits of lime which make the plants resemble corals. In fact, "coralline" algae have often outranked corals as builders of limestone reefs.

Plants more complex than algae belong to eight or nine principal groups, which different authors divide among four to nine phyla. Simplest of these, and presumably oldest, are the mosses and liverworts. The latter are sheetlike affairs that grow on damp soil or rocks. Some authorities think they covered moist lowlands of very ancient times while lichens (which are compounds of fungi and blue-green algae) grew upon dry rocks.

"Higher" plants have roots, stems, leaves, and tubes that carry sap from one part of the organism to another. These tubes first appeared among aquatic or swamp-dwelling plants that apparently ranged round the world. This phylum presumably evolved from green algae that lived near the mouths of rivers, and its members became largest and most abundant during the Pennsylvanian Coal Age, more than 230,000,000 years ago.

Family Tree of Plants. **P.** *Lash-bearing protist ancestors.* **1.** *Green algae.* **2.** *Mosses and liverworts.* **3.** *Psilophytes.* **4.** *Horsetails and lycopods (club mosses and lepidodendrons).* **5.** *Ferns.* **6.** *Seed ferns.* **7.** *Cycads.* **8.** *Ginkgos.* **9.** *Conifers.* **10.** *Flowering plants, which branch into monocotyledons* **(M)** *and dicotyledons* **(D)**. *Some books separate the horsetails and their relatives from lycopods.*

Family Tree of Animals. **1.** *Sponges, whose relationships are uncertain.* **2.** *Comb jellies, which seem to be descended from very early coelenterates.* **3.** *Coelenterates.* **4.** *Flatworms.* **5.** *Brachiopods.* **6.** *Bryozoans.* **7.** *Rotifers.* **8.** *Proboscis worms.* **9.** *Roundworms.* **10.** *Mollusks.* **11.** *Annelids.* **12.** *Onychophores.* **13.** *Arthropods.* **14.** *Echinoderms.* **15.** *Arrow worms.* **16.** *Hemichordates.* **17.** *Tunicates.* **18.** *Cephalochordates (amphioxids).* **19.** *Vertebrates.*

Seed ferns also reached their zenith in Pennsylvanian times, and they seem to have been ancestors of all subsequent phyla. These include the cycads, conifers and their allies, and flowering plants, all of which developed during the last 200,000,000 years.

Compared with plants, the family tree of animals seems to have suffered from lack of pruning. It begins with an inferred ancestor whose body probably was cup-shaped and contained two layers. This creature produced two types of offspring, the sea nuts, or comb jellies, and coelenterates. The latter diverged into several classes—but before going too far, it also produced two types of offspring. In one of these a third body-layer (the mesoderm) developed from within the rim of the cup, expanding into muscles and other organs and enclosing a body cavity. In the second type, the third body-layer came from the inner part of the cup, which was the digestive tract. Pouches that formed there became the mesodermal organs and contained the body cavity, whose technical name is coelom.

Now we see how little such terms as "higher" mean when they are applied to classification. Old systems would make this second body-plan the "higher," since it is found in backboned animals and their relatives. Yet this "enterocoel" plan is limited to just a few phyla—to the six that are numbered 14 to 19 in our family tree of animals. The "lower" (schizocoel) plan, on the other hand, is found in a much larger series of phyla, ten of which appear in our condensed tree. Though none of these phyla equals some chordates in size, intelligence, or complexity of structure, they vastly exceed the enterocoel groups in variety and abundance. Indeed, one schizocoel class (the insects) contains more individuals and species than do all other animal groups combined.

CHAPTER IV

Earth's Oldest Remains

Until the early 1900's, most geologists were sure the earth had begun as a cloud of gas that condensed into a white-hot, molten ball. Slowly that whirling mass lost heat, until its surface solidified into a granite crust. But the molten core still heated that crust, which turned falling rains into steam that returned to a dense, cloud-filled atmosphere.

This primitive planet supposedly was barren, for nothing could live in boiling water or on almost red-hot rock. Life was a late-comer to our earth, the product of a degenerate age in which the planet's surface had lost so much heat that water could accumulate instead of boiling away. Still, early plants and animals supposedly dwelt in tepid water, under constant threat of being parboiled when lava from the still-molten core burst through weak spots in the crust. Life's later story was one of adjustment, first to progressively cooling waters, and then to less and less warmth on land. The last Ice Age was a warning of worse times to come, when the earth's core would lose its original heat and everything at the surface would freeze.

This word picture was dramatic, but it was not true. The earth may or may not have been molten; only theories answer that question, and they disagree. But rocks leave little doubt that our planet has had a firm, cool surface for a very long time—perhaps as long as 3,700,000,000 years. On that surface rains fell and ran into rivers that drained into low places, filling them with lakes or seas. Waves beat against rocky lands, which were either divided into islands or heaved upward until they formed continents. Fragments worn from those lands also settled, building up sedimentary rocks.

Such an earth simplifies life's beginning but makes it incomprehensibly remote. Since the primeval earth was normally cool, living things presumably could exist as soon as water provided them with habitats. That this actually happened is indicated by the variety of organisms that developed before their remains first became abundant, roughly a half billion years ago. Fossils of

Newlandia sarcinula F. & F., a typical stromatolite. Belt of Glacier National Park, Montana

Eozoon canadense Dawson, from the Grenville marble of Quebec

Filled worm burrows of Belt age, Glacier National Park, Montana

Lingulella montana F. & F., a Belt brachiopod. Near White Sulphur Springs, Montana

Typical fossils of late Precambrian (Eozoic) age

that period, the Cambrian, include seaweeds and other plants, one-celled protists, and animals ranging from sponges to crustaceans, jointed worms, and relatives of vertebrates. They show that most of the great steps in animal evolution had taken place before the Cambrian began. Though plants were less progressive, they too had made substantial progress and must have been plentiful during Precambrian times.

THE "DAWN-ANIMAL OF CANADA"

Where there once was life there may now be fossils; the problem has been to find them. Once found, they must be interpreted. What are they and how did they live? What do they tell about life's progress during very ancient times?

The first serious effort to answer these questions began in 1859. In that year Sir William Logan, director of the Geological Survey of Canada, exhibited specimens "of probably organic character" from rocks supposed to be little younger than the so-called primeval crust. Logan submitted the fossils to his friend, J. William Dawson, an outstanding paleontologist. He called them colonial foraminifers, one-celled creatures described in Chapter V, which covered themselves with limy incrustations. Dawson named one species *Eozoon canadense,* the "dawn-animal of Canada."

This he did in 1864, with the approval of an outstanding authority on modern "forams." Some scientists were enthusiastic; others were more reserved, and several became hostile. In 1866 two Irish mineralogists dismissed the "dawn-animal" as a mere mixture of minerals developed as steam and heat from the earth's core changed beds of impure limestone to marble. Another critic compared the supposed fossils with blocks of limestone thrown out of Monte Somma, the ancient volcano on which Mount Vesuvius now stands.

Thus began an argument that is not quite dead today. On one side were Dawson and his supporters, who tried to prove that *Eozoon* was a fossil and described similar things from other very old formations. The opposition included geologists and mineralogists who maintained that all these supposed fossils were inorganic. Most of these critics based their opinions on thin sections, ignoring Dawson's insistence that *Eozoon* should also be seen in its native rock. One German, however, crossed the Atlantic to examine the dawn-animal in ledges and quarries on the Quebec side of the Ottawa River. His verdict agreed with that of his fellows: *Eozoon* showed structures produced by both heat and pressure and therefore was not a fossil.

THE PUZZLING STROMATOLITES

This might have settled the problem had not Dawson found fossils resembling *Eozoon* in rocks of Hastings County, Ontario. Not only were these eozoons virtually unmodified by heat, steam, or compression. They were undeniably related to structures that have come to be known as stromatolites, a term that means "layer stones."

This relationship, however, did not immediately establish the Ontario eozoons as fossils. Stromatolites had been known for many years, and some of them had been described as calcareous protozoans. That theory, however, had lost standing; when interest in the fossils revived they were transferred to the plant kingdom as algae. But several geologists promptly called them inorganic concretions, while an eminent paleobotanist declared that only fossils preserving cells could be referred to algae. Other critics, less specific, were content to dismiss all concern with stromatolites as "unfortunate."

Unfortunate or not, the concern persisted. Today stromatolites are widely, if not generally accepted as fossils produced by stony algae. Indeed, stromatolites are now being formed by algae inhabiting both lakes and seas.

Here again we digress to clarify our words. The term *algae* is a general one; we apply it to plants or plantlike organisms that range from single cells in water or jelly to seaweeds with stalks and leaflike blades, or to jointed growths that resemble corals. According to one theory, stromatolites are the work of very simple blue-green "algae," or cyanophytes, which live in chains or mats and cover themselves with jelly. They also take carbon dioxide from water in order to make food, and in doing so compel limy material to settle

Hadrophycus immanis F. & F. is one of the oldest and largest algal stromatolites, some masses being more than 16 feet in diameter. Found in Precambrian rocks of the Medicine Bow Mountains, Wyoming

in layers upon the jelly. Thus the organisms build stony replicas of their colonies, but not their cells, while they are still alive.

There are three reasons for this interpretation of ancient stromatolites. One is their general lack of cells; only a few specimens contain balls that seem to be cellular. A second reason is the resemblance of a few stromatolites to the spongy, calcareous "lake balls" built by a few modern blue-greens. Finally, a long-standing theory declared that blue-green algae had to be the earliest organisms. If Precambrian stromatolites were algal, it seemed proper that they should have been cyanophytes.

This conclusion, however, has been questioned. On one hand, both green and blue-green algae are now building stromatolites in Walker and Pyramid lakes, Nevada. On the other hand, most really ancient stromatolites are massive—and modern marine structures of this type are the work of red algae. Their cell walls often vanish before the colonies die, and cells that survive are smaller than the grains of dolomite in which the majority of stromatolites are preserved. In other words, the very absence of microscopic structure provides at least negative evidence that stromatolites are red algae, not blue-greens.

With this cautious conclusion we come back to *Eozoon* and other very ancient fossils. *Eozoon* itself is found in limestone and marbles termed the Grenville series, which may be more than 800,000,000 years old. The fossils are convex or vase-shaped and consist of crumpled or gently convex layers whose structure suggests matted tubes and rods.

Hadrophycus ("mighty sea-plant") includes stromatolites that form beds in the Medicine Bow Mountains of Wyoming. Colonies range from irregular sheets to flattened biscuits, swollen heads, and broad-based domes, and structure varies with preservation. Fossils in which dolomite alternates with grainy chert show only crenulate layers. Others, made up of fine-grained chert, contain both layers and thick, irregular pillars. They show most plainly in broken, weathered domes and in those that were scraped smooth by glaciers of the last Ice Age.

Stromatolites have been found in other very old deposits of New Brunswick, the Northwest Territories of Canada, and the Lake Superior region. The most beautiful are those in the dark red iron ore known as jaspilite. Blocks make fine polished slabs, and selected blood-red pieces may be cut for gems.

Algae of Glacier National Park. We now skip long ages and many miles to reach a happy hunting ground for algae in the northern Rockies. There a huge block of Eozoic rocks has been broken and thrust upward and eastward over much younger formations for a distance of thirty-five miles. In the end it formed the spectacular mountains of Glacier National Park, Montana, and Waterton Lakes National Park in adjacent Alberta.

Though shattered along the break, or thrust fault, rocks in the mountains have suffered little change. All show the layers in which their sediment settled, often rapidly but sometimes so slowly that the deposits of two centuries are only one inch thick. Ridges piled up by rippling waves are common, as are cracks that opened when the water retreated, leaving broad mud flats to dry in the sun. Other beds consist of fragments stirred up by floods or violent storms.

Amid these records of a shallow, shifting sea are vast numbers of stromatolites. Some form massive beds near the thrust fault; others are scattered through a thick formation of buff-weathering dolomite. Compact biscuits are found in the lowermost beds; flat-topped colonies appear higher in the series, beside trails and along a paved highway that crosses Glacier National Park. This road also cuts ledges made up of conical masses, and reefs as fine as those built by corals during later times. Those reefs grew while the muddy sea bottom was soft, for their weight squeezed the sediment below them and pushed it up at their sides.

Most surprising of all are algal biscuits found in red and green strata along the Continental Divide. These stromatolites almost always grew upon mud flats that had dried and cracked and then were covered by shallow water. Sudden storms often rolled the biscuits over; others were caught in floods of

Collenia frequens Walcott (left), *and Collenia versiformis F. & F.* (right). *Two types of algal stromatolites from Eozoic (Belt) deposits of Glacier National Park, Montana*

lava that issued from cracks. These lavas tore up mud and rolled it into twisted masses and turned stromatolites into lumps of iron-stained chert. So persistent were the algae, however, that they reappeared as soon as the lava hardened and was covered by a thin coat of mud.

Most of these fossils have been called *Collenia*, a name applied to stromatolites made up of convex layers that are flattened near the center. They form biscuit-shaped or columnar colonies, and many columns may unite in one larger colony. Stromatolites that grew on cracked mud or hardened lava are now placed in *Cryptozoon*. Unfortunately stromatolites varied with the conditions under which they developed, and these variations do not fit under any name.

STONY ALGAE OF LATER AGES

Stromatolites were not limited to the earliest eras but grew abundantly in seas of Cambrian and later times. Some may be called *Collenia*, but others must be placed in different genera.

Cryptozoon ("puzzling animal") was named in the days when *Eozoon* was regarded as a foraminifer. It generally grew in crumpled layers that formed biscuits or domes whose upper surface resembled cauliflower, though at least one species spread out in undulating layers. The most spectacular form, *Cryptozoon proliferum,* was crowded into great barrier reefs around an island

A reef of algal stromatolites called Collenia (above) in Belt strata. Going-to-the-Sun Highway in Glacier National Park, Montana. (Below) A bed of Cryptozoon proliferum Hall. Late Cambrian of the "Petrified Sea Gardens" near Saratoga Springs, New York

which now forms the Adirondack Mountains. Part of one reef, scraped smooth by glaciers, is to be seen in the "Petrified Sea Gardens" near Saratoga Springs, New York. Good collecting grounds may be found near State College, Pennsylvania. A very different species occurs at Fountain, Minnesota, and in a bank beside U. S. Highway 52, 6.8 miles north of that town.

Solenopora is known to be a red alga, for its biscuits and heads are made up of tiny calcareous tubes that formed around algal filaments. *Girvanella* also is made up of tubes, but its small colonies are spheroidal or egg-shaped. *Ottonosia* looks like a little, crumpled *Cryptozoon* that developed around a shell, pebble, or some other solid body.

Algae of Fresh-water Lakes. Some 50,000,000 years ago two broad lakes described in Chapter XXI covered parts of what now are Wyoming, Colorado, and Utah. Near the shores were rich growths of what seems to be a blue-green alga known as *Chlorellopsis*. Its cells were covered by small limy shells; the shells accumulated in layers, and the layers built biscuit-shaped masses resembling *Cryptozoon*. *Chlorellopsis* also grew around logs or upright stumps which finally were replaced by chalcedony. Some of these have been mistaken for geyser tubes or cones.

OTHER PRECAMBRIAN FOSSILS

We now return to Precambrian times and formations. What records of life do they provide in addition to stromatolites?

Cells of bacteria and blue-green algae have been identified in Huronian rocks of northern Michigan, where some slates also contain coal and lumps that seem to be jellylike masses resembling those formed by the modern blue-green alga, *Nostoc*. The Gunflint cherts, of early Huronian age, contain filaments that seem to be both blue-greens and aquatic fungi, as well as amino acids, which are sometimes called the "building blocks" of living material. The age of these varied remains may be estimated at 1,600,000,000 to 1,800,000,000 years.

Dots of carbon found in Glacier National Park also resemble *Nostoc*. Other films may belong to brown algae related to rockweeds. Tiny green algae have been found in India, and carbonized films that seem to be plants come from Archeozoic rocks of Finland. Some skeptics, however, say that the carbon is inorganic.

Precambrian animals are less plentiful than algae. Remains of sponges have been found in limestone about 1,000,000,000 years old. Filled worm burrows have been found in Belt deposits of Glacier National Park, where an arthropod fragment was discovered many years ago. Small disks of carbon from India seem to be algae, but brachiopods have been described from Belt strata near Little Birch Creek, west of White Sulphur Springs, Montana. These shells, which reach 1.5 inches in length, are flat and wrinkled and may have been largely chitinous. They covered animals whose habits resembled those of the modern *Lingula,* though it is not clear that they burrowed so effectively.

In 1928 one-celled protists, annelids, and arthropods were reported from late Precambrian rocks of Adelaide district, in South Australia. Illustrations seem to show recognizable fossils, including creatures much like the euryp-terids described in Chapter XIX. Many paleontologists are skeptical, how-ever, and demand more evidence before they will accept these Australian specimens as animals.

WHY ARE PRECAMBRIAN ANIMALS RARE?

Several theories have tried to explain why remains of Precambrian animals are the rarest and often the poorest of fossils. The most likely explanation seems to be that animals took a long time to evolve and that still more ages passed before they built hard shells, solid supports, or tough chitinous crusts on their skins. Wrinkled surfaces suggest that the first brachiopod shells were tough and stiff rather than hard; some Ordovician corals built small and simple cups, and supposed Precambrian arthropods from Australia had such thin coverings that they can barely be distinguished as fossils. Though most great groups of animals existed, they had not yet got round to protecting themselves with structures that could last long enough to be buried and preserved as fossils.

CHAPTER V

A Variety of Protists

ONE THEORY holds that protists began when a purple bacterium that swam with a lash produced offspring whose cells contained nuclei. The mixture of red and green material changed, too, becoming either yellow or green and increasing its ability to make food from carbon dioxide and water. The new organisms, in short, were essentially like the plantlike stage of *Chrysamoeba*. Many later types lost their food-making materials, however, and began to feed upon their neighbors.

STONY FLAGELLATES

This story is theoretical, but lash-bearing protists, or flagellates, are important though microscopic fossils. Those called coccoliths are ball-shaped or buttonlike bits of silica with varied ornamentation and even collars of spines. They go back at least to the Jurassic and perhaps to the Silurian period.

Silicoflagellates resemble radiolarians, which we describe later, but are less symmetrical. Some silicoflagellates have radial spines, but others are round or star-shaped. Fossils are found in Cretaceous and later formations.

Dinoflagellates move by means of two lashes, and many build shells of a substance that resembles wood. Modern dinoflagellates include the organisms that cause "red rain" and "red snow" on land as well as "red tides" in the ocean. Still other types produce much of the phosphorescence that makes sea water glow at night. Fossil dinoflagellates vary greatly in size, in shape, and in ornamentation, which ranges from frills and knobs to branched spines. The group appears in Pennsylvanian strata, and its members are common in Jurassic to Recent deposits.

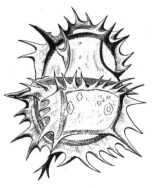

Ctenidodinium, Jurassic

Peridinium
Cretaceous

Palaeogleodinium
Cretaceous

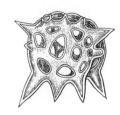

Cannopilus, a
Miocene chrysomonad

Three dinoflagellates of Mesozoic age

Coccolithus
Jurassic-Recent

Thoracosphaera
Tertiary-Recent

Two typical coccoliths

Actinoptychus
Miocene-Recent

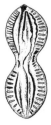

Diploneis
Pliocene

Melosira
Tertiary-Recent

Three diatoms of Cenozoic age

Though they are often divided among plants and animals, these fossils find less confusing places among the protists. All enlarged

DIATOMS

Modern diatoms are enormously abundant in cool seas as well as in streams and lakes. They are solitary or colonial creatures that build ornate shells, or frustules, of silica. Each frustule contains two parts, one of which partly covers the other, as a lid fits over a box. Shapes vary endlessly, as does ornamentation, but marine species tend to be round, while fresh-water types are often elongate. The oldest marine diatoms are found in late Cretaceous strata; fresh-water species appear in lake beds of Tertiary age.

Modern diatoms form a large part of the sediment that settles on ocean bottoms, especially in arctic and antarctic regions. During the Tertiary period, diatoms were even more important in seas that encroached upon California, where the Monterey shale, of Miocene age, exceeds 200 feet in thickness. It seems likely that many pre-Tertiary cherts also were first formed by these protists, whose boxlike shells disappeared during later ages. Their silica, however, remains in layers of compact rock.

ROOT-FEET AND GLASSY SHELLS

Most fossil protozoans belong to the rhizopods, or Sarcodina. The former name means "root-feet" and aptly describes the pseudopods which these creatures put out as they feed, crawl, or drift about in fresh and marine waters. Once thought to be primitive, they now are known to possess simplified bodies from which ancestral flagella have not quite disappeared. Though some are bare, soft, and shapeless, others build up shells that are beautiful as well as complex.

Radiolarians. If beauty were our criterion, radiolarians would rank as the most important rhizopods. The typical radiolarian consists of a spherical or compressed body supported by a shell of glassy silica that may contain several netlike layers and is commonly studded with spines. Another porous capsule lies in the jellylike flesh, or protoplasm, and divides it into two regions. The outer one sends out raylike pseudopods and digests food; the inner contains one or more nuclei and carries on reproduction. When necessary, the protist can use food produced by tiny algae that live in its protoplasm. They, in turn, utilize carbon dioxide and nitrogen-bearing wastes that are given off by the protists.

This is the typical plan; one that has many variations. Some radiolarians have a capsule but no shell, or exoskeleton. Others have no spines, are shaped like small pine cones, or divide into radiating lobes. One group has shells made of strontium sulfate instead of silica.

Radiolarians were once thought to be rare and unimportant fossils. They are now known to be common in the Eozoic quartzites of France, and they make up many siliceous strata in Devonian and later formations. Especially rich deposits are found in late Cretaceous and Tertiary rocks of California.

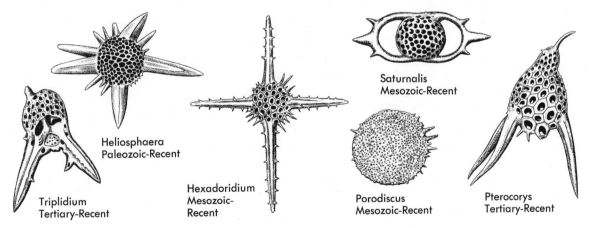

Triplidium
Tertiary-Recent

Heliosphaera
Paleozoic-Recent

Hexadoridium
Mesozoic-
Recent

Saturnalis
Mesozoic-Recent

Porodiscus
Mesozoic-Recent

Pterocorys
Tertiary-Recent

Recent and Fossil Radiolarians. All enlarged

THE VARIED AND USEFUL "FORAMS"

Many a paleontologist has lived a long and useful life without seeing fossil flagellates, ciliates, or even radiolarians. But no one who deals with so-called invertebrates can afford to overlook the Foraminifera, whose name is commonly shortened to "forams." Not only are they the most abundant and best-preserved fossil protists; they also are the most useful of index fossils. No one knows how many oil wells they have helped to locate or how many formations they have helped to identify.

The word *foraminifer* means "bearer of openings"—openings in a capsule or shell which is better termed a *test*. Though some foraminifers have only a tough surface layer, the majority build tests provided with one or many openings. The jellylike flesh, or protoplasm, may be confined inside the test and send out pseudopods through one large foramen. More commonly, protoplasm both fills the test and covers it, flows freely through many foramina, and sends forth pseudopods from any part of the surface. These "false feet" are slender and commonly branch, but they also run together and fuse. This happens when food is captured, forming islands in which it is digested outside the central body and test.

Cells and Life Cycles. Long before anyone knew that "forams" were useful, students of fossils discovered that many species came in two different forms. One, called megalospheric, began with a relatively large part called the proloculum ("first little chamber") but developed a small test. The other form, termed microspheric, began with a small proloculum but produced a test which was much larger than that of the microspheric form.

The reason for this contrast became clear when biologists got round to study reproduction in modern foraminifers. Microspheres are sexless creatures whose nuclei divide until many are scattered through each cell. When the latter reaches maturity, its protoplasm flows from the test and divides into balls, one for each nucleus. These balls, which are young forams, construct large prolocula and go on to build megalospheres.

Though produced by asexual reproduction, the megalospheric form itself reproduces sexually. At maturity its nucleus divides into many tiny parts, each of which becomes the core of a lash-bearing swarm-cell that resembles a small, gray *Chrysamoeba*. Many of these swarm-cells die, but a few come together in pairs, unite, and build new microspheres. They, of course, reproduce asexually and thereby continue the cycle of alternating generations.

This is the "typical" cycle—but, like many other typical things, it is subject to variation. This is true when megalospheres produce still more megalospheres for two, three, or even more generations before going back to microspheres. Since the prolocula of these generations differ in size, they seem to give such species more than their normal two forms.

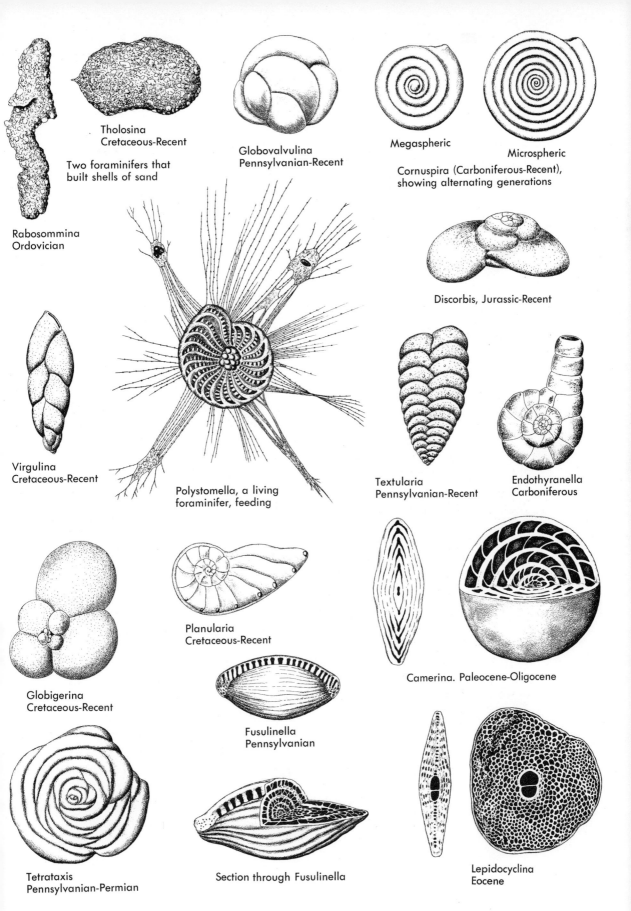

Tholosina
Cretaceous-Recent

Two foraminifers that
built shells of sand

Globovalvulina
Pennsylvanian-Recent

Megaspheric

Microspheric

Cornuspira (Carboniferous-Recent),
showing alternating generations

Rabosommina
Ordovician

Discorbis, Jurassic-Recent

Virgulina
Cretaceous-Recent

Polystomella, a living
foraminifer, feeding

Textularia
Pennsylvanian-Recent

Endothyranella
Carboniferous

Globigerina
Cretaceous-Recent

Planularia
Cretaceous-Recent

Fusulinella
Pennsylvanian

Camerina. Paleocene-Oligocene

Tetrataxis
Pennsylvanian-Permian

Section through Fusulinella

Lepidocyclina
Eocene

Foraminifers, all enlarged

Tests of Several Kinds. The tests of some Foraminifera are 0.1 millimeter in diameter, or one two hundred fiftieth of an inch. Others are 25 to 75 millimeters (1 to 3 inches) in length, and the largest have diameters ranging from 4 to 7.6 inches. The commonest diameter, however, is roughly one fiftieth of an inch, or one third that of a small pinhead.

Chitinous tests are the simplest and may be the most primitive. They are round, oval, or flask-shaped and consist of material that looks rather like clear plastic or the crisp layer that covers insects. This so-called chitin also survives in the early stages of very different tests.

Agglutinated tests are just what their name suggests. They consist of mud, sand, or other material glued together by cement which may be chitinous, limy, glassy, or an iron compound. Some foraminifers use anything they can get; others use only one substance, such as sand, tiny flakes of mica, or tiny particles of shell. A few, such as *Textularia,* employ quartz sand where they inhabit cold water, but select limy particles where the water is warm.

Calcareous tests also are limy, but they are not agglutinated. They consist of calcite secreted by the living protists, just as snail shells are made of calcite secreted by living snails. The calcite may be either grainy or crystalline, and the shells may be impunctate or filled with foramina.

Siliceous, or glassy, tests are not common and their significance has been disputed. One theory says their silica is secreted by the creatures that build them, but others think it has replaced calcite or other material.

Varied Forms and Structures. The simplest tests, as we have said, are round, oval, or flask-shaped structures made up of so-called chitin. Similar forms are found among agglutinated and calcareous Foraminifera.

Next in the scale of organization come stellate tests and tubes. The former contain a hollow central body and radial arms, both made up of material collected on the body and pseudopods and fastened together by their secretions. Tubes start out as oval or ball-shaped chambers and increase in length as their makers grow larger. Some tubes remain straight; others curve and twist like worms; many form flat, tightly coiled spirals which may straighten at the end. Most surprising are tubes that branch like so many tiny bushes that stand on sand or mud.

Chambered shells also start out with a proloculum, either large or small. As the creature grows, its protoplasm flows out of this chamber and builds others of ever-increasing size. These new chambers may form in a straight series; more often they coil or overlap in one, two, or three series. Since these changes take place in regular order, they build up tests that characterize different genera and species. So do structures in the walls, which range from thin and solid to thick and very complex. Other characteristics are found in the walls, which are smooth or fluted partitions between successive chambers.

Some Typical "Forams." Foraminifers have been reported from Precambrian strata in northern France, and from Cambrian rocks of New Brunswick and several other regions. But all these supposed fossils have been questioned, so that the first undoubted "forams" are agglutinated capsules and tubes from middle Ordovician rocks of Oklahoma. Coiled tubes appear in the Silurian, and chambered tests that are closely coiled are found in upper Devonian formations. Foraminifers of later ages achieved great variety.

Three groups that deserve special mention are the fusulinids, camerinids, and orbitoids. The first appeared in late Mississippian seas, spread widely and evolved rapidly, and then died out before the Permian period closed. Early species were thin and almost disk-shaped; later types became spheroidal or spread sidewise until they resembled grains of oats or small cucumbers. They also increased in size from bodies less than 2 millimeters thick and 4 wide to others whose width—it seems to be length—was as much as 3 inches.

Camerinids (once called nummulites) were large discoidal foraminifers that appeared in Pennsylvanian seas, ranged widely during the Tertiary period, and still survive. They were especially abundant in a sea that filled the present Mediterranean basin and covered adjacent parts of Europe, Asia, and Africa. Limestone made largely of camerinid tests was used to build the pyramids of Egypt. The fossils were regarded as petrified lentils by the Greek historian Herodotus, who thought them to be remains of food which the Egyptians provided for their slaves.

The orbitoids also are large and are disklike, saddle-shaped, or stellate; some of them were once placed among the camerinids. The best-known American species belong to the genus *Lepidocyclina* and are found in Tertiary formations from Florida to Texas as well as in California.

Ways and Environments. Though most modern foraminifers are marine, some inhabit brackish water. A few have also been found in Hungarian lakes and in desert wells of Asia and North Africa. The vast majority of Paleozoic and early Mesozoic species lay or crawled on the bottoms of shallow seas, a way of life that was shared by camerinids and orbitoids. All were most abundant near shores, a condition that prevails among bottom-dwellers today.

During the latter half of the Mesozoic era, a variety of small foraminifers took up life in the open sea. There they drifted near the surface, where currents carried them far and wide. Some also evolved rapidly, developing new types at a rate rivaling that of the bottom-dwelling fusulinids. Since most of these new forms were short-lived, their remains were preserved in one or a few related formations.

Foraminifers also are limited by temperature and by conditions of the sea bottom. Off our modern Atlantic coast, for example, four different groups of these protists are found in four zones that differ in temperature as well as in depth. A lower Cretaceous formation in northern Texas contains one lot of bottom-dwelling species in dark, thin-bedded shale, another in brown to gray shales and marls, and a third in places where the rocks are yellow marls and limestones. Comparable differences are found in several other formations.

Tales Told by "Forams." These facts show that different fossils can be used to trace conditions in long-vanished seas. An abundance of bottom-dwelling species means shallow water; if they grow more plentiful as we travel in a given direction, we are nearing the ancient shore. Different types of bottom-dwellers imply different bottoms, but varied drifting forms apparently record variations in temperature. If the fossils are closely related to modern species, we can tell which assemblages indicate warm water and which show that it was cool or cold.

Of still greater practical importance is the fact that many species are excellent index fossils whose value is increased by the fact that most of them are small enough to be found in the cores removed from test borings and oil wells. This means that they can be used to identify formations that lie deep down in the ground as well as those at the surface. Thus one formation in an oil-bearing series has been traced from Nebraska to New Mexico by its fusulinids. An agglutinated species, *Vulvulina advena,* marks upper Cretaceous formations from Cuba to Alabama and eastern Mexico, and so on. So important are these index species that oil companies maintain staffs of experts to identify them and so guide geologists and drillers.

CHAPTER VI

Sponges, True and Probable

Placing sponges among animals, we accept them as a phylum called the Porifera, or pore-bearers. Those we see every day are soft-bodied creatures that have little chance of becoming fossils. Other sponges, however, build skeletons of silica or calcite that are readily preserved. As a result, fossil sponges are found in some Precambrian and many later formations.

Throughout most of their history sponges have lived in shallow seas, though a few have retreated into deep water, and one family of fifty-odd species now inhabits lakes, ponds, and streams. Young sponges may drift in the water, but adults are attached to muddy or sandy bottoms, to rocks, or to other organisms. The creatures live alone or in colonies that range from a few simple branches to complex masses whose members interfinger and unite. Some sponges are smaller than a pinhead, but others reach 3 to 4 feet in diameter and height.

Though many colonies become complex, the basic plan of all sponges is simple. It consists of a cup-shaped or vaselike body that is attached at the bottom, open at the top, and pierced by many small tubes or canals. Half of these start at the surface and extend inward; the rest begin in the body wall and open into a central cavity commonly called the cloaca. Water enters the outer canals, goes through the inner ones to the cloaca, and then out of the opening at its top, termed the osculum. During this journey the sponge removes oxygen and bits of food but gives off wastes of various sorts and reproductive cells.

The cells in this simple body belong to three general types and are found in three different layers. First among these is the ectoderm ("outer skin"), which both covers the body and lines the outer, or incurrent, canals. Most cells of the ectoderm are thin and flat, but others overlap to form funnels that contain the openings that lead to the inner canals. These funnels can be closed, stopping the flow of water when that becomes necessary.

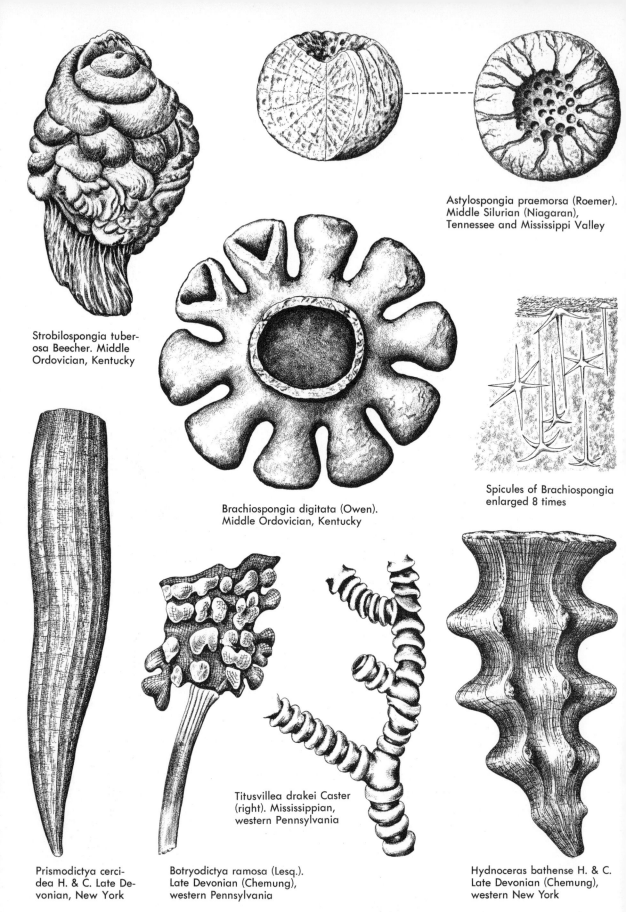

Astylospongia praemorsa (Roemer).
Middle Silurian (Niagaran),
Tennessee and Mississippi Valley

Strobilospongia tuber-
osa Beecher. Middle
Ordovician, Kentucky

Spicules of Brachiospongia
enlarged 8 times

Brachiospongia digitata (Owen).
Middle Ordovician, Kentucky

Titusvillea drakei Caster
(right). Mississippian,
western Pennsylvania

Prismodictya cerci-
dea H. & C. Late De-
vonian, New York

Botryodictya ramosa (Lesq.).
Late Devonian (Chemung),
western Pennsylvania

Hydnoceras bathense H. & C.
Late Devonian (Chemung),
western New York

Some typical Paleozoic sponges

The endoderm ("inner skin") lines both the cloaca and the inner, or radial, canals. Cells in the cavity are thin, but those that line the canals are thick and have lashes surrounded by cuplike collars. As the lashes beat to and fro they produce the currents that bring water into the sponge and send it out again. Food particles are captured as they settle on the collars and are carried into the cells.

The sponge's third layer lies between ectoderm and endoderm. It consists of jelly in which are irregular cells that send out pseudopods and is quite different from the mesoderm of other three-layered animals. Some of the cells wander about, digesting food or distributing it and collecting waste materials. Others build up fibers of tough spongin or make sharp-pointed spicules of calcite or silica. These fibers or spicules form the skeleton of the sponge.

Sponges and two receptaculitids

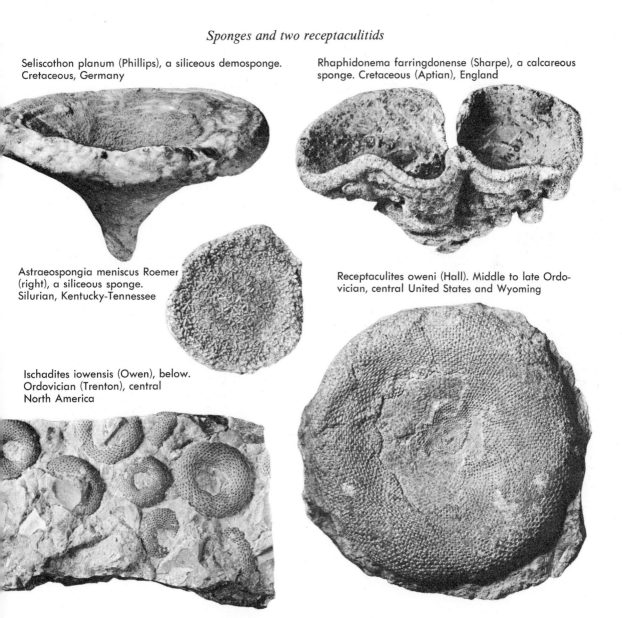

Seliscothon planum (Phillips), a siliceous demosponge. Cretaceous, Germany

Rhaphidonema farringdonense (Sharpe), a calcareous sponge. Cretaceous (Aptian), England

Astraeospongia meniscus Roemer (right), a siliceous sponge. Silurian, Kentucky-Tennessee

Receptaculites oweni (Hall). Middle to late Ordovician, central United States and Wyoming

Ischadites iowensis (Owen), below. Ordovician (Trenton), central North America

A SURVEY OF FOSSIL SPONGES

Like most creatures that have lived through the ages, sponges have divided into several very different groups whose histories overlap. All three, indeed, seem to be so ancient that no one can tell which came first or how they developed.

Calcareous Sponges (Calcispongea). This group includes the simplest sponges, and on that ground might be ranked as the most primitive. But these simple forms are known only from modern seas, which suggests that their simplicity may have come about through degeneration instead of being the product of survival from very ancient times.

The calcareous, or limy, sponges have skeletons made of calcite or the related mineral called aragonite. Though some spicules are needle-shaped, others have three or four branches. They also may be separate or fastened together in firm but porous masses.

Modern members of this group live near the shores of shallow seas, and fossils seem to have had similar habitats. They appear as small, branched colonies of Cambrian age, become chains of overlapping spheres in late Paleozoic formations, and achieve moderate variety in Jurassic and Cretaceous formations of Europe. Most American species are found in Pennsylvanian and Permian rocks of the Southwest.

Glass Sponges (Hyalospongea). These sponges have siliceous spicules with six rays, one of which may be so much longer than the others that it looks like a wisp of spun glass. Though most ancient members of this group lived in shallow water, their descendants are found at depths of 300 to 17,000 feet.

Glass sponges were present in early Cambrian seas and achieved great variety by mid-Cambrian times. The best specimens, with impressions of spicules and carbonized films representing the vase-shaped bodies, are found at the famous quarry west of Burgess Pass near Field, British Columbia, described in Chapter XVI.

Glass sponges are rare in Ordovician and Silurian formations but are preserved in enormous numbers in late Devonian formations of western New York. The fossils lie in dark, fine-grained sandstone and are hardened fillings, or internal molds, which show the shapes of the fossils as well as impressions of their long, fibrous spicules. Anyone who wants to know what the skeletons looked like may compare them with the modern Venus's-flower-basket (*Euplectella*), which lives in the Pacific Ocean near the Philippine Islands and Japan. Fossils range in length from a few inches to as much as 10 feet.

Though glass sponges declined after Devonian times, they continued to live and evolve. One of the most interesting of later types is *Titusvillea*, from early Mississippian deposits of northwestern Pennsylvania. It consists of branching

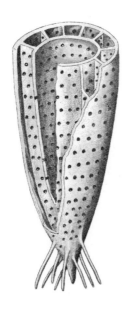

Diagram of a pleosponge (right), *showing walls, pores, and props.* (Left), *Ajicicyathus nevadensis (Okulitch), an early Cambrian pleosponge from Nevada. Enlarged 8 times*

Vauxia dignata Walcott, a colonial glass sponge of middle Cambrian age. Burgess Pass, near Field, British Columbia. Enlarged about 4 times

colonies made up of cuplike individuals whose cavities are continuous. They open in a single osculum at the end of each branch.

Brachiospongia is an Ordovician form which may or may not be an aberrant glass sponge. It looks like a broad, ornate pot with its lower part squeezed out into a series of hollow pouches. The most familiar species is found in middle Ordovician deposits of Kentucky and Tennessee, but others occur in late Ordovician rocks.

Astraeospongia is another fossil of uncertain relationships, though many books call it a glass sponge. It is a bowl-shaped organism that seemingly lay on the bottom without attachment. Its spicules, which are very coarse, have six rays arranged like those of a star and two more in the form of buttonlike bumps at right angles to the others. A single species, *A. meniscus,* is common in middle Silurian (Niagaran) rocks of Kentucky and Tennessee. Since it generally is silicified, it weathers out cleanly as beds of limestone are destroyed by solution.

Siliceous and Horny Sponges (Demospongea). This is the largest and most complex group of sponges, with the longest history. It includes forms with needle-shaped or four-branched siliceous spicules, which may or may not be supported by spongin. It also includes our familiar "modern" sponges, from which spicules have disappeared, leaving spongin to form the skeleton of both single sponges and colonies.

Spicules of demosponges have been found in Eozoic rocks, but the first fossils that show entire bodies appear in the middle Cambrian Burgess shale. After them comes a long and varied array of spheroidal, vaselike, and irregular forms, some of which might be mistaken for corals. Rocks containing silicified specimens may be cut and polished to show their structure, which is made up of spicules cemented together into a firm network.

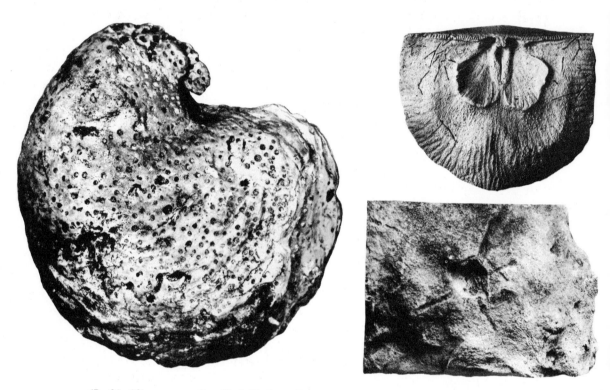

(Left) *Cliona cretacica F. & F., late Cretaceous sponge borings that are common in fossil shells of the Atlantic and Gulf Coastal Plains.* (Upper right) *Clionolithes hackberryensis (Thomas); burrows in late Devonian shells of Iowa.* (Lower right) *Topsentopsis devonica (Clarke), a supposed boring sponge found in Devonian formations from Iowa to New York*

The best and most varied fossil demosponges are found in Jurassic and Cretaceous rocks of France and Germany. Shapes range from stemmed goblets to flattened mushrooms, cones, and crumpled cups.

Some modern demosponges grow upon rocks and shells, dissolving pits or tubes in them and then spreading over their surfaces. Similar cavities have been found in fossil shells of Devonian and later ages. Some are assigned to the modern genus *Cliona,* but others have been given names such as *Clionolithes* and *Clionoides.*

PLEOSPONGES AND "PROBLEMATICA"

Pleo means "full" or "true," and many paleontologists think that pleosponges deserve their name. Others think they are only relatives of sponges, or aberrant descendants of very primitive corals. An alternate name for the group, archaeocyathids ("ancient cups") implies relationship to horn corals.

These conflicting opinions add up to this: Pleosponges probably are not closely related to anything that lives today. In shape they range from saucers to vases and cylinders; conical species generally are pointed at the bottom but have platelike or root-shaped expansions that anchored them to the sea floor. The simplest species have only a thin outer wall of calcite, but others possess an inner wall as well. The space between the walls is divided by vertical partitions which, like the walls themselves, are pierced by many small holes, or pores. Crossbars, platforms, and curved plates that form blisterlike structures appear between the partitions.

A Precambrian fossil, *Atikokania,* looks rather like a pleosponge; it was found in early Proterozoic strata of northwestern Ontario. Except for this problematical form, pleosponges appear only in early and middle Cambrian formations. During those epochs they ranged round the world and often built massive banks or reefs. One Australian deposit in which they are plentiful is 400 miles long and many miles in width.

Receptaculitids. These creatures are commonly called "sunflower corals." Their fossils generally are shaped like saucers or bowls, but these contain only the lower portion of creatures that actually resembled beets or broad turnips turned upside down. Most fossils also are hardened fillings or external molds and so are solid where the creatures were soft and have pits in place of the original skeleton. It consisted of thick calcareous pillars whose ends spread out into flat plates. Both plates and pillars were arranged in spiral rows. Between the skeletal elements were canals resembling those in the walls of undoubted sponges; the osculum was located at the apex.

Receptaculites itself contains twenty or more species, one of which (*R. oweni*) reaches diameters of 12 to 24 inches. During middle and late Ordovician epochs, *Receptaculites* ranged from Nevada to Wyoming, and from Missouri and Maryland to the Arctic, but was most plentiful in the region that is now the upper Mississippi Valley. Several species also are found in Silurian formations, as well as in Devonian and Mississippian deposits of North America, Europe, and Australia.

CHAPTER VII

Simple Coelenterates

Along the Lackawanna railway near East Bethany, New York, lie gentle slopes of gray Devonian shale that is famous for its well-preserved fossils. Lamp-shells, or brachiopods, are abundant, snails of several kinds are common, and molds of clams are not rare. Most abundant, however, are massive and horn-shaped fossils whose structure shows that they belong to two of the four orders of corals.

Corals, in turn, introduce us to the coelenterates, which—with the possible exception of sponges—are the simplest true animals. Corals, however, do not rank as the simplest coelenterates. That honor, if it is one, belongs to the modern hydra, which inhabits quiet streams and fresh-water pools and is illustrated in Chapter III.

Though named for a mythical water serpent with many heads, the real hydra is a little, harmless creature whose body is a slender tube containing two layers of cells separated by a sheet of tough jelly. The base of this tube is loosely attached to a stick or pebble; the upper end contains a mouth. Hollow tentacles stretch out to capture food, which is digested in a central cavity that takes the place of stomach, intestine, and several other organs. Cells in the two body-layers feel, taste, sting prey and twine around it, contract as if they were muscles, and send messages through a network of nerves. Some cells also have pseudopods or lashes, but the latter are not surrounded by collars. This is one good reason for saying that hydra is not closely related to sponges.

The body-plan of hydra is simple, but it has three great advantages. The first of these is efficiency, which has enabled the animal to live and prosper for untold ages. Second, the plan can be changed in many ways, producing creatures that range from delicate colonial organisms to massive polyps and free-swimming jellyfish. Third, early relatives of hydra were able to produce a third layer of cells, thereby giving rise to all animals more complex than the phylum of coelenterates.

COLONIAL HYDROZOANS

This final virtue does not concern us now. Our present task is to become acquainted with the modifications of hydra's plan among the coelenterates.

Hydroids. Our first major group, the hydrozoans, disappoints collectors who want records of innovations made while they still were new. Hydrozoans such as hydra itself presumably evolved early in Precambrian times, since specialized descendants appeared before the Paleozoic era began. But simple hydrozoans are and presumably have always been too soft to be fossilized, and their nearest relatives first achieved that state during the Cambrian period. Their chitinous skeletons have been found in mid-Cambrian and later formations of Australia, Tasmania, Asia, Africa, Europe, and North America. North American occurrences range from Texas to Virginia and New York.

Millepores, or Hydrocorallines. Millepores are colonial hydrozoans that build up limy hard parts. Each colony contains two basic types of animals, or zooids. One type (the gastrozooids) captures food and swallows it; the second type is mouthless and therefore gets nourishment secondhand from the gastrozooids. The noneaters are further divided into relatively long, branched creatures (dactylozooids) whose tentacles help to capture the food which they cannot devour, and short reproductive zooids (ampullae) whose task is to produce young in the form of tiny jellyfish. These, in turn, develop cells that give rise to new colonies. The whole colony is joined by a fleshy sheet that covers the stony base and by tubes that run through it.

Fossil millepores appear in Cretaceous rocks and continue into Recent deposits. Some are massive but many more branch; their surfaces show large pores that once housed gastrozooids and smaller pores that contained dactylozooids. Clusters of still smaller pores contained the reproductive polyps.

Stromatoporoids. These are the most abundant of fossil hydrozoans, though they died out near the end of Cretaceous times. Their name, which means "layer-pores," refers to the fact that these fossils consist of limy layers. Actually, each layer is made up of thin sheets, or laminae, held together by solid or hollow pillars which may branch so many times that the layers become networks. Typical stromatoporoids also show structures called astrorhizae ("root-stars") which consist of central cavities and radial canals or tubes. These resemble the canals and cloacal cavities of fresh-water sponges and are the principal reason why some authorities have placed these fossils among the demosponges. Further evidence is provided by needle-shaped spicules found near astrorhizae.

Stromatoporoids formed massive, sheetlike, encrusting or branched colonies that sometimes spread out upon the sea bottom, sometimes grew upright, and sometimes were interlayered with corals. They appeared in early Ordovician times and continued to the Cretaceous, when they became extinct. During the

Silurian and Devonian periods they built thick beds and limestone reefs in what now are Michigan, Indiana, Illinois, and Iowa, as well as in northern Canada. Individual colonies range from a half inch to 5 feet in thickness and up to 11 feet in width.

Labechiids. These cylindrical or twisted fossils are often placed in the stromatoporoids, though they may belong elsewhere. They have no well-defined laminae but consist of rodlike structures and blister-shaped cysts. *Beatricea* and *Cryptophragmus,* of the Ordovician, have central regions in which the blisters are very large.

ANCIENT JELLYFISH

Living jellyfish belong to two classes, hydrozoan and scyphozoan. Fossils add two others, as well as some lesser groups.

Protomedusans. The oldest known jellyfish is a cast found in Proterozoic sandstone in the Grand Canyon of Arizona. Related types are found in Cambrian rocks of North America and in the Ordovician of Sweden and France. Specimens from the Conasauga shale of the Coosa Valley, Alabama, are preserved as cherty nodules 1 to 10 centimeters in diameter and are locally known as "star cobbles."

The protomedusan body was soft and watery, yet so tough that it often was fossilized. It was divided into irregular lobes, which numbered four to fifteen or even more and were largest on the upper surface. No tentacles hung from the edge of the body, though four or five "arms" projected near the center of the under surface. Tubes, or oral canals, which opened at the tip of each arm secured food and took it to a ventral pouch; other tubes (axial canals) carried it to a round stomach near the upper surface. Radial canals, which extended from the stomach, took digested food to the outer parts of the body.

Dipleurozoans. These early Cambrian jellyfish were discovered in South Australia and should be sought elsewhere. They were oval in shape with scalloped edges; a furrow ran lengthwise through the upper surface, which was divided into many segments by diverging grooves. One small tentacle hung from the tip of each segment.

Scyphomedusans. These members of the class Scyphozoa are sometimes called "true" jellyfish. The most familiar types are umbrella-shaped, with tentacles at the edge of the body and four arms around the central mouth. There is no real stomach, for it divides into four lobes that run out to the edge of the body and are joined by a circular tube. Four U-shaped organs under the "stomach" lobes produce reproductive cells. A band of muscles enables the animals to swim by expanding and then contracting their bodies.

Although jellyfish are soft and consist mostly of water, they become very tough when they lie on beaches and dry out in the sun. As a result, fossil

Peytoia nathorsti Walcott, a jellyfish.
Middle Cambrian, British Columbia

Parapsonema cryptophya Clarke, a hydrozoan jellyfish of late
Devonian age, New York. Upper surface, about 6 inches wide

Paropsonema cryptophya Clarke. Late Devonian
(Portage), Canandaigua Lake, N.Y.

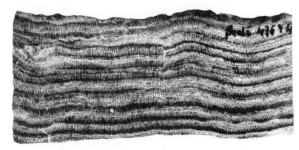

Section of Actinostroma, a stromatoporoid, x 3.
Late Devonian (Shellrock), Iowa

Three stromatoporoid colonies of late Devonian age, from
northern Iowa. Those at the left and right lay on the bottom;
the middle colony stood erect. The dark pits were made by the
supposed boring sponge Topsentopsis devonica Clarke.

Fossil jellyfish and stromatoporoids

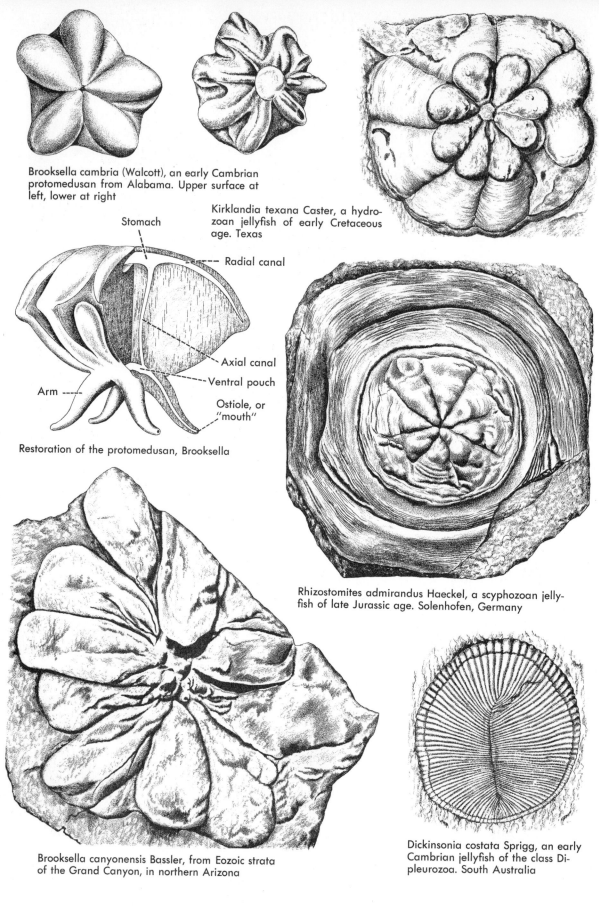

Brooksella cambria (Walcott), an early Cambrian protomedusan from Alabama. Upper surface at left, lower at right

Kirklandia texana Caster, a hydrozoan jellyfish of early Cretaceous age. Texas

Stomach

Radial canal

Axial canal

Ventral pouch

Arm

Ostiole, or "mouth"

Restoration of the protomedusan, Brooksella

Rhizostomites admirandus Haeckel, a scyphozoan jellyfish of late Jurassic age. Solenhofen, Germany

Brooksella canyonensis Bassler, from Eozoic strata of the Grand Canyon, in northern Arizona

Dickinsonia costata Sprigg, an early Cambrian jellyfish of the class Dipleurozoa. South Australia

Jellyfish, or medusae

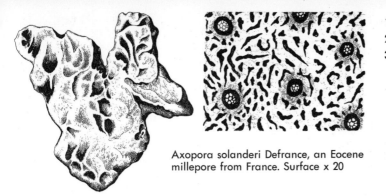

Axopora solanderi Defrance, an Eocene millepore from France. Surface x 20

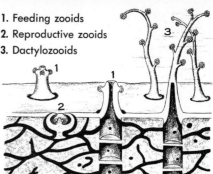

1. Feeding zooids
2. Reproductive zooids
3. Dactylozooids

Diagram of a millepore showing canals (black) and the three types of zooids

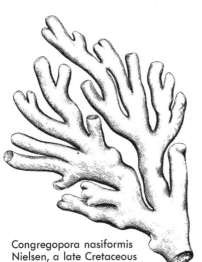

Congregopora nasiformis Nielsen, a late Cretaceous hydrozoan from Denmark

Conchopeltis alternata Walcott, a broad and low conularian. Middle Ordovician of New York

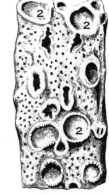

Congregopora enlarged to show pits of the reproductive zooids (2)

Shells of two typical conularians. Restorations at the lower right show one floating and one attached species.

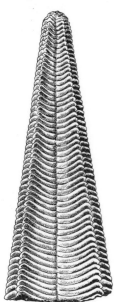

Paraconularia Mississippian

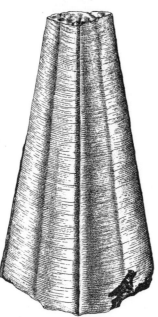

Conularia undulata Conrad Middle Devonian

Exoconularia in the free-swimming state. Ordovician

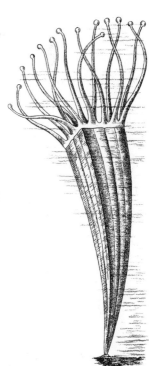

Archaeoconularia, attached. Ordovician and Silurian

Hydrozoans and conularians

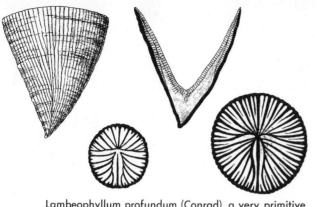

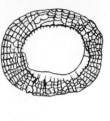

Lambeophyllum profundum (Conrad), a very primitive rugose coral, has septa but no tabulae. Mid-Ordovician, eastern North America

Streptelasma corniculum Hall, with irregular septa. Middle Ordovician, eastern N.A.

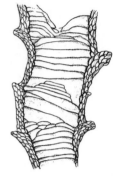

Breviphyllum cliftonense (Amsden). Silurian (Niagaran) of Tennessee

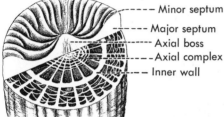

- - - - Minor septum
- - - - Major septum
- - - - Axial boss
- - - - Axial complex
- - - - Inner wall

Some of the structures found in rugose corals

Calyx

Fossula - - - - - - - -
Cardinal septum - - - - - - -
Alar septum and groove - - - -
Growth line - - - - - - -
Septal groove - - - - - - -
Interseptal ridge - - - - - - -

Epitheca

- - - - - Septum
- - - - - Dissepiments
- - - - - Tabulae
- - - - - Septa

Rejuvenation in Heliophyllum halli Edwards & Haime. Middle Devonian of eastern North America

Reproduction, or budding, in rugose corals. Marginal increase at left, lateral increase (center), and axial increase at right

Heliophyllum, species undetermined. Middle Devonian of New York

Lithostrotion. Mississippian, Scotland

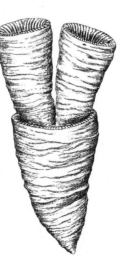

Unidentified "horn" coral. Middle Devonian, Louisville, Kentucky

Structures and features of reproduction in rugose, or horn, corals

jellyfish are much less rare than one might expect. They range from early Cambrian to Recent in age. The finest specimens come from the Jurassic lithographic limestones of Germany.

Conularians. This group of early jellyfish appears among worms or mollusks in books published before 1937. It is typified by *Conularia,* a pyramidal, horny shell with four sides, each with a lengthwise groove and many fine cross ridges. At first the shells were attached to the sea bottom or to other shells; later many species broke loose near their tips and the animals drifted or swam. Tentacles extended from the edge of the body, reaching upward while the creature was attached, but hanging downward when it became a drifter. *Conchopeltis* departed from the norm by building a shell that was low and broad, with the four lobes one expects to find in a jellyfish. The tentacles, which were many, also were very short.

Fossils that resemble *Conularia* have been found in late Precambrian rocks of Montana and South Africa. Other conulates range through the Paleozoic and into Jurassic formations of Europe. The most familiar North American species come from Ordovician, Silurian, and Devonian rocks.

Hydrozoans. Hydrozoan jellyfish range from early Cambrian to Recent but are unusual fossils. Some Recent forms produce eggs that develop into new jellyfish, but the offspring of others settle down and become bottom-dwelling hydrozoans such as millepores. These jellyfish have a central mouth on the under side of the body, which is not divided into lobes. Tentacles hang down from the edge of the body, which may be either shallow and saucerlike or bell-shaped.

Kirklandia is a hydrozoan jellyfish of early Cretaceous age from Texas. *Crucimedusina,* from the Pennsylvanian of Nebraska, had a quadrangular body that was bluntly pyramidal.

Siphonophores are colonial hydrozoans that include individuals of various specialized types. All bud from one original stem, which may be long and slender or may spread out in a disk that is attached to a float. Some fossils are related to the living *Velella,* which has a crest or sail; others lack that structure. All are rare, though specimens have been found in Ordovician and Devonian strata.

CORALS AND THEIR KIN; THE ANTHOZOANS

Corals were once regarded as plants or plant-animals (zoophytes); writers who are indifferent to science sometimes call them insects. Actually they belong to the Anthozoa, a subclass made up of coelenterates that never go through the jellyfish stage and have a tubelike gullet, or stomodaeum, that leads from the mouth to a large central cavity that does the work of a stomach. The tentacles are hollow, like those of hydra. One group, the sea anemones,

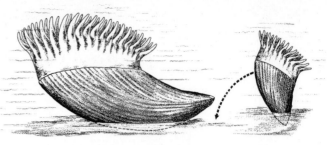

Microcyclus   Hadrophyllum

These corals lay on the sea bottom.

Aulacophyllum stood upright while young. Later it sank on its convex side and lay upon the muddy bottom.

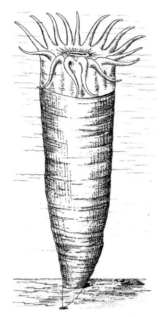

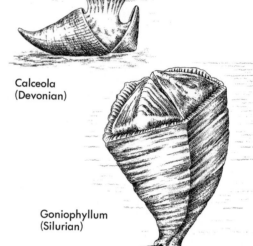

Calceola
(Devonian)

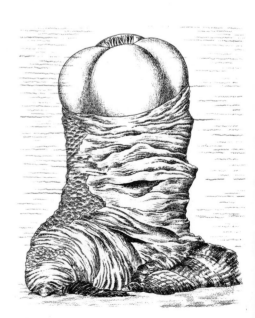

Goniophyllum
(Silurian)

Omphyma kept itself upright by means of rootlike props.

Streptelasma remained upright by sinking into the mud.

Calceola and Goniophyllum covered their soft bodies with stony lids, or opercula. Gonio-phyllum is European; Calceola occurs in Europe, Asia, Australia, and North America.

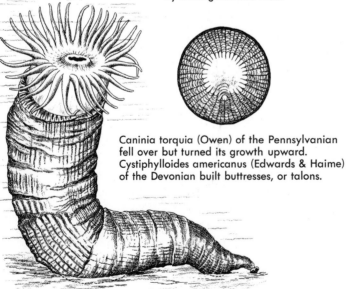

Caninia torquia (Owen) of the Pennsylvanian fell over but turned its growth upward. Cystiphylloides americanus (Edwards & Haime) of the Devonian built buttresses, or talons.

Life habits of some rugose corals

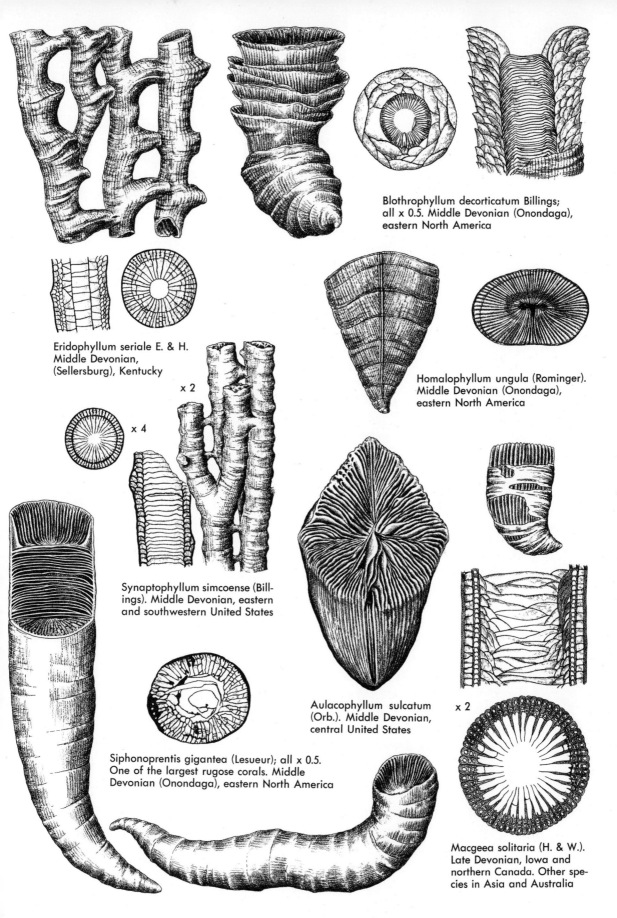

Blothrophyllum decorticatum Billings; all x 0.5. Middle Devonian (Onondaga), eastern North America

Eridophyllum seriale E. & H. Middle Devonian, (Sellersburg), Kentucky

x 2

x 4

Homalophyllum ungula (Rominger). Middle Devonian (Onondaga), eastern North America

Synaptophyllum simcoense (Billings). Middle Devonian, eastern and southwestern United States

Aulacophyllum sulcatum (Orb.). Middle Devonian, central United States

x 2

Siphonoprentis gigantea (Lesueur); all x 0.5. One of the largest rugose corals. Middle Devonian (Onondaga), eastern North America

Macgeea solitaria (H. & W.). Late Devonian, Iowa and northern Canada. Other species in Asia and Australia

Some typical rugose corals

has no hard parts; others build horny or stony structures that serve as skeletons.

It is not hard to imagine how creatures with the body plan of hydra evolved into primitive corals. The first step, apparently, was to thicken the original body-layers until each contained several sublayers and variously specialized cells. The mouth also became elongate, and upright radial folds of endoderm, called mesenteries, partly divided the body. The bottom of the tube began to secrete a limy base, or exoskeleton, whose function was to keep the soft body from toppling over into the mud, which would have smothered it. At first the base was a tiny disk, but since it increased in size with the growth of the coral, it took on the shape of a cup or curved horn.

The Structure of Rugose Corals. Horn corals belong to the subclass Rugosa, so called because their surface is commonly marked by wrinkles. Rugose corals are common in Paleozoic formations all over the world, but species of Silurian and later ages are products of long-continued evolution. To find a primitive type we select *Lambeophyllum,* which appears in middle Ordovician strata of eastern North America.

The name *Lambeophyllum* honors a Canadian paleontologist, L. M. Lambe, and is a cumbersome term for the exoskeleton of one small coral, also termed a corallite. This much-named structure actually is only a slightly curved cone of calcite containing a cup, or calyx, in which the body rested. The cone is covered by an outer layer, or epitheca, marked by growth lines and length-wise grooves that correspond to internal partitions called septa. Half of these septa are short and half are so long that they reach the center of the calyx.

Many books call *Lambeophyllum* a tetracoral, a term that explains itself when we find that two septa arise near the base (not at it) and are called cardinal and counter septa. They are followed by two alar septa, which divide the cone into unequal sections. Other septa, both long and short, are added in these quadrants as the coral increases in size. This arrangement, not surface wrinkles, is the feature that really distinguishes rugose corals from other anthozoans.

Such is one early tetracoral; since it starts out with nothing more than a cone, it seems to be close to the primordial form. But its simple plan, like that of hydra, was one that could be improved upon as well as elaborated—and both processes began early. *Streptelasma,* which also appeared in middle Ordovician seas, added curved plates (tabulae) under the calyx. Extensions from the septa also reached the central part of the corallite and seemed to twist at the bottom of the calyx.

Corals such as *Breviphyllum,* of Silurian age, added a zone of blisterlike plates around the tabulae. Other forms developed gaps (fossulae) as one or more of the original septa ceased to develop fully. These and further elaborations appear in our diagram of tetracoralline structure.

Reproduction and Colonial Growth. Modern corals reproduce both sexually and asexually. The former method depends upon eggs and sperms produced by glands on the fleshy mesenteries, which grow between the septa. The sex cells pass out of the mouth and into the sea, where some sperms fertilize eggs which then develop into simple larvae. These drift about for a while before they settle down to complete their development. Drifting, of course, gives them a chance to be widely distributed.

We must infer that ancient corals also used this method, since their soft parts have not been preserved. Asexual reproduction, however, is clearly shown by countless fossils. In some, new corallites developed by a process called peripheral increase or marginal budding. In it the outer portion of the old corallite divided into sections, or buds, which proceeded to grow upward and outward. The parent animal sometimes ceased to exist; at other times it became smaller but continued to live amid its offspring. In axial increase the parent polyps divided into two or more buds which developed in the calyx of the parent and replaced it. Lateral increase took place when new corallites grew from the walls of old ones, building up branching colonies or adding to the size of those that were massive.

Rejuvenescence was almost as common as asexual reproduction. All rugose corals grew faster at some times than others, producing thickenings and wrinkles on the surface of horn-shaped species. Many corallites also suddenly became much smaller, lost some of their septa, and then began to grow larger again. This sometimes happened only once, but in many species it took place again and again during the life of every corallite.

Both marginal budding and axial increase sometimes did no more than produce new corals that were independent even though they were attached to the skeleton of their parent. Commonly, however, asexual reproduction gave rise to colonies in which dozens, hundreds, or even thousands of individual polyps formed compact, branched, or netlike masses. Though some modern colonies are very large, few of those formed by tetracorals were more than 6 inches thick or 8 to 12 inches in width. In most of them the individual bases, or corallites, have characteristic shapes as well as the same internal structures found in their solitary relatives.

Devices for Support and Protection. *Lambeophyllum* and *Streptelasma* must have kept themselves upright by letting their pointed tips sink into the mud, which also piled up around the corals and kept them from toppling over. But as tetracorals increased in size and built colonies, they outgrew this simple sort of support.

Some, it is true, evaded the problem by remaining small or by ceasing to build their corallites upward. Several genera of Silurian, Devonian, and later corals are smaller than *Streptelasma* and must have stood upon the mud just as easily. Others, forming the family of paleocyclids, built their corallites upward very slowly but grew outward into buttonlike affairs that could lie flat on the mud with small danger of being overturned.

Still other horn corals tipped slowly as they grew, but turned enough to keep their bodies erect. Those that turned in one direction became smoothly curved, but others that rolled from side to side assumed irregular shapes. One of the most amazing, *Siphonophrentis,* reached lengths of 7 to 24 inches. In closely packed banks it curved gently or remained almost straight, but in open places it fell over, rolled this way and that, and grew in directions changed by each new position.

A still better means of achieving support was to grow upon shells, stromatoporoids, or other corals. Some of these formed firm foundations throughout life; others tipped when the corals became top-heavy. Colonial species often spread out over the bottom, and some solitary species imitated sponges by sending out buttresses (talons) or rootlike projections that kept the creatures upright.

Modern coral polyps protect themselves with stinging cells on their tentacles and by contracting into tight balls when they are disturbed. Some small Silurian forms developed one or four lidlike opercula, which were hinged to the sides of the calyx. When such corals contracted, they pulled the opercula down, thus covering their bodies.

Sections. Rugose, or tetracorals, once were identified like shells, by examining their external characters, especially those appearing in the calyx. Today most species and genera are based on internal structures, which are found by cutting thin sections lengthwise and crosswise through colonies or single corallites. Such sections show much that cannot be seen at the surface, and can be used even though calyxes have been destroyed or are filled with rock.

SIX ORIGINAL SEPTA; SCLERACTINIANS

Scleractinians are also called hexacorals. As that name implies, the septa and mesenteries are arranged on a basic plan of 6, with successive cycles of 6, 12, 24, and so on. There is equally great variation in the manner of growth and the nature of the base, or exoskeleton. Hexacorals are both solitary and colonial; though the former may be as much flattened as the paleocyclids, none has the height and hornlike shape of *Cystiphylloides* or *Siphonophrentis.* The individual corallites in colonies may be uniformly round or hexagonal, but they also may vary in shape and size or even run together, as they do in the modern brain coral. Fossulae are not developed, and the primary septa can be recognized only because they begin at the base instead of higher up in the growing corallite.

Scleractinians first left remains in middle Triassic deposits, and before that period closed were building reefs in southern Europe, southeastern Asia, California, and Alaska. Other reef-building epochs occurred in middle and late Jurassic, early and late Cretaceous, Tertiary, and later times. Most of the

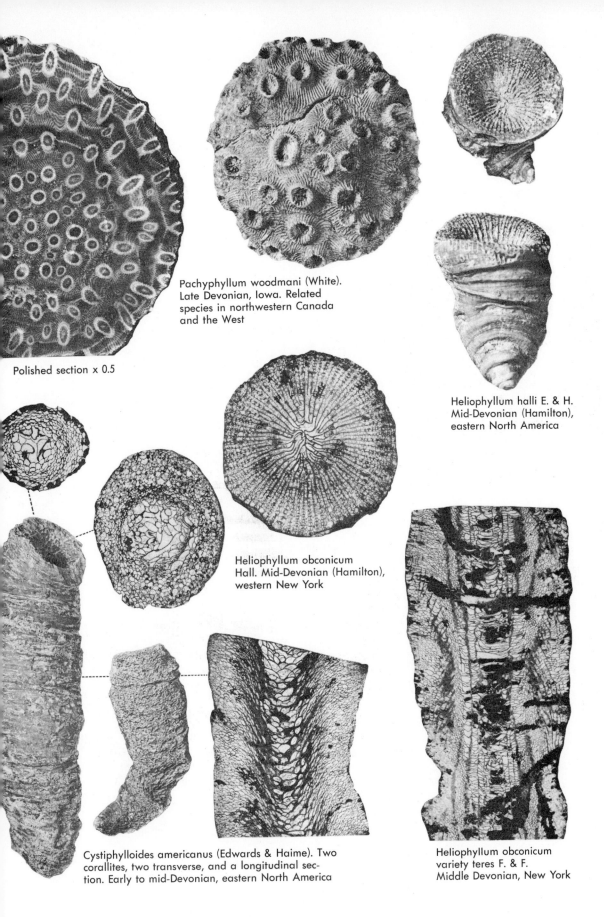

Pachyphyllum woodmani (White).
Late Devonian, Iowa. Related
species in northwestern Canada
and the West

Polished section x 0.5

Heliophyllum halli E. & H.
Mid-Devonian (Hamilton),
eastern North America

Heliophyllum obconicum
Hall. Mid-Devonian (Hamilton),
western New York

Cystiphylloides americanus (Edwards & Haime). Two
corallites, two transverse, and a longitudinal section. Early to mid-Devonian, eastern North America

Heliophyllum obconicum
variety teres F. & F.
Middle Devonian, New York

Rugose corals of Devonian age

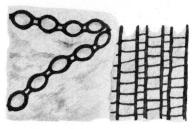

Sections of Halysites amplitubatus
Lambe, x 2. Silurian, Anticosti
Island, Canada

Catenipora microporus (Whitfield). Middle Silurian (Niagaran),
Ohio Valley, Mississippi Valley, and Manitoulin Island, Ontario

Alveolites goldfussi Billings.
Middle Devonian (Hamilton),
eastern North America

Entelophyllum rugosum (Smith).
Middle Silurian (Niagaran),
eastern North America

Aulopora michiganensis F. & F.
Middle Devonian (Traverse),
Michigan

Hexagonaria percarinata Sloss,
often called "Petoskey stone."
Middle Devonian (Traverse), Michigan

Lithostrotionella castelnaui Hayasaka.
Middle Mississippian, eastern United States

Tabulate and rugose corals

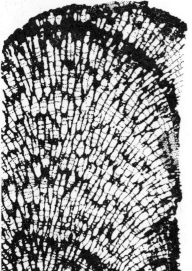

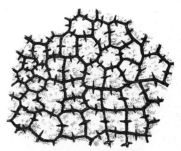

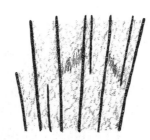

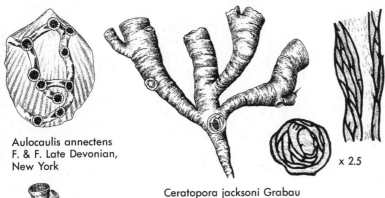

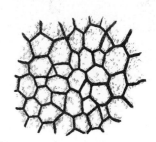

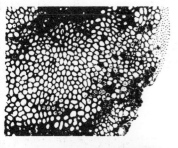

Aulocaulis annectens
F. & F. Late Devonian,
New York

Ceratopora jacksoni Grabau
Middle Devonian, eastern North America

x 2.5

Heliolites interstinctus (Linnaeus), x 5.
Middle Silurian (Niagaran), eastern
North America

Cladochonus beecheri (Grabau).
Mississippian, Mississippi Valley

Tetradium fibratum Safford, x 6. Middle and late
Ordovician of eastern North America

Lichenaria typa Winchell & Schuchert; section x 4.
Middle Ordovician, Mississippi Valley

Chaetetes septosus Fleming, x 4.
Late Mississippian (Viséan),
France (From Hill and Stumm)

Syringopora retiformis Billings (sections x 3). Middle Silurian
(Niagaran), Mississippi Valley and eastern North America

Tabulate corals

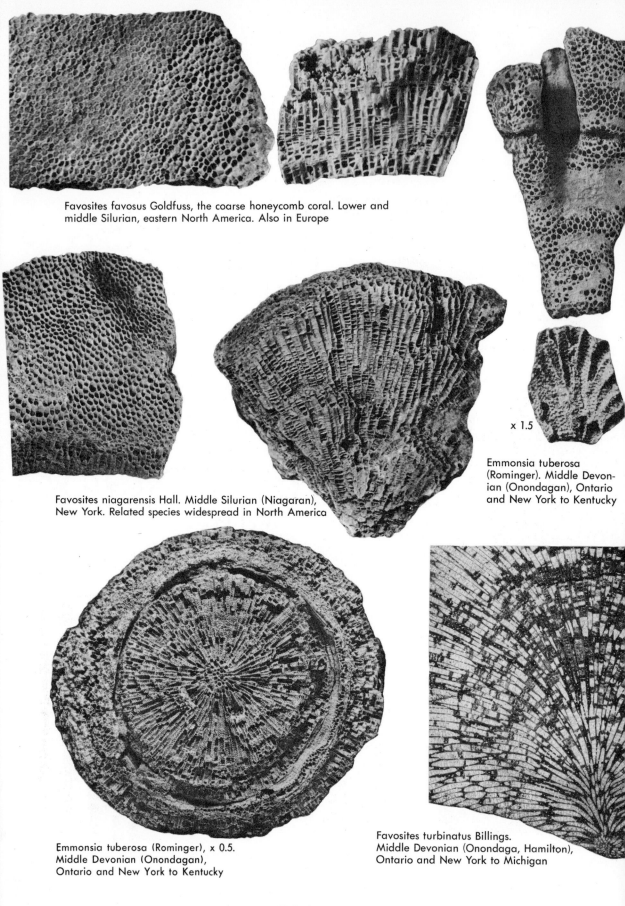

Favosites favosus Goldfuss, the coarse honeycomb coral. Lower and middle Silurian, eastern North America. Also in Europe

Favosites niagarensis Hall. Middle Silurian (Niagaran), New York. Related species widespread in North America

x 1.5

Emmonsia tuberosa (Rominger). Middle Devonian (Onondagan), Ontario and New York to Kentucky

Emmonsia tuberosa (Rominger), x 0.5. Middle Devonian (Onondagan), Ontario and New York to Kentucky

Favosites turbinatus Billings. Middle Devonian (Onondaga, Hamilton), Ontario and New York to Michigan

Tabulate corals

large coral reefs found in southern seas today have survived from the Pleistocene epoch, and some may be even older.

Corals are not common in most Mesozoic deposits of North America, in
spite of the fact that reefs were built in California, Alaska, and elsewhere.
Collecting is much better in Europe, where late Triassic, Jurassic, and Cretaceous formations contain great numbers of well-preserved corals. Solitary
species are now common in the Gulf of Mexico, and colonial forms ("reef-
builders") are widespread in Miocene and later deposits. Some of the most
attractive come from the Miocene "Silex" beds near Tampa Bay, Florida. On
the surface they show cups and septa thinly coated with white limestone, but
when broken or sawed they prove to be geodes lined with chalcedony.

THE ABUNDANT TABULATES

A great array of Paleozoic corals makes up the subclass termed Tabulata—
in English, the tabulates. All its members are colonial, consisting of small
corallites that may spread out in chains or nets but generally are so closely
crowded that they become prisms with four, five or six sides. There are no
dissepiments; tabulae may be missing but generally are well developed and
extend from wall to wall. Septa may be absent too; if not, they are few and
may be reduced to mere ridges or rows of spines. Shapes range from creeping
chains or nets to crusts, balls, curved cones, and branched colonies.

The Schizocorals. *Schizo* means "to split"; schizocorals reproduced by the
splitting, or fission, of parents, which then grew upward into two or more new
corallites. One of the best-known types, *Tetradium*, built massive, sheaflike,
or branched colonies composed of tiny, prismatic corallites with four principal septa and few to many tabulae. After fission the septa came together at
the center, forming the outer walls of four new corallites.

Schizocorals may be as old as the tetracorals, for a supposed mid-Cambrian
bryozoan seems to belong to this group. *Lichenaria* appears in early Ordovician strata, and Chaetetes (a complex group of fossils that resemble *Tetradium*
but lack septa) ranges through the Ordovician of North America and the
Jurassic of Europe.

Tubes, Chains, and Honeycombs. Chain corals range from late Ordovician to
early Devonian but are especially characteristic of Silurian deposits. The
genus *Catenipora* consists of small oval tubes that grew side by side in rows
called ranks, which resemble chains in cross section. Each tube contains
twelve ridgelike septa whose edge is set with spines, but tabulae may not
appear. The ranks are covered with wrinkled epitheca. *Halysites* resembles
Catenipora in general appearance but has small angular corallites between
those that are oval in section. Tabulae are well developed, but septa are absent.

Favosites, the honeycomb coral, is aptly described by its popular name.

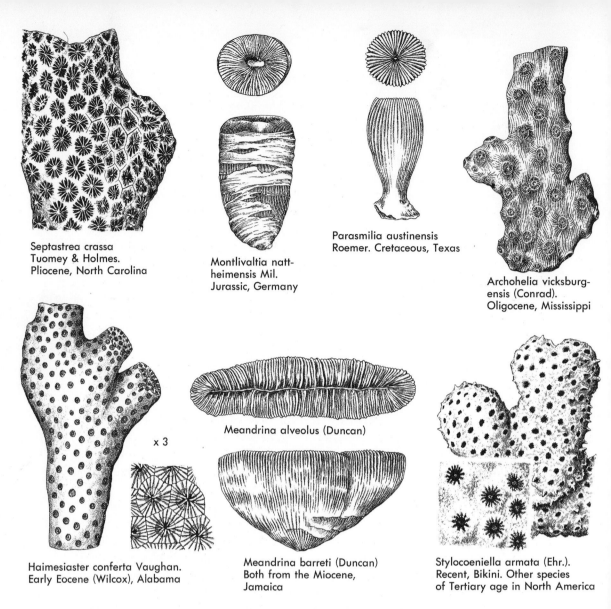

Septastrea crassa
Tuomey & Holmes.
Pliocene, North Carolina

Montlivaltia natt-
heimensis Mil.
Jurassic, Germany

Parasmilia austinensis
Roemer. Cretaceous, Texas

Archohelia vicksburg-
ensis (Conrad).
Oligocene, Mississippi

x 3

Meandrina alveolus (Duncan)

Haimesiaster conferta Vaughan.
Early Eocene (Wilcox), Alabama

Meandrina barreti (Duncan)
Both from the Miocene,
Jamaica

Stylocoeniella armata (Ehr.).
Recent, Bikini. Other species
of Tertiary age in North America

Some typical scleractinian corals

Colonies consist of closely packed corallites, most of which are prismatic and have thin walls that remain distinct, allowing large masses to split easily. Small pores extend through the walls, showing that the flesh of adjacent polyps was continuous; tabulae are well developed and extend from wall to wall. In some species old corallites were covered by limy layers after the polyps died.

There are many species of *Favosites,* ranging from small sheets to massive domes and from compact cones to branched colonies. Some bear small corallites of uniform size, but others, such as *F. argus,* have large corallites scattered among what seem to be small ones, as autopores are scattered among siphonopores in *Heliopora.*

Several other genera are commonly grouped in one family with *Favosites.* Some differ in details; *Emmonsia,* for example, has incomplete tabulae that look like spines when we see them in section. Others possess such thick walls that they resemble branched hexacorals. Still others have large corallites with many coarse septal ridges and tabulae that form blisterlike structures. The collector who likes to cut, polish, and make sections can distinguish varied genera and species on a basis much firmer than the one used to classify them in most books.

Aulopora consists of small tubes with thick, wrinkled walls, faint septal ridges, and few or no tabulae. The polyps reproduced by budding, forming chains, networks, or even crusts that spread out over firm though muddy bottoms or were attached to shells, stromatoporoids, and other corals. Related genera had tubes of different shapes, grew upward into short columns, or formed bushy colonies.

CHAPTER VIII

"*Moss Animals,*" *or Bryozoans*

Shale banks near Cincinnati abound in fossils that suggest stony hydroids or corals dotted with minute openings. Some form biscuitlike or irregular lumps; others suggest twigs and crumpled leaves or are crusts that adhere to shells. A few are tapering blades marked by pits in neatly alternating rows.

These fossils actually are not corals, hydroids, or even coelenterates. Instead they belong to a phylum that contains branched, creeping, or encrusting creatures that now live in many streams and ponds but are much more plentiful in the sea. Their usual name, bryozoans, means "moss-animals" and refers to the plantlike appearance of many species. The British, however, call them polyzoans ("multiple-animals") in recognition of the fact that they are colonial.

THE BRYOZOAN AND ITS WALL

Though tiny, the living bryozoan, or zooid, is much more highly organized than any coelenterate. Its saclike body contains three layers: the same three found in flatworms and all other many-celled creatures more complex than coelenterates and sponges. The hinder end of the body is closed; the other (which is not a head) bears a ring or loop of tentacles (the lophophore) around the mouth. Cilia on these tentacles beat to and fro, producing currents that carry food along until it is caught in mucus and swallowed. Digestion takes place in a U-shaped or V-shaped tract that terminates in an anus lying outside the tentacles and a little below the mouth. Supposed bryozoans whose anus lies inside the tentacles—the Entoprocta—apparently form a separate phylum.

Though the bryozoan has no head or brain, it does possess a nerve ganglion lying between mouth and anus. Muscles run through the fluid-filled body, causing it to contract when the creature is alarmed. Other organs extend the body when the zooid is ready to feed.

Each bryozoan can produce eggs and male sperm cells, though it may not do both at one time. After eggs are fertilized they develop into larvae that swim feebly but are often carried far by currents. Most of these larvae are eaten by other invertebrates; the survivors attach themselves to seaweeds, shells, or other objects and establish new colonies. Thereafter they reproduce by budding and cover themselves with jelly, tough membranes, or walls that

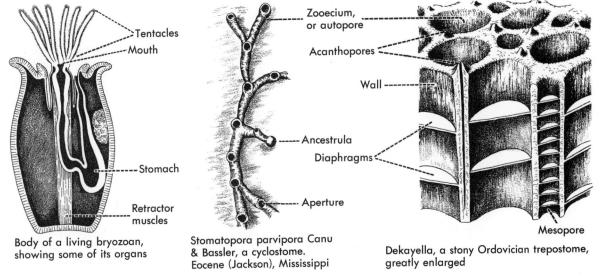

Body of a living bryozoan, showing some of its organs

Stomatopora parvipora Canu & Bassler, a cyclostome. Eocene (Jackson), Mississippi

Dekayella, a stony Ordovician trepostome, greatly enlarged

Structures of some modern and fossil bryozoans

form open boxes, sacs, or tubes. These walls may be either chitinous—often called "horny"—or limy. Bryozoans with limy walls are abundant as fossils, their colonies ranging from slender, branched structures to masses 24 inches in diameter. The latter are exceptions, of course, for a bryozoan colony more than 4 inches thick is unusually large.

We say that the walls form boxes, sacs, or tubes, for these words describe their shapes. Technically, however, the wall around one bryozoan animal is a zooecium, the structure formed by many such walls being a zoarium. The creature itself is a zooid or polypide. In colonies whose zooids belong to more than one type, zooecia of the largest zooids are called autopores. Smaller zooecia are mesopores. Still smaller tubes, which end in spinelike projections, are termed acanthopores.

How to Tell Bryozoans From Corals. Many limy, or calcareous, bryozoans closely resemble corals. *Stomatopora,* for example, looks like a small *Aulopora; Cyclotrypa* suggests *Favosites; Polypora* reminds us of the modern sea-fan,

Eliasopora siluriensis
(Vine), a ctenostome, x 10.
Silurian, New York

Vinella repens Ulrich, a
ctenostome, x 1. Ordovician
(Black River), Minnesota

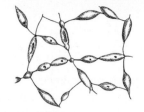

Rhopalonaria venosa Ulrich,
a ctenostome, x 25. Late
Ordovician, Ohio Valley

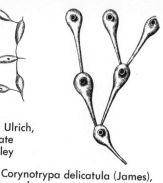

Corynotrypa delicatula (James),
a cyclostome, x 25. Late Ordovician, Ohio Valley

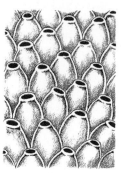

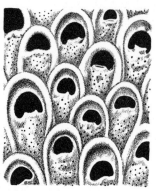

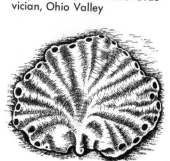

Floridinella vicks-
burgica C. & B., a
cheilostome, x 25.
Oligocene, Alabama

Steganoporella vicksburgica
C. & B., a cheilostome, x 20.
Oligocene (Vicksburg), Ala.

Micropora coriacea
(Esper), a cheilostome,
x 20. Eocene to Recent

Flabellotrypa rugulosa Bassler,
a cyclostome, x 15. Early Devonian (Helderberg), Tennessee

Some typical bryozoans

Gorgonia. Differences generally can be recognized in the small size of bryozoan zooecia and in details of structure. The best evidence, however, is provided by the earliest stages of colonies. The coral larva develops directly into
an ordinary polyp as soon as it becomes attached, and that polyp produces
others like itself. A larval bryozoan, however, becomes a round ancestrula,
from which a tubelike zooid buds. This zooid buds again, thus starting the
development of a colony. The ancestrula is most easily seen in attached, tubular forms such as *Stomatopora,* but careful search will show it in "coralline"
types. Indeed, the round original zooid is the thing that finally convinced
skeptics that these fossils were not corals.

Another distinctive feature of many, though not all, bryozoans is the ovi-
cell, or chamber in which fertilized eggs lie while they develop into larvae. It
may be a special, enlarged zooecium, or it may be a hollow swelling in an
otherwise normal zooecial wall.

HOW "MOSS-ANIMALS" ARE CLASSIFIED

Although bryozoans are abundant fossils, few come from rocks older than
middle Ordovician. The group also is often neglected by collectors, who overlook small species or complain that many large ones look alike. Others take

Hallopora ramosa (Orbigny).
Late Ordovician (Cincinnatian),
Ohio Valley

Constellaria florida Ulrich.
Late Ordovician (Cincinnatian),
Ohio Valley

Upper surface of a dome-shaped zoarium
of Amplexopora. Late Ordovician (Cincinnatian), Ohio Valley

Archimedes wortheni (Hall),
axis and drawing showing
the spiral fronds. Mis-
sissippian (Warsaw), Illinois

Lyropora subquadrans (Hall).
Late Mississippian (Chester),
Mississippi Valley

Broad frond of a fenestellid, crushed.
Devonian (Cedar Valley), eastern Iowa

Batostoma implicatum (Nicholson).
Ordovician (Cincinnatian), Ohio

Some typical bryozoans

specimens from clay or weathered shale but reject those in hard limestone since they cannot be separated from the rock.

The opinion that bryozoans do not reward careful study was once shared by professional paleontologists. A glance through old books reveals that small species are neglected, while large ones appear under "omnibus" names such as *Chaetetes lycoperdon* or *Stenopora fibrosa,* with descriptions based on such characters as shape and surface. Later, especially during the 1880's, came the discovery that fossils with few surface peculiarities may show quite different structure in sections cut lengthwise with and across the tubes. Such longitudinal and transverse sections, moreover, tell as much about specimens embedded in limestone as about those weathered from soft clay or shale. By this means, and by careful study under low-power microscopes, paleontologists have distinguished some 4,600 kinds of ancient bryozoans: 1,600 from Paleozoic formations, 1,000 from the Mesozoic, and 2,000 of Cenozoic age. These numbers are sure to increase, and almost 3,000 species are alive today.

Class Phylactolaemata. The 7,600 named species of bryozoans belong to two very unequal classes. One, the Phylactolaemata, contains 1,200 species that now inhabit shallow fresh waters and a few deep lakes; no fossil member of the group has yet been recognized. They differ from other bryozoans in having a horseshoe- or U-shaped lophophore, a lip that overhangs the mouth, and body cavities that run together instead of remaining separate. Some zoaria are chains or mats of leathery tubes; others are wormlike gelatinous masses that reach lengths of 8 to 10 inches and are provided with flattened soles on which the colonies crawl.

Class Gymnolaemata. This group contains all other bryozoans: some 6,400 species. Living members of the class are distinguished by a complete ring of tentacles, by the lack of an overhanging lip, and by distinct body cavities that are separated by walls. Though some species live in brackish or fresh water, the vast majority are marine. Most gymnolaematous bryozoans also build calcareous walls, a fact that explains why all known fossils belonging to the phylum are members of this class.

MAIN GROUPS OF FOSSIL BRYOZOANS

Ctenostomata, or "Comb-mouths." The known story of bryozoans begins with small fossils from early Ordovician rocks of Estonia. They belong to a simple but still extant order whose zooecia bud from central stems, or stolons, and form clusters, chains, networks, or sheets. The zooecia are gelatinous or horny but the stolons may be calcified. Many of these bryozoans sink both stolons and tubes into shells or corals, so that fossils are mere depressions or holes. The order's name, which means "comb-mouths," comes from a comb-like structure that covers each zooecium after the tentacles are drawn in.

Vinella, whose stolons resemble tubular threads, is a ctenostome that appeared in middle Ordovician seas and lived on to the middle Silurian. *Rhopalonaria* (late Ordovician) is a network of stolons that swell into vesicles with porous walls and uncertain function. *Ascodictyon* (Silurian to Mississippian) has ovate or pear-shaped vesicles that form clusters or are scattered along threadlike stolons.

Cyclostomata, the "Round-mouths." Bryozoans belonging to this order are larger, more varied, and more complex than the ctenostomes. Typically, however, the zooecia are simply limy tubes with round apertures that have neither comb nor other means of closing. Walls are simple, thin, and contain many fine pores; the tubes of some species are divided by crosswise partitions called diaphragms. Like the tabulae of corals, these diaphragms provide floors on which the animals rest between periods of active growth.

Cyclostomes appeared in mid-Ordovician seas and persisted throughout the Paleozoic with only moderate success. In Jurassic times they began to prosper, reached their zenith in Cretaceous seas, and continued in reduced numbers into modern times. They have varied greatly in size and general form, from simple chains of tubes or pear-shaped zooecia to sheets, disks, crumpled fans, and massive or many-branched colonies that stood erect upon expanded and attached bases. The simplest types, such as *Stomatopora* and *Corynotrypa,* consist of prostrate tubes cemented to shells, corals, or even other bryozoans. No diaphragms divide the tubes, which branch variously but do not form crusts or grow over each other.

Fistulipora is typical of cyclostomes with massive, irregular zoaria; it also is one of the largest cyclostomes, since it reaches a diameter of 15 inches. The upper surface bears shallow pits and rounded elevations; the under surface is covered by a wrinkled layer that resembles the epitheca of corals and sometimes is given that name. Large, tube-shaped zooecia (autopores) are separated by much smaller tubes with closely spaced transverse partitions. Instead of being true zooecia, however, these small tubes are parts of the coenosteum, a porous mass built up by the colony in general. The rear wall of each autopore is thickened and abruptly curved, forming a lunarium that may appear as a hood over part of the aperture. Edges of the lunarium also may curve so abruptly that they project as pseudosepta that show plainly in transverse sections.

Trepostomata, the "Changed-mouths." This order is exclusively Paleozoic, since it appeared in early Ordovician seas and died out as the Permian period closed. All trepostomes were stony and many were large. Because of this they outnumber other Paleozoic bryozoans in specimens, though not in species.

Trepostome zooecia consist of long rounded or prismatic tubes that lack combs but commonly have hoods. The inner (immature) portion of each tube has thin walls and widely spaced diaphragms that suggest rapid and continuous growth. The outer (mature) region, however, has thick walls and crowded

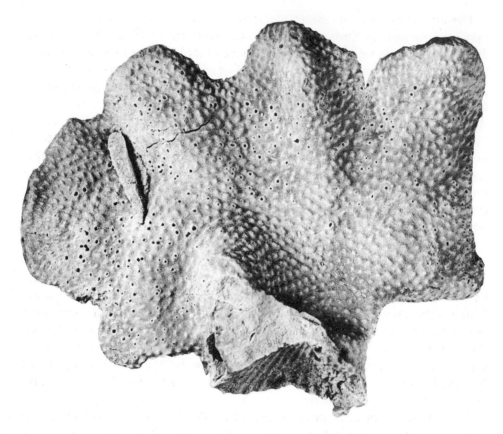

*Monticulipora molesta Nicholson. A large colony of this cyclostomatous bryozoan;
it grew upon a clamshell. Ordovician (Cincinnatian), Cincinnati, Ohio*

diaphragms that are evidence of slow growth and many "resting" periods.
The change from one region to the other explains the order's name.

The characteristics of trepostomes are well shown by *Dekayella*, a moderately thick-branched genus of middle to late Ordovician age. Longitudinal
sections show that the immature region contains only large tubes, or autopores, with the usual thin walls and widely spaced diaphragms. With maturity
the autopores thicken and turn obliquely outward. Small tubes called mesopores also appear; their diaphragms are still more closely spaced. Transverse
sections show even smaller tubes (acanthopores), whose relatively thick walls
commonly project as short spines. Both mesopores and acanthopores presumably contained specialized zooids, but since the trepostomes are extinct we
cannot tell what these zooids were like or what tasks they performed in the
colony.

Mesopores are missing from some species of *Monticulipora*, and acanthopores commonly are few. Acanthopores are rare in *Prasopora*, a buttonlike

to subconical genus, one of whose species is sometimes called the gumdrop bryozoan. Its autopores contain steeply curved plates (cystiphragms), which lie outside or surround the diaphragms, very much as dissepiments surround tabulae in horn corals such as *Blothryphyllum*. The under side of each zoarium is covered by a wrinkled layer; the upper generally bears raised clusters of mesopores, called monticules, which are surrounded by larger than average autopores.

Some trepostomes have incomplete or perforated diaphragms; others, such as *Hallopora*, lack them. In several genera, clusters of mesopores are on a plane with the general surface or form shallow pits and therefore are called maculae, or spots. The attractive *Constellaria* has depressed maculae between which autopores form starlike elevations. In the species called *florida* these stars suggest little flowers.

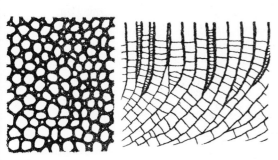

Transverse and vertical sections through Dekayella praenuntia Ulrich, x 10. Middle Ordovician, Minnesota

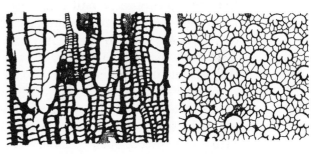

Fistulipora proiecta (Moore & Dudley), a stony cyclostome, x 10. Early Permian (Leonard), western Texas

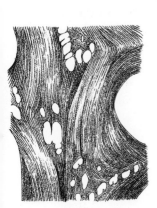

Section through axis, or "screw," of Archimedes, a cryptostome, x 20, showing layers, or lamellae

Structure of Rhombopora, a cryptostome, x 8. Ridges consist of acanthopores.

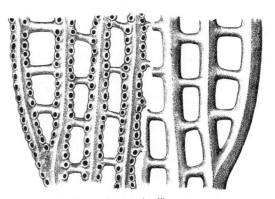

Fenestrellina elegans (Hall), a cryptostome, x 15. Both sides of a frond. Middle Silurian (Rochester), Ontario and New York

Some typical bryozoans

Virtually all the many species of trepostomes have been determined by structures shown in thin sections. Now that this basic work has been done, many of the fossils can be recognized by external characters such as the stars of *Constellaria*. Internal characters may also be revealed by grinding transverse and longitudinal surfaces flat and etching them lightly with dilute acid. This brings out acanthopores, mesopores, walls, and even tabulae, though a low-powered binocular microscope is needed to see them well.

Cheilostomata, the "Rimmed-mouths." Mesozoic to Recent formations abound in Bryozoa whose zooecia are short, saclike chambers of limy or horny material, or of both combined. In life these chambers bear hinged chitinous lids (opercula) which fit against narrowed lips, closing the apertures when the body is contracted and the tentacles are withdrawn. The delicate colonies include mats, disks, and bushlike affairs with flat or chainlike branches. The living animals possess stalked structures (avicularia) that snap like the beaks of birds and may help in capturing food. The vibracula bear lashes that whip to and fro but have no known function. Both vibracula and avicularia are specialized zooids whose bases show plainly in fossils.

Cheilostomes first appeared in mid-Jurassic seas; during the Cretaceous they became the most abundant and varied of bryozoans. The order continued to prosper during the Tertiary period, and today it outnumbers all other groups by about six to one. Cheilostomes are the bryozoans most often washed ashore by storms, either loose, attached to shells and pebbles, or cemented to blades of seaweed. Such specimens make significant additions to a collection of cheilostome fossils.

Cryptostomata, the "Hidden-mouths." Many rocks of Ordovician to Permian age contain fossils that look like lacy nets or minute versions of the modern sea-fan, the coral *Gorgonia*. Actually they are so-called Cryptostomata—bryozoans with short zooecia whose apertures seem to lie at the bottoms of thick-walled vestibules. Many authorities, however, have decided that the supposed vestibules are merely the mature regions of zooecia, lying above projections known as hemisepta. These mature regions contain no diaphragms, and the immature regions may lack them. Some genera, such as *Rhombopora*, possess rows of large acanthopores; in others the space between autopores is filled with a porous coenosteum. Lunaria may be absent or well developed, forming pseudosepta.

Though cryptostomes have been called an order, they seem to be early cheilostomes that had not developed structures such as avicularia and retained some other features lost by their later relatives. The group appears in mid-Ordovician rocks as branched or blade-shaped colonies, most of which require thin sections for reliable identification. In the Silurian and Devonian come lacy genera such as *Fenestrellina*, formerly called *Fenestella*. They grew in fanlike or conical colonies attached to shells and other supports by means of expanded bases or structures resembling roots. Their zooecia contain straight or flexuous branches joined by crossbars; apertures appear only on one surface.

Still more remarkable was *Archimedes,* in which the lacy net had become a spiral extending from a central column in the form of a wide-flanged screw. The whole colony stood erect upon an expanded base but toppled over after death. Fossils consist of screws with fragments of the lacy spiral or portions of the latter separated from their central support. *Archimedes* is abundant in some early and late Mississippian deposits, is found in several Pennsylvanian formations of the West, and makes its final appearance in the Permian of Russia.

CHAPTER IX

The Sturdy Brachiopods

Among late Precambrian fossils are a few brachiopods. Some authorities question their nature, however, and others agree that they tell little about this segment of the animal kingdom. For brachiopods, like other invertebrates, did not become important fossils until the Paleozoic era. Then, after a laggard start, they filled the role now held by pelecypods among denizens of shallow sea waters. For seven long ages they prospered greatly and then declined before the Mesozoic era dawned. Only about 220 species inhabit modern seas.

Even as late as 1913, a standard textbook of paleontology grouped brachiopods with bryozoans in a phylum called Molluscoidea. Since that time the two groups have been separated, even though they appear in the same general part of animals' family tree.

WHAT ARE BRACHIOPODS?

Brachiopods are exclusively marine animals that cover their soft bodies with shells made up of two parts, or valves. In this brachiopods resemble mussels, yet the two are not difficult to distinguish. The typical mussel has valves that are similar but opposite; the shells can be divided into equal halves just by separating them. Brachiopods, however, have valves that are both unlike and unequal; to divide such shells into matching halves we should have to cut across both valves, not pull them apart.

The Brachiopod Body. Shells are essentially lifeless structures which organisms build as combined skeleton and armor and then leave to fate. The real brachiopod is a living body whose four main parts are mantle, brachia, internal organs, and stalk, or pedicle. The mantle is a sheet whose two halves are folded over the rest of the body and secrete the shell. Edges of the mantle bear fringes of hairlike setae, which are long and stiff in such genera as *Lingula* but are short and soft in others. The mantle also encloses the body cavity and internal organs, which lie mainly in the hind part of the shell. Channels in the mantle provide for the flow of watery blood, their course being marked by depressions on the inside of the shell.

The brachia lie outside the body cavity but inside the mantle. Collectively termed the lophophore, they consist of two loops or spirals of flesh whose edges are set with tentacles. They bear cilia that beat to and fro, driving currents

Clam   Brachiopod

A line drawn between the valves divides this clam into equal parts. In a brachiopod, the line must be drawn across the valves.

of food-bearing water over sticky mucus. When this mucus has trapped small creatures, it is swallowed by the mouth, which opens between the brachia. The lophophore once was thought to carry on respiration, but that seems to be done by the mantle.

Internal organs include muscles, a digestive tract, nerves, and glands of several kinds; there may or may not be a heart. The nervous system branches but is very simple, with no distinct sense organs. In the digestive tract, the round mouth leads to an esophagus and saclike stomach; then comes an intestine that is either short or long and V-shaped and is closed at its end. This, of course, means that waste matter passes out of the mouth when mucus is not being swallowed.

Muscles run through the body cavity; the hard parts to which they are fastened permit them to open and close the shell. The opening never is very wide, for even when a brachiopod feeds, its valves are separated by little more than a slit.

The pedicle is a fleshy or leathery tube that projects between the valves or through an opening in one of them. In primitive brachiopods this tube is long and flexible and contains muscles that contract to cause shortening or even coiling. To lengthen the pedicle, muscles relax and fluid is pumped into the tube from the body cavity. Many pedicles, however, are so short and stiff that they move little or not at all. They attach their owners to solid objects, and so do flexible pedicles that are not very long. Elongate—even wormlike—organs burrow into sand or soft mud.

The name *brachiopod* ("arm-foot") was devised many years ago, when the brachia were regarded as molluscan feet that had somehow evolved into arms. Since that is not true, the name no longer has any real meaning, but the English lamp-shell is not much better. It fits one valve of such genera as *Laqueus* and *Cranaena,* which do suggest an ancient bronze lamp with a spout to hold the wick. But the term does not describe the opposite valve and is even less

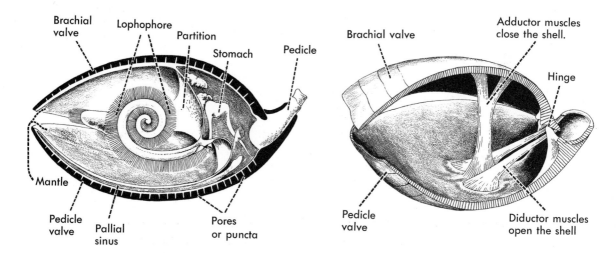

Section through the body of a modern brachiopod, and a diagram of muscles that open and close the shell

appropriate for shells that are wedge-shaped, gently convex, flattened, deeply and variously ribbed, or cuplike and covered with spines. Our best course is to ignore translations and retain brachiopod, which at least enjoys the advantage of established scientific use.

Classes Based upon Shells. Brachiopods may be classified according to the way in which valves and pedicles develop, the microscopic structure of their shells, or the devices that hold both valves together. The first probably would distribute the creatures among two phyla that closely but falsely resemble one another. Microstructure of shells would preserve one phylum but divide it into one class whose shells are pierced by tiny holes and another whose shells are solid. The third system of classification makes a much more obvious division based on the presence or absence of structures forming a hinge between the two valves. This again results in two classes, the Inarticulata and Articulata. Though they may mean less than either of the other groupings, they are generally used by American paleontologists and are adopted here.

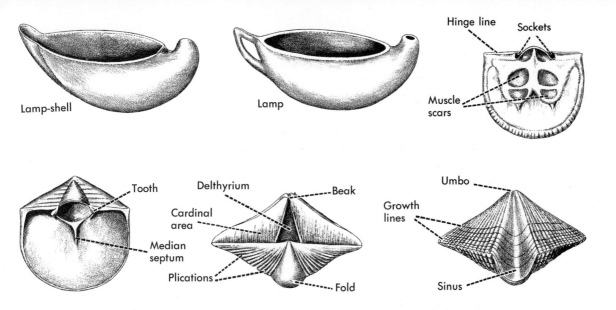

The first two drawings show why brachiopods are sometimes called lamp-shells. The other drawings illustrate some terms used to describe brachiopods.

Inarticulate brachiopods are hingeless. They also are old and primitive, even though they still survive in *Lingula* and *Glottidia*. Most inarticulates have thin—even flexible—shells whose valves are held together without ligaments or hinges like those to be seen in clams or oysters. The short valve may be moved from side to side, and the two often separate after death. Both valves may be so thin that fossils are almost flat.

Articulate brachiopods have valves that are hinged along a line that is either straight or curved and may extend beyond the rest of the shell. The hinge is strengthened by *teeth* that fit into pits or sockets, keeping the valves in line. In both classes the valves develop a variety of internal and external structures, as well as elevations, depressions, and so on. Since these are important in identification, they are illustrated and briefly defined.

Shell Materials and Structure. Most inarticulates, but by no means all, have chitinophosphatic shells. In less compact terms this means that the shells consist of calcium phosphate combined with chitinous material and minor substances. Such shells are always thin and commonly are glossy, the latter being a character that survives in fossils, many of which are black. The two principal materials may be mixed or may combine in alternating layers, like sheets of varicolored paper piled upon each other.

Almost all articulates and a few inarticulate brachiopods have shells composed chiefly of calcium carbonate in the form of the mineral calcite. Such shells have an outer, thinly laminate layer and a much thicker inner one made up of oblique fibers or rods. In impunctate shells both layers are solid; punctate shells contain pores (puncta) left by threadlike projections from the mantle that extend into the laminar layer but stop just below the surface. Pseudopunctate shells contain rods of calcite in the fibrous layer. They formed pustules on the inner surface and look deceptively like true puncta in transverse sections of shells.

Naming the Valves. For many years scientists assumed that one valve of the brachiopod shell was upper, or dorsal, while the other was lower, or ventral. These two terms appear in many old articles and books.

The weakness of this assumption should have been shown by *Lingula* and other inarticulates that were known to burrow in muddy sand, keeping their shells upright. But *Lingula* received little attention before the early 1900's, and many more years went by before much was learned about ways of life among the articulates. Then it was found that species with short pedicles live in almost any position, though the "ventral" valve is often upward. Attached forms with long pedicles vary greatly, for the shells hang downward, slant obliquely upward, or have either valve in the dorsal position. Other types, especially fossils, started out with that valve obliquely upward; but, as proportions changed, the animals turned till the pedicle valve became the lower. This also was true of most brachiopods that lost their pedicles and lay upon the bottom, though such genera as *Strophonella* and *Strophomena* apparently lay on the brachial valve.

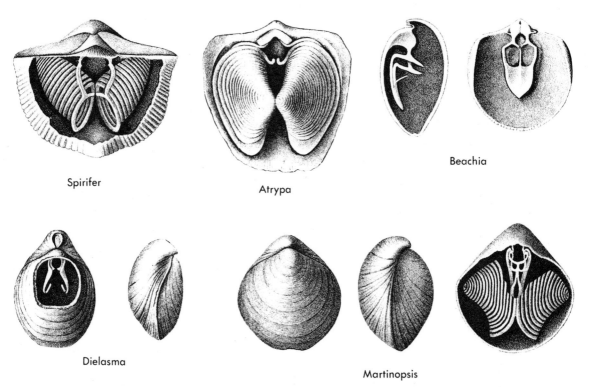

Beachia

Spirifer

Atrypa

Dielasma

Martinopsis

The hard structures, or brachidia, that supported the lophophores in five genera of brachiopods. Though Dielasma resembles Martiniopsis, the brachidia show that they are not related.

Such facts made the terms *dorsal* and *ventral* almost useless and focused attention on other essential features. Since the pedicle of many brachiopods is attached to one half of the shell, it became known as the pedicle valve. The other valve, to which the brachia are fastened, was called the brachial. These terms are applied to primitive inarticulates as well as to specialized articulate genera.

THE ORDERS OF BRACHIOPODS

We already have divided brachiopods into two classes, the Inarticulata (hingeless) and the Articulata (hinged). The former contains two orders, but the latter includes eight.

Class Inarticulata

Atremata. The modern *Lingula* typifies this order, which includes the most primitive and probably the oldest brachiopods. Atremates have an ill-defined pedicle opening formed by shallow notches in both valves, allowing the stalk to emerge between them. The original shape probably is that of *Lingulella,* which has an elongate, pointed pedicle valve and a shorter, blunter brachial, both with gently curved margins. Advanced genera specialized in various ways, some becoming almost round while others became elongate with slender beaks or subangular margins. Plates on the brachial valve of some genera tended to force the pedicle to emerge from the opposite valve.

Lingula, the commonest living atremate, once was supposed to range from the early Cambrian to Recent. Cambrian species are now placed in other genera, and further deletions may be made. Still, both linguloids and *Lingula* itself establish a record for sturdy durability among animals. As things now stand, the genus has prospered for almost 400,000,000 years.

Neotremata. In this order the pedicle has been crowded into an opening at the apex of its own valve, from which it disappears if the shells are cemented to other objects. *Paterina* is a good and ancient example of the former condition; *Crania* and its relatives are neotremates in which the pedicle disappears and the pedicle valve is cemented to corals or other objects. When these bear ridges, the brachial valve of the brachiopod generally mimics their markings. Though a great variety of these sessile species were once called *Crania,* most of the fossils are now assigned to other genera in its family.

Class Articulata

Palaeotremata. Though all articulates have hinges, their teeth and sockets are poorly developed in this early Cambrian order. It contains only a few rare genera from Vermont, Pennsylvania, and the West.

Lingula anatina Linnaeus. Interior of both valves, showing muscle scars. Recent, Philippines

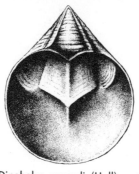

Dinobolus conradi (Hall), pedicle valve. Middle Silurian (Niagaran), central United States and Europe

Lingula elderi Whitfield, internal molds showing scars. Middle Ordovician, central United States

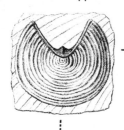

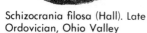

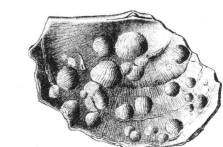

Petrocrania scabiosa (Hall). Late Ordovician, Ohio Valley and Wisconsin

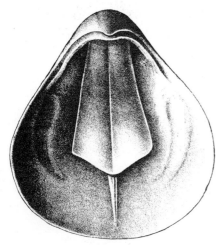

Schizocrania filosa (Hall). Late Ordovician, Ohio Valley

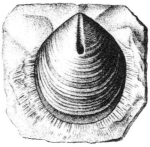

Schizambon canadensis Ami, pedicle valve. Late Ordovician, Ontario and New York

Trematis ottawaensis Billings. Middle Ordovician (Trenton), eastern North America

Trimerella ohioensis Meek, brachial valve. Middle Silurian (Niagaran), eastern North America

Lingulepis pinnaformis (Owen), internal molds of both valves. Late Cambrian, Wisconsin

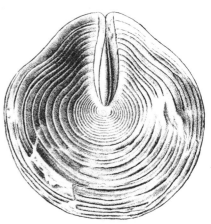

Lindstroemella aspidium Hall & Clarke. Middle Devonian (Hamilton), New York and Pa.

Inarticulate brachiopods (after Hall & Clarke)

Rustella edsoni Walcott, a true
palaeotremate brachiopod. Early
Cambrian, Vermont

Kutorgina cingulata (Billings), a palaeotremate
or primitive orthid. Early Cambrian, Vermont

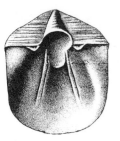

Billingsella pepina Hall & Clarke,
x 3. Late Cambrian, upper Mississippi Valley

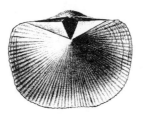

Retrorsirostra carleyi (Hall). Late
Ordovician (Richmond), Ohio Valley

Hesperorthis tricenaria (Conrad), Middle
Ordovician, eastern North America

Plaesiomys subquadrata (Hall). Late
Ordovician (Richmond), Manitoba to
Ohio, Texas and New Mexico

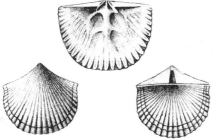

Dinorthis pectinella (Conrad). Middle Ordovician (Trenton), eastern North America

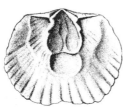
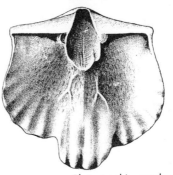

Platystrophia ponderosa Foerste,
interiors. Late Ordovician (Cincinnatian), Ohio

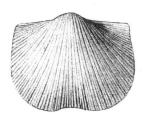

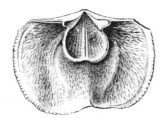

Hebertella sinuata (Hall). Late Ordovician (Cincinnatian,
Richmond), widespread in eastern North America

Palaeotremate brachiopods and orthids (after Hall & Clarke)

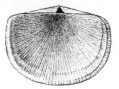

Dicaelosia biloba (Linnaeus). Middle
Silurian (Niagaran), widespread
in North America

Heterorthis clytie (Hall). Middle Ordovician

Rhipidomella hybrida (Sowerby). Middle
Silurian, eastern United States

Dicaelosia varica (Conrad). Early
Devonian, New York to Oklahoma

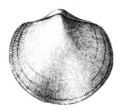

Enteletes hemiplicatus (Hall).
Pennsylvanian, Nebraska to Texas

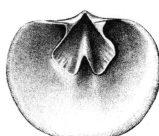

Levenea subcarinata (Hall). Early
Devonian, Oklahoma to New York

Schizophoria swallovi (Hall).
Mississippian (Burlington),
Mississippi Valley

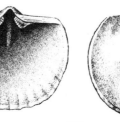

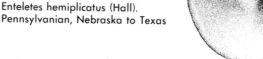

Schizophoria tulliensis (Vanuxem).
Mid-Devonian, New York

Rhipidomella penelope (Hall).
Middle Devonian (Hamilton),
Ontario, New York, Pa.

Tropidoleptus carinatus (Conrad). Middle to late Devonian,
eastern United States and New Mexico

Orthid brachiopods (after Hall & Clarke)

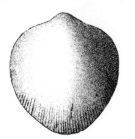
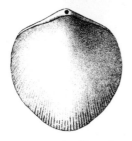

Beachia suessana (Hall). Early
Devonian, Missouri to Quebec

Cranaena iowensis (Calvin). Middle
Devonian (Cedar Valley), Missouri
and Iowa

Cryptonella planirostra (Hall), with internal
mold of brachial valve. Middle Devonian
(Hamilton), New York and Virginia

Dielasma bovidens (Morton). Pennsylvanian and
early Permian, Missouri to Texas

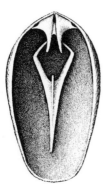

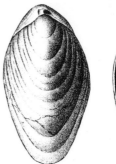

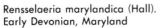

Rensselandia johanni (Hall). Middle Devonian,
Iowa and Missouri

Rensselaeria marylandica (Hall).
Early Devonian, Maryland

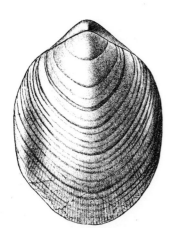

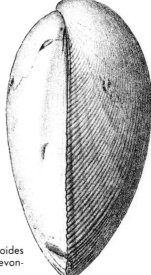

Amphigenia elongata (Vanuxem). Middle
Devonian (Onondaga), New York to Kentucky

Rensselaeria ovoides
(Eaton). Early Devon-
ian, New York

Terebratulid brachiopods (after Hall & Clarke)

Anastrophia verneuili (Hall). Early Devonian, Greenland and New York to Oklahoma

Gypidula romingeri Hall & Clarke. Middle Devonian (Traverse), Michigan

Conchidium nysius (Hall & Whitfield). Middle Silurian (Niagaran), Kentucky

Pentamerella arata (Conrad). Middle Devonian, Ontario to New York and Indiana

Gypidula. Middle Devonian, Iowa

Camerella volborthi Billings. Middle Ordovician (Trenton), Ontario and Quebec

Stricklandia castellana White. Middle Silurian, Iowa

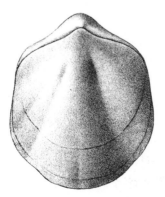

Virgiana decussata (Whiteaves). Middle Silurian, North America

Pentamerus laevis Sowerby. Middle Silurian, North America

Pentamerid brachiopods (after Hall & Clarke)

Rhynchotrema capax (Conrad). Late Ordovician (Richmond), Ohio Valley; close relatives in many other regions

Rhynchotreta americana Hall. Middle Silurian, Ontario and New York to Tennessee and Wisconsin

Camarotoechia congregata (Conrad). Middle Devonian (Hamilton), New York to Indiana

Orthorhynchula linneyi (James). Late Ordovician (Cincinnatian), Tennessee and Ohio Valley

Hypothyridina venustula (Hall), with internal mold of pedicle valve. Middle Devonian (Tully), Pennsylvania and New York

Pugnoides calvini Fenton & Fenton. Late Devonian (Hackberry), Iowa. Also internal molds of a related species from the Chemung of New York

Eatonia medialis (Hall). Early Devonian, Quebec to New York

Triplesia ortoni (Meek). Early Silurian (Brassfield), Ohio to Tennessee and Oklahoma

  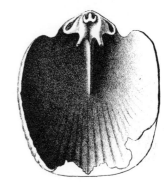

Plethorhyncha speciosa (Hall). Early Devonian (Oriskany), Quebec to Tennessee and Oklahoma

Rhynchonellid and triplesiid brachiopods (after Hall & Clarke)

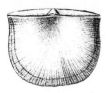   

Strophomena planumbona Hall. Late Ordovician (Richmond), Ohio Valley

Strophomena exigua Fenton. Middle Ordovician (Plattin-Platteville), Mississippi Valley

  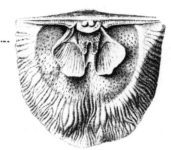 

Strophonelloides reversus (Hall) and interior of S. hybrida (H. & W.). Late Devonian (Hackberry), Iowa

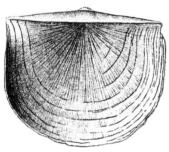  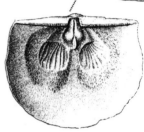

Stropheodonta demissa (Conrad). Middle Devonian (Hamilton), New York and Pennsylvania. Similar species are found in other regions.

Douvillina inaequistriata (Conrad). Middle Devonian, eastern North America

 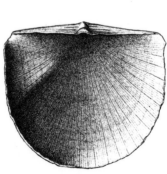 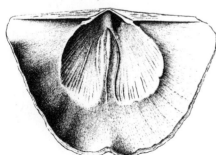 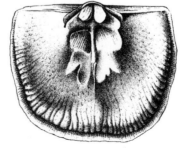 

Rafinesquina alternata (Emmons). Late Ordovician (Cincinnatian), Ohio Valley

Schuchertella woolworthana (Hall). Early Devonian, eastern North America

Strophomenid brachiopods (after Hall & Clarke)

 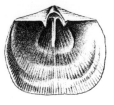  

Derbyia crassa (Meek & Hayden). Pennsylvanian, central United States

Derbyia bennetti Hall & Clarke. Late Pennsylvanian, Missouri and Nebraska to Texas

 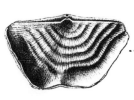 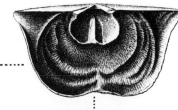

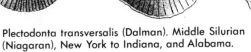

Leptaena rhomboidalis Wilckens. A name used for wrinkled Leptaenas which doubtless belong to several species. Silurian and Devonian, North America

  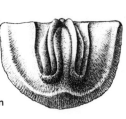

Plectodonta transversalis (Dalman). Middle Silurian (Niagaran), New York to Indiana, and Alabama.

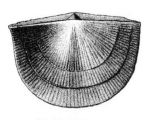  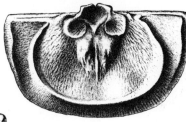

  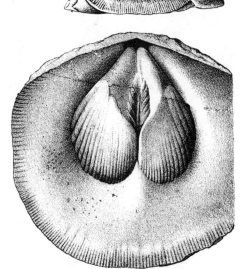

Fardenia subplana (Conrad). Middle Silurian, widespread in the United States

Meekella striatocostata (Cox). Pennsylvanian and Permian, North America

Hipparionyx proximus Vanuxem, internal molds. Early Devonian (Oriskany), Quebec to Oklahoma

Strophomenid brachiopods (after Hall & Clarke)

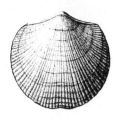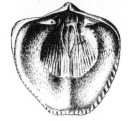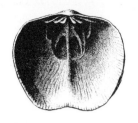

Atrypa "reticularis Linneaeus." Complete shell as well as interiors of both valves of specimens for which this name is used. Middle Devonian (Hamilton), Ontario and New York

Atrypa hystrix Hall. Late Devonian (Chemung), New York and Pennsylvania

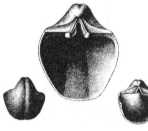

Zygospira modesta (Say). Late Ordovician (Cincinnatian and Richmond), Quebec to Ohio Valley and Tennessee

Atrypa occidentalis Hall. Middle Devonian (Cedar Valley), Iowa and Illinois

Athyris spiriferoides (Eaton). Middle Devonian (Hamilton), Appalachians and New York

Torynifera setigera (Hall). Mississippian (Chester), Alabama and Kentucky to Arkansas

Ambocoelia umbonata (Conrad), interior of pedicle valve enlarged. Middle Devonian, Ontario to Ohio and Kentucky

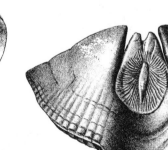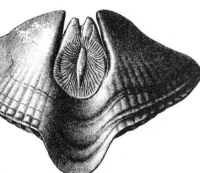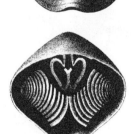

Merista typa (Hall). Late Silurian, Pennsylvania and Maryland

Syringothyris texta (Hall). Mississippian (Keokuk), Virginia and Kentucky to Iowa

Elytha fimbriata (Conrad). Middle Devonian (Hamilton, Tully), Ontario to Tennessee and Illinois

Meristina maria (Hall). Late Silurian, Indiana, Tennessee, and New York

Spiriferid brachiopods (after Hall & Clarke)

Eospirifer radiatus (Sow.). Middle Silurian, eastern North America

Cyrtia exporrecta (Wahlenberg). Niagaran of Quebec, Indiana, and Kentucky

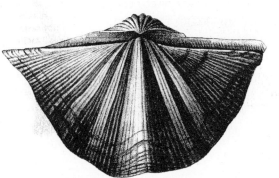

Mucrospirifer mucronatus (Conrad). Middle Devonian (Hamilton) New York and Pennsylvania to Virginia

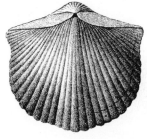

Costispirifer arenosus (Con.). Early Devonian, eastern North America and Great Basin

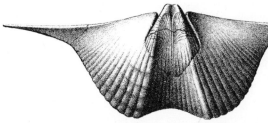

Cyrtospirifer disjunctus (Sowerby). Late Devonian, New York, Appalachians, and Utah

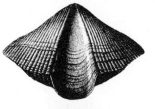

Brachyspirifer audaculus (Conrad). Middle Devonian, eastern North America

Neospirifer cameratus (Morton). Early Pennsylvanian, Pennsylvania to Texas

Spirifer keokuk Hall. Mississippian (Keokuk), Appalachians to Iowa

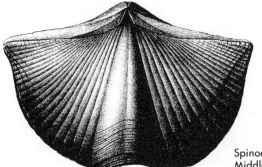

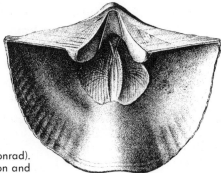

Spinocyrtia granulosa (Conrad). Middle Devonian (Hamilton and Tully), Ontario, New York, and Pennsylvania

Spiriferid brachiopods (after Hall & Clarke)

C. hamiltonensis (Hall)

C. alpenensis (Hall)

C. curvilineatea (White)

Homoeospira evax (Hall). Middle
Silurian (Niagaran), New York,
Indiana, and Tennessee

Three species of Cyrtina of Devonian age from
New York, Iowa, and northern Michigan

Trematospira multistriata (Hall). Early
Devonian, New York to Oklahoma

Reticulariina spinosa (Norwood &
Pratten). Mississippian (Chester),
Mississippi Valley and Alabama

Spiriferid brachiopods with punctate shells. All resemble genera whose shells are not punctate (after Hall & Clarke).

Orthida. A more progressive and much more varied order, the orthids are characterized by broad and generally biconvex shells with radial costae, well-developed teeth, simple or divided cardinal processes, and short projections to which the brachia were attached. Beginning with small subquadrate forms of early and middle Cambrian age, orthids achieved considerable variety and widths of 1 to 2 inches before that period closed. Late Cambrian and earliest Ordovician genera included shells with rounded to high, pointed pedicle valves, sharp to obtuse extremities, and fine to coarse ridges called costae.

These brachiopods had impunctate shells and belonged to one suborder termed the Orthacea, which lived on into early Devonian times. In the mid-Ordovician, punctate shells appeared, establishing a second suborder, the Dalmanellacea. Both groups then produced a great variety of genera and species, some of which resembled members of the other suborder and even of unrelated groups. Thus *Schizophoria,* of Devonian age, resembles the mid-Ordovician *Hebertella.* Another Ordovician orthid looked like a strophomenid, and a third developed both shape and ornamentation which were paralleled in later times by the spiny productids. *Platystrophia* anticipated the spirifers in both shape and habit and even went through similar changes in the evolution of its species.

Terebratulida. These punctate shells apparently evolved from orthids in early or middle Silurian times and are characterized by short hinge lines and calcareous loops supporting the lophophores. Early genera were almost circular to elongate-oval, with smooth or finely costate shells. During the Cretaceous and Tertiary periods, many shells became coarsely plicate. Terebratulids are important today, especially on the Pacific coast of North America. Some species inhabit rocky shores, though others are found in waters that are deep, quiet, and cold.

Chonetes coronatus (Conrad), surface and internal molds. Middle Devonian (Hamilton), widespread in North America

Productella spinulicosta Hall. Middle Devonian, eastern United States

Dictyoclostus burlingtonensis (Hall). Mississippian (Burlington), Appalachians and Mississippi Valley

Productella lachrymosa (Conrad), of different shapes. Late Devonian, New York and Appalachians

Spiny strophomenids (productids), (after Hall & Clarke)

Pentamerida. These biconvex, impunctate shells appeared in mid-Cambrian seas, became common in the Ordovician, and lived on to the end of Devonian times. They have short hinge lines, open notches for the pedicle, and—with one exception—well-developed spondylia. The Silurian *Pentamerus laevis* (often called *oblongus*) lived in closely packed colonies with pedicles sunk into the mud and elongate shells directed upward. Such colonies are often found on the under side of beds of fine sandstones. When cleaned and exhibited in museums, they appear upside down.

Triplesiida. This small group of Ordovician and Silurian brachiopods includes biconvex shells with well-developed fold and sulcus, either smooth or covered with costae. The brachial valve contains short crura and a prominent, branched cardinal process. *Triplesia ortoni* is a characteristic early Silurian fossil of the Ohio Valley.

Rhynchonellida. These wedge-shaped or nutlike brachiopods range from middle Ordovician to Recent, being especially common in some Mississippian formations. They have short hinge lines, prominent beaks, and plications which generally are coarse. Some species are excellent index fossils; others belong to superficially similar genera that can be distinguished only by internal characters and punctate or impunctate shells.

Strophomenida. These are the brachiopods most often referred to as "petrified butterflies." The strophomenid shell seems to be punctate but is not. It has a wide hinge line, costate surface, and one concave valve, which may be either brachial or pedicle. Appearing in the mid-Ordovician, strophomenids soon became both varied and abundant but declined after the Devonian. A few species, however, survive in modern seas.

Though the strophomenid body was very thin, it generally built a thick shell with prominent muscle scars. Such shells are abundant Paleozoic fossils, and well-cleaned pedicle valves are exceedingly attractive. Many species are marked by growth lines that show how shapes changed with increasing size.

Spiriferida. These brachiopods, which range from mid-Ordovician to Jurassic, are united by spiral structures (brachidia) supporting the lophophore. Aside from this, the group varies greatly. Its oldest suborder, the Atrypacea, contains shells with short hinge lines, inconspicuous beaks, and spirals that rise directly into the brachial valve. Shells may have fine costae or coarse plications; some possess wide "wings," or alate lamellae, that are commonly missing from fossils. In other species the lamellae fold into spines, which also are easily broken.

This suborder contains *Atrypa reticularis,* which once was said to range through both Silurian and Devonian deposits. Actually *reticularis* is a complex lot of varieties and species, none of which lived through a whole period and many of which are so restricted in range that they serve well as index fossils.

Shells of the suborder Spiriferacea have, in the main, a characteristic "spirifer" shape with wide or extended hinge line, prominent beaks, and well-developed sulcus and fold. The spiral brachidia extend outward toward the extremities rather than into the brachial valve. The surface is either plicate or costate and may bear much finer markings.

The original genus *Spirifer* has been split into many genera which range from mid-Silurian to Permian but reach their greatest variety in Devonian formations. Related genera with high cardinal areas and coarse plications lived on into the Triassic of California and Alaska, as well as the Jurassic of Europe.

The Rostrospiracea include smooth-shelled genera of mid-Silurian to Jurassic age. Some resemble such terebratulids as *Dielasma* and *Kingena,* but others can readily be distinguished by their costae or growth lamellae. Internally, of course, the Rostrospiracea have spirals, which no terebratulid possesses.

Punctospiracea consist of punctate shells that have spiral brachidia. Ranging from late Silurian to Jurassic, they contain genera that look like *Spirifer* itself and others that resemble rhynchonellids. *Cyrtina,* with its deep pedicle valve and opening for a large pedicle, is a well-known Devonian genus.

NATURAL HISTORY

As with other groups of animals and plants, we learn the natural history of brachiopods by comparing ancient with modern species, by examining strata in which the former are found, and by carefully studying the fossils themselves.

Depths and Habitats. Many brachiopods inhabit bottoms 150 to 1,500 feet deep, and others thrive at depths of 2,500 to more than 18,000 feet. The majority, however, lived and still live in shallow water or even in the intertidal zone. Thus *Terebratalia* of the northern Pacific coast often grows on rocks exposed by low tides, while *Lingula* and *Glottidia* burrow in sandy shoals where storms tear them up and sometimes wash them ashore in heaps that extend for miles and contain millions of animals. Though many shoals are brackish and hostile to most shelled invertebrates, modern linguloids apparently find them

Resserella meeki (Miller) from the late Ordovician of the Ohio Valley. These brachiopods lived near the place where their shells were buried, for most of them are not broken or worn. One shows a hole bored by a carnivorous snail.

A specimen of Atrypa petrified where it lived on a colonial coral, Hexagonaria, from the Devonian of Iowa. The coral grew around the brachiopod but not against it, so the shell could be opened for feeding.

desirable habitats. Fossils in sandstone bearing rill marks and wave marks indicate similar habits as far back as the Cambrian.

Landlocked seas of the Paleozoic provided vast areas in which the water was rarely much more than 600 feet deep and commonly less than 150. There brachiopods and other invertebrates found light, placid water and almost incredible supplies of microscopic food. Thus favored, brachiopods became both varied and abundant. The former is shown by the number of genera, species, and subspecies or varieties that are found; the latter by the large number of specimens and by "banks" in which they are crowded as closely as blue mussels on modern shores. *Pentamerus laevis* colonies of this type have already been described.

There is no doubt that many ancient linguloids lived on sandy bottoms, as their descendants do today. There is a strong suggestion that some thin-shelled strophomenids also did so, and they may have been joined by wide-hinged

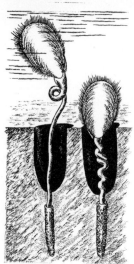

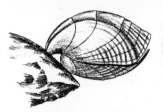

Hesperorthis had a thick pedicle that could have been attached to a shell or might have dug into the bottom.

Two specimens of Terebratalia (Recent). Both are attached by short, stiff pedicles that permit very little movement and cause distortion of the beaks.

Barroisella, which looked and presumably lived like the modern Lingula, with its pedicle in the sea bottom

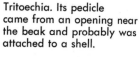

Composita was attached by a strong pedicle, probably in varying positions, like Terebratalia.

Brachyspirifer had a thick pedicle that probably was attached to large shells, corals, etc., throughout the animal's life.

Tritoechia. Its pedicle came from an opening near the beak and probably was attached to a shell.

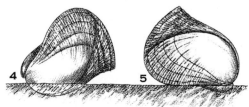

Schizophoria used its pedicle throughout life, though the pedicle valve sometimes rested on the bottom.

Stages in growth and orientation of a large Atrypa. A few old shells lay in position 4, but most came to rest in position 5.

Paraspirifer was attached when young, but its pedicle disappeared in maturity and the shells lay in the mud.

Platystrophia also lost its pedicle and lay in the mud as it grew old.

Orientation and attachment of typical brachiopods

members of the Spiriferacea, whose sharp extremities acted as anchors. If so, these shells were buried where they lived and died. Many of the brachiopods found in limestone and shale also were buried where they had lived, since they preserve delicate frills, spines, and surface markings that would have been destroyed had they been washed into other regions. But some strata contain only worn shells or crowded fragments which show that waves broke dead brachiopods to bits and mixed them with mud or swept them together in beds that resemble the coquina formed by Recent clamshells along the coast of Florida. In other places currents sorted broad valves, depositing brachials in one set of channels and pedicles in another.

Movement and Attachment. Larval brachiopods both drift and swim, but their travels are so limited that they generally settle down in clusters near their parents and relatives. Having done so, they cease to move about, spending the rest of their lives in one spot.

Different groups have various means of attaching themselves to the bottom. The primitive linguloids have a very long, tough pedicle that bores into sand or mud and covers its tip with a tough mucus to which sand grains are attached. By alternately contracting and relaxing its pedicle, the animal moves its shell up and down until it excavates a small burrow. When the creature is feeding, its shell extends about halfway out of the burrow. Any disturbance makes the pedicle contract, pulling the body into its hole.

We have found that storms often tear up banks of sand in which linguloids burrow. Those that are washed ashore perish, but the rest must burrow again. This they normally do with the pedicle, but injured animals may use their setae. Others travel short distances by pushing the setae into the sand and forcing themselves along on one side. In this way a creature that comes to rest in a crowd can pull itself away to a spot where it has room to burrow. Ancient linguloids doubtless shared these habits, though thicker atremates, such as *Trimerella,* probably were content to force their pedicles into the bottom without excavating burrows. Many of these creatures lived on mud rather than on banks of sand.

Most neotremates kept their pedicles, though some were exceedingly small. Many members of the Craniacea lost them, however, as their pedicle valves were cemented to corals or other shells.

Most telotremates also retain their pedicles, which differ greatly in flexibility and length. The short, stiff pedicle of *Terebratalia* holds both valves directly against the rocks or shells to which they are attached; such pedicles may be traced among fossils by thick shells that are worn or distorted by pressure. Thin-shelled genera such as *Laqueus* have longer, slender, more flexible pedicles that allow the shells to move freely. Some modern species attach themselves to seaweeds. Several ancient genera, such as *Oleneothyris, Rensselaeria,* and *Beachia* may have done the same. Both shapes and thin shells are consistent with this type of life.

Middle Devonian brachiopods of western New York and Ontario, shown in the positions they occupied during life; about half natural size. **1.** *Spinocyrtia granulosa (Conrad).* **2.** *Mucrospirifer mucronatus (Conrad).* **3.** *Meristella barrisi Hall.* **4.** *Athyris spiriferoides (Eaton).* **5.** *Tropidoleptus carinatus (Conrad).* **6.** *Pustulina pustulosa (Hall).* **7.** *Productella truncata Hall.* **8.** *Atrypa "reticularis."* **9.** *Camarotoechia sappho (Hall).* **10.** *Rhipidomella penelope (Hall).* **11.** *Stropheodonta demissa (Conrad). All these species are found in the famous exposures along Eighteen Mile Creek, Erie County, New York.*

Many Paleozoic telotremates have openings that accommodate very large pedicles. Such shells also show little distortion or wear of the sort that might have come from attachment. We conclude that these brachiopods had long pedicles which either became stiff or remained so strong that the shells were held well above mud and solid objects to which the pedicles were attached. Indeed, it would not be hard to picture spirifers with deep valves and wide pedicle openings as creatures that reverted to habits much like those of *Lingula,* with stout pedicles that pierced the mud but held the shells above it.

Many brachiopods apparently were attached when young but lost their pedicles during maturity. This allowed the shells to lie upon the bottom or sink part way into it. *Rafinesquina, Strophomena,* and other concavo-convex genera apparently did this, resting upon their convex valves. *Hypothyridina* probably came to rest on its moderately curved pedicle valve, as did other genera of similar shape.

A variety of spines and wide projections kept aging specimens of *Atrypa* in position, though some probably rolled over onto their deepening brachial valves. *Paraspirifer* and *Platystrophia* apparently rested upon their deep pedicle valves, which sank more and more deeply into the mud. Some of these shells show growths of bryozoans, corals, and other encrusting organisms upon valves which must have been exposed.

Advanced as well as lowly brachiopods cemented themselves to solid supports. Many did so by means of spines, or by spines and part of one valve. In

Richthofenia, of Permian age, the cemented valve comes to a point and is thickened so much that it looks like a horn coral. The uncemented valve is flattened and is little more than a lid.

LIFE HISTORIES AND ACCIDENTS

During the 1880's two paleontologists washed and sieved a huge collection of Silurian fossils from Waldron, in Decatur County, Indiana. They secured a large number of brachiopods, from very small shells to large ones whose size and irregular growth indicate that they were old. Four species were illustrated in *Memoir I* of the New York State Museum, published in 1889.

Methods of washing and sieving for fossils have been greatly improved, yet few "life histories" like those from Waldron have been collected and described. They really are not needed, however, for growth lines trace changes in shape and size from early stages to old age. Some genera also have minute surface markings that go through an equally precise sequence. Though they can be seen only through a good lens or a low-powered binocular microscope, they are well worth examination.

Ancient Injuries. Many modern brachiopods are sturdy creatures—linguloids live in wave-swept shallows, surviving storms that fill the water with sand or reduce salinity; *Terebratalia* endures beating surf and exposure at low tide. It also inhabits shallow, sunlit pools filled only by spray during storms, with long periods when the water bubbles with gas from decaying seaweeds. At least one *Terebratalia* grew to good size inside the shell of a snail whose mantle had been torn.

Ancient brachiopods probably were as hardy as their modern relatives. Fossils show that they survived injuries which caused distortion and twisting of the valves or even sharply broken shells. A specially good example is seen in a shell whose valves grew around a bryozoan that had been forced against them. Though distorted and kept from opening normally, the brachiopod survived and almost regained its normal shape. Such specimens, like others that show attachment or change in orientation, are helpful clues to the natural history of ancient brachiopods.

CHAPTER X

Armored Echinoderms

A LIMESTONE QUARRY near Le Grand, Iowa, has long been famous for its fossils. Though some beds and layers are barren, others contain well-preserved remains which quarrymen as well as collectors call sea lilies, or crinoids. Both names (*crinoid* means "lilylike") are justified by bodies that look like flowers on jointed stalks.

Sea lilies introduce us to the phylum of echinoderms, or spiny-skinned animals. Their whole group, like the brachiopods, is marine; its twelve classes, five of which are still living, include such creatures as starfish, sand dollars, and sea cucumbers, as well as crinoids and their relatives. Some have stalks but many lack them; some are hard while others are soft-skinned and flabby; they include sessile stay-at-homes as well as drifters, burrowers, and crawlers. Colors of living animals range from the dingy gray-green of mud to blue, purple, and vermilion.

In spite of these differences, echinoderms have a few basic characters in common. All, for instance, begin as animals with right and left sides, though most adults develop bodies whose parts are arranged in five starlike sections, or rays. All echinoderms also possess skeletal supports in the form of plates or spines of calcite, which looks porous or netlike under the microscope yet splits into flat-sided blocks as if it were crystalline. These supports are built up in the skin and flesh instead of along the edge of a mantle, as they are in the shells of brachiopods and mollusks. The plates may be joined together but seldom are fused, which means that they can increase in size as long as their owners live. Growth is often recorded in fine lines or wrinkles that show upon plates, though spines merely grow longer and thicker with age and increasing size.

124

PRIMITIVE ECHINODERMS

Echinoderms, like most other phyla, began to leave remains that formed fossils during Cambrian times. Unfortunately we have no assurance that the Cambrian fossils are the most primitive echinoderms. On theoretical grounds, that honor belongs to a group called cystoids, whose fossil record goes back only to the mid-Ordovician. Collectors constantly hope for older specimens.

Cystoids. These creatures, whose name means "bladderlike," had compressed egg-shaped or spherical bodies covered by a calyx of plates. Some genera were attached directly to other objects; some had short stalks (columns) made up of round flat sections (columnals), each with a central hole through which ran a stalk of flesh. The stemless state seems to be primitive, and so does one in which plates number as many as 250 and have no definite arrangement. A small number of plates, with distinct shapes and positions, is a specialized character.

The cystoid mouth lies on the upper surface, generally at the center of radiating grooves (ambulacra) which must have been lined with cilia that beat to and fro, carrying food to the mouth. Some genera lack appendages; others have armlike brachioles that rise in a cluster around the mouth or run along both sides of food grooves that extend far down the sides of the calyx. Food grooves branch and extend along brachioles of the former type, which may also bear jointed branches called pinnules. The anus lies to one side of the mouth and is covered by plates.

These specimens show that remains of echinoderms form a large part of some limestones. The sea urchins (Melonechinus) are well preserved, but the crinoids have gone to pieces. Many of those in the encrinal limestone have also been worn to bits.

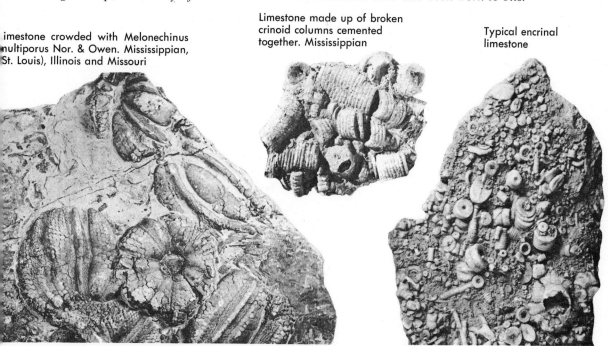

imestone crowded with Melonechinus
nultiporus Nor. & Owen. Mississippian,
St. Louis), Illinois and Missouri

Limestone made up of broken
crinoid columns cemented
together. Mississippian

Typical encrinal
limestone

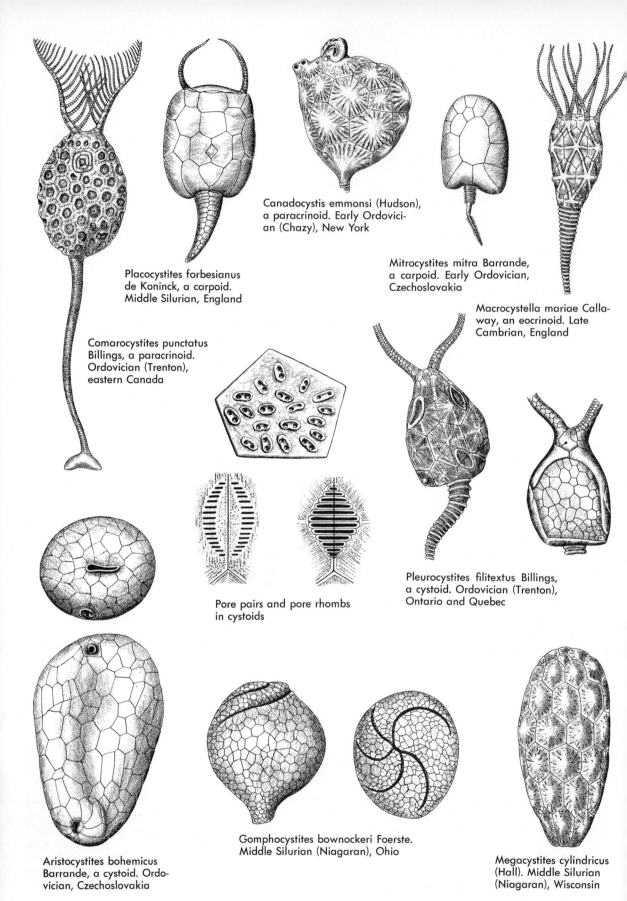

Placocystites forbesianus
de Koninck, a carpoid.
Middle Silurian, England

Canadocystis emmonsi (Hudson),
a paracrinoid. Early Ordovician (Chazy), New York

Mitrocystites mitra Barrande,
a carpoid. Early Ordovician,
Czechoslovakia

Macrocystella mariae Calla-
way, an eocrinoid. Late
Cambrian, England

Comarocystites punctatus
Billings, a paracrinoid.
Ordovician (Trenton),
eastern Canada

Pore pairs and pore rhombs
in cystoids

Pleurocystites filitextus Billings,
a cystoid. Ordovician (Trenton),
Ontario and Quebec

Aristocystites bohemicus
Barrande, a cystoid. Ordovician, Czechoslovakia

Gomphocystites bownockeri Foerste.
Middle Silurian (Niagaran), Ohio

Megacystites cylindricus
(Hall). Middle Silurian
(Niagaran), Wisconsin

Carpoids, eocrinoids, paracrinoids, and cystoids

Cystoids are divided into two orders by differences in the pores that took water through plates of the calyx, apparently to secure oxygen. In one order the pores are arranged in rhomblike patterns and open either through slits or small holes; in the second order the pores are arranged in pairs that seem to be scattered hit-or-miss. Rhomb cystoids appear to be the more primitive of the two orders, though fossils of both are equally old. Most of the 250 or more species of cystoids lived between mid-Ordovician and the end of Silurian times. Barely a dozen are known from Devonian and Mississippian strata.

Eocrinoids. The typical "dawn crinoid" has an elongate stalk, a vase-shaped calyx whose plates have definite shapes, and five brachioles. The last are either simple or branched and consist of two interlocking series of plates. During life the brachioles doubtless carried cilia that took food to the mouth, which lies on top of the calyx. Though eocrinoids never were plentiful, they lived from mid-Cambrian to mid-Ordovician, a span of 100,000,000 years. The best-known species are European.

Paracrinoids. These creatures, whose name means "allied to crinoids," are found in mid-Ordovician strata. Paracrinoid plates show no definite arrangement but commonly contain pores that are covered and show only on deeply weathered specimens. In the best-known genus, *Comarocystites,* plates of the calyx are concave. The two arms bear side branchlets which are relatively thick.

Carpoids. Most of these echinoderms have compressed bodies with large, solid plates on one side and smaller plates on the other. There may be two armlike organs or none; the stalk has become a taillike affair containing two rows of plates which, in some genera, bear spines. Carpoids apparently lay on the flat or convex side and fed by taking water into the mouth. A ratchetlike structure at the base of the stalk may have enabled the creatures to creep. They range from mid-Cambrian to early Devonian.

Blastoids. These fossils are often called "petrified nuts," though their technical name means "budlike." Ranging from mid-Devonian to latest Permian, they are most plentiful in Mississippian formations. Weathered "pockets" sometimes provide thousands of fine specimens.

The blastoid calyx may be recognized by its shape, its five broad, cross-ribbed ambulacra which are deeply grooved at the center, and the V-shaped plates that partly enclose them. The mouth lies at the apex of the "bud"; around it are five holes (spiracles), one of which commonly served as an anus. During life the mouth was covered by small movable plates and so were the ambulacra. These plates are generally missing from fossils, and so are the jointed brachioles that once extended at both sides of the ambulacra and carried branches of the food grooves.

The respiratory apparatus of blastoids begins with rows of pores on both sides of the ambulacra. The pores lead to tubes with folded walls, called hydrospires, two of which open through each spiracle. Water came in through

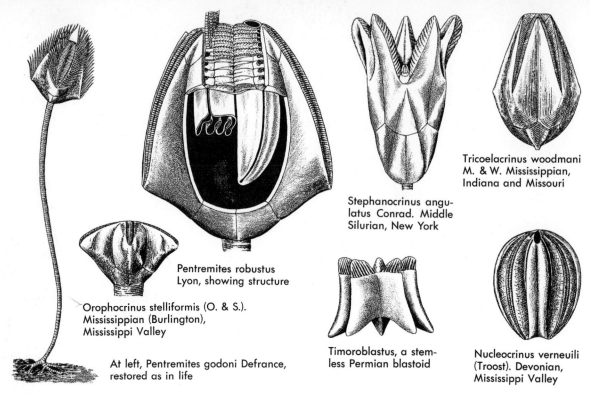

Tricoelacrinus woodmani
M. & W. Mississippian,
Indiana and Missouri

Stephanocrinus angu-
latus Conrad. Middle
Silurian, New York

Pentremites robustus
Lyon, showing structure

Orophocrinus stelliformis (O. & S.).
Mississippian (Burlington),
Mississippi Valley

Timoroblastus, a stem-
less Permian blastoid

Nucleocrinus verneuili
(Troost). Devonian,
Mississippi Valley

At left, Pentremites godoni Defrance,
restored as in life

Blastoids of various ages

the many pores, gave up oxygen to soft membranes lining the hydrospires, and passed out of the spiracles.

Most blastoids had short stalks that were anchored to the sea bottom by means of rootlike extensions. A few became stemless, however, and lay on the mud or were partly embedded in it. Some of these stemless genera developed winglike extensions or structures suggesting the feet of old-fashioned jardinieres. Such forms as *Timoroblastus* must have sat on smooth, hardened mud under water too quiet to topple the creatures over, even though they were not attached.

The Stalkless Edrioasters. The edrioasters ("seated stars") are a unique group of echinoderms that appeared in the early Cambrian and lived on into the Pennsylvanian period. Though more ancient than any known cystoids, they are much less primitive.

An edrioaster looks rather like a tiny starfish attached to a relatively large, rough button. Actually the button is a calyx made up of overlapping plates that seem to have no special arrangement. The star consists of ambulacra with food grooves radiating from the mouth. As in blastoids, the food grooves must have been ciliated and were covered by movable plates.

Some mature edrioasters may have been able to creep slowly over muddy bottoms. Typically, however, the larval animal swam for a while and then settled down and attached itself to a shell or some other solid object. The cilia captured food and took it to the mouth, but water entered through a perfor-

Edrioaster bigsbyi (Billings).
Ordovician (Trenton), eastern U.S.A. and Ontario

Foerstediscus splendens Bassler.
Ordovician (Decorah), Minnesota

Two typical edrioasters

Three views of the blastoid
Pentremites showing plates
and apex

Caryocrinites ornatus
Say. Silurian (Niagaran),
eastern U.S.A. and Canada

Troostocrinus reinwardti
(Troost), a blastoid. Si-
lurian (Niagaran), Tennessee

Pleurocystites filitexta Billings, a
cystoid. Ordovician (Trenton), Ontario and Quebec

Edrioasters, blastoids, and cystoids

ated plate near the anus. From this plate the water went to a ringlike tube below the mouth and then into radial canals under the ambulacra. Branches from the canals formed muscular sacs that ended in soft tube feet which projected through pores at the sides of the ambulacra. Starfish crawl with similar tube feet, but edrioasters probably used them to secure oxygen from sea water.

THE VARIED AND SUCCESSFUL CRINOIDS

Crinoids, the so-called sea lilies, include the most complex and beautiful group of stalked echinoderms. During the Paleozoic era they also were the

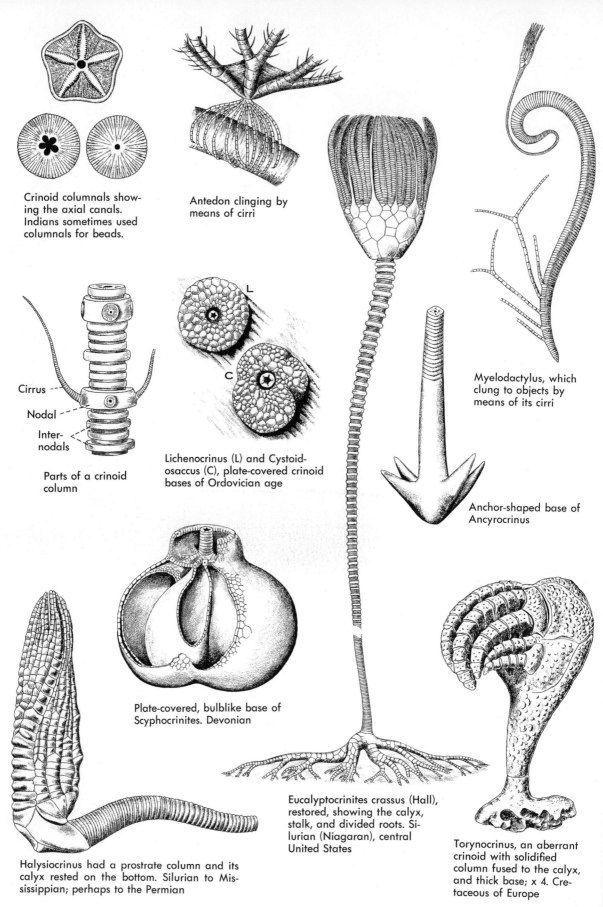

Crinoid columnals showing the axial canals. Indians sometimes used columnals for beads.

Antedon clinging by means of cirri

Cirrus

Nodal

Internodals

Parts of a crinoid column

Lichenocrinus (L) and Cystoidosaccus (C), plate-covered crinoid bases of Ordovician age

Myelodactylus, which clung to objects by means of its cirri

Anchor-shaped base of Ancyrocrinus

Plate-covered, bulblike base of Scyphocrinites. Devonian

Eucalyptocrinites crassus (Hall), restored, showing the calyx, stalk, and divided roots. Silurian (Niagaran), central United States

Halysiocrinus had a prostrate column and its calyx rested on the bottom. Silurian to Mississippian; perhaps to the Permian

Torynocrinus, an aberrant crinoid with solidified column fused to the calyx, and thick base; x 4. Cretaceous of Europe

Structures and habits of crinoids

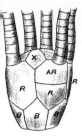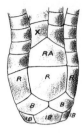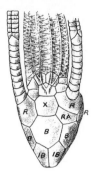

Plates in the calyx of three typical crinoids.
B, basals; IB, infrabasals; R, Radials; X, anal;
AR, aniradial; RA, radianal

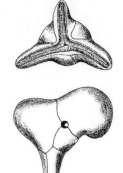

Carabocrinus, with
very short arms

Cornucrinus mirus,
an armless crinoid

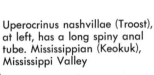

Arms of Petalocrinus (right)
became broad plates radiating from the calyx

Uperocrinus nashvillae (Troost),
at left, has a long spiny anal
tube. Mississippian (Keokuk),
Mississippi Valley

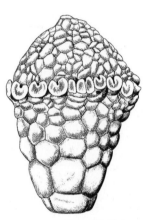

Cactocrinus glans (Hall) has
smooth plates. Mississippian
(Keokuk), Iowa and Missouri

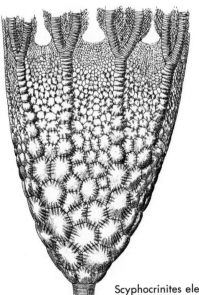

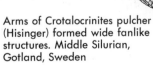

Arms of Cyathocrinites
divided several times

Scyphocrinites elegans Zenker
had great numbers of plates
in its calyx. Early Devonian, southern Missouri

Arms of Crotalocrinites pulcher
(Hisinger) formed wide fanlike
structures. Middle Silurian,
Gotland, Sweden

Structures of various crinoids

largest, the most successful, and the most abundant. Crinoids appeared in the early Ordovician, and though many died out some 320,000,000 years later, others lived on into modern times. Their range is almost as wide as the seas and oceans and extends from sunlit shoals and reefs to dark, frigid waters at depths of 13,000 feet or more. A few modern species are 50 to 60 feet long, a Cretaceous genus bore arms 4 feet in length, and some Silurian species had bodies 4 inches wide and 5 inches high. Vast colonies lived in shallow seas of Devonian, Mississippian, and Pennsylvanian ages, where their remains built up beds of limestone. Many of these range from 6 to 30 inches in thickness, and some lie on top of one another in massive series. One of these series in the Rocky Mountains near Banff, Alberta, reaches a total of 200 feet.

Most beds of crinoidal, or encrinal, limestone consist mainly of broken columns and separate columnals, with only a few calyxes. This may mean that mature crinoids broke loose from their stalks and drifted away, to be scattered widely when they died. If that is true, calyxes found in the crinoidal beds or attached to stalks belong to species that did not develop this habit or to individuals that died before they had time to break loose.

The basic plan of crinoids resembles that of eocrinoids and cystoids; it also has been compared to a starfish resting bottom side up on a jointed column, with both mouth and anus directed upward. The arms suggest those of *Macrocystella,* though they always begin with only one series of brachial plates. Water enters the body through a perforated plate, as in edrioasters, passes through a ring and radial canals, and fills tube feet that extend through pores in the arms and are used for breathing. Cilia along grooves in the arms and their branches gather food and take it to the mouth.

This is the general plan; it allows for a great deal of variation and a corresponding abundance of terms. Most of these may be ignored, but we must note that the arms and calyx together are often called the crown, while the stalk with its roots or base of attachment becomes the pelma. The latter term appears in *Pelmatozoa,* the subphylum containing all echinoderms that have or once had stalks, as well as the edrioasters.

Roots and Other Bases. Variations begin at the very bottom of the pelma. In many crinoids it consists of rootlike structures that grew into mud as the roots of land plants grow into soil. The stalk may also spread into a plate that is cemented to a shell, a coral, or some other hard object. This foundation was sometimes overturned by waves; a late Ordovician formation in the Cincinnati region contains many flat, thin concretions that have had crinoid bases attached to both sides and even to their edges. Crinoid rootlets also have been found on petrified wood of Devonian age, suggesting that some of these echinoderms hung downward from floating logs.

Lichenocrinus and *Cystoidosaccus* are plate-covered bases of crinoids with very small calyxes. Each base looks rather like an edrioaster minus its food grooves and must have covered a pad of flesh. *Ancyrocrinus* is another base which generally bears four prongs that enabled it to serve as an anchor. The roots of *Scyphocrinites* grew into a thick, plated bulb that was divided into sections. Once regarded as a float which enabled the crinoid to drift with its body hanging downward, the bulb apparently was a weight that rested on the bottom, where it sometimes was covered with mud.

The Stalk, or Column. Restorations sometimes show crinoids waving gracefully in the water or coiling and bending this way and that to reach levels where food might be plentiful or avoid disturbing currents. Such pictures ignore the nature of the stalk, which generally consists of flat columnals fastened face to face with little freedom for movement. In some genera, however, the columnals are narrow with ridged or curved faces which allowed them to tip from side to side. Columnals of *Platycrinites* also are twisted, so that the sum of their tiltings enabled the column to bend in any direction.

Columnals vary greatly in shape, from round to elliptical, quadrangular, star-shaped, or even crescentic. Their surfaces bear ridges and varied flutings whose principal function must have been to strengthen their linkage. In many crinoids the columnals changed shape during growth. One of the commonest changes led some to become larger than others, the two types being distinguished as nodals and internodals. Branchlets from stalks are called cirri; they may appear only on nodals, upon otherwise ordinary columnals, or upon every other one in stalks with two interlocking series.

Since both stalks and bases grew throughout life, they had to be supplied with food and dissolved lime salts that could be turned into calcite. Most of this was done by a fleshy cord that ran through the axial canal seen in columnals or fragments of stalks. These canals range from large or small cylindrical tubes to others with five well-defined sections.

Most stalks served as means of support that were firmly anchored or cemented at the base. But *Myelodactylus* has no base, only a tip that could coil around corals or other crinoids and cling to them by means of cirri that were single in some species but long and branched in others. The lower part of the stalk generally is thick, but more than halfway up to the calyx it contracts and commonly curves so abruptly that the column surrounds the crown. Except for a few species that were long enough to direct their bodies upward, *Myelodactylus* must have resembled a living question mark.

Still more extreme were changes in which the stalk was lost. That happened several times in four different orders, producing such forms as the modern *Antedon* and the ancient *Uintacrinus,* of late Cretaceous age. The former builds a stalk, breaks away from it, and clings to shells or other objects with a tuft of clawlike cirri, releasing its hold to swim slowly by waving its arms. *Uintacrinus* did not even have cirri, but swam or floated at the surface in hordes that sometimes drifted into shallows from which they could not escape.

The Calyx. The crinoidal calyx consists of two parts: the cup, or dorsal cup, and the tegmen. The former is aptly described by its name, for it is a cuplike, bowl-shaped or vase-shaped structure made up of plates that have definite forms and occupy definite positions in different genera. The tegmen ranges from a leathery covering over the cup to a roof of thick plates that may rise in a tall anal sac or tube, or may form a solid roof over both the mouth and the food grooves.

The oldest and most primitive crinoids have small cups with two circlets of plates called basals and radials, the former being attached to the stalk while the latter support the arms. Another plate, the anal, rests between two radials and above a plate called radianal in some genera and aniradial in others.

This brings the total number of plates to twelve, a very modest beginning.

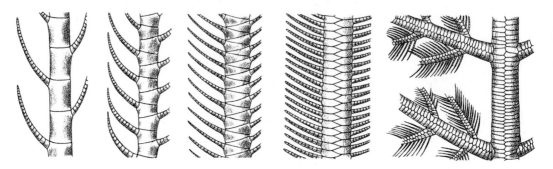

As brachials became shorter and shorter, and formed two series, the number of pinnules on crinoid arms increased. There was still further increase when arms with two series of brachials branched repeatedly.

Other crinoids added three to five infrabasals, inserted new plates near the anal, took arm plates into the cup while increasing their number, and developed new interradial plates that were not connected with the anal. Because of the changes, small crinoids such as *Uperocrinus* had seventy-seven plates in the cup, *Ichthyocrinus* one hundred and twenty-eight, and *Scyphocrinites* more than three hundred. Paleozoic genera then died out, and most of those that lived in the Mesozoic and Cenozoic eras reduced both the size of the calyx and the number of its plates. *Uintacrinus,* however, retained a bulbous calyx that contained a large number of plates.

We have mentioned crinoids whose stalks were coiled so deeply that they surrounded the calyx. These aberrant types were erect, but *Halysiocrinus* lay on the bottom or arched down to it with the calyx bent sharply upward. One side also was flattened, as if to form a surface on which the calyx could lie. This may mean that the creature lived where strong currents flowed in one or in opposite directions, as they do where tides run across reefs.

Torynocrinus, of Cretaceous age, had a short stalk that was broadly attached at its base, the calyx turned sidewise at a right angle, and its plates as well as columnals were fused into one solid mass from which thick arms projected.

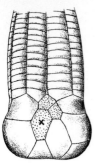

Phanocrinus

Botryocrinus

Two inadunate crinoids
X, anal plate; RA, radianal

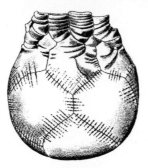

Marsupites
(articulate)

Rhizocrinus
(articulate)

Pentacrinites
(articulate)

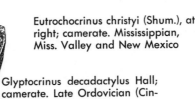

Eutrochocrinus christyi (Shum.), at
right; camerate. Mississippian,
Miss. Valley and New Mexico

Glyptocrinus decadactylus Hall;
camerate. Late Ordovician (Cincinnatian), Ohio Valley

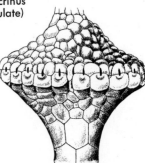

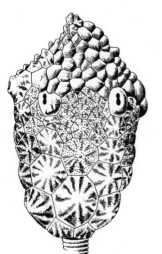

Lampterocrinus tennesseensis
Roemer, a camerate. Mid-
Silurian, Tennessee

Calliocrinus murchisonianus (Angelin),
a camerate. Middle Silurian, Sweden

Eutaxocrinus fletcheri
(Wor.), Mississippian

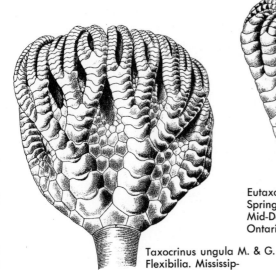

Taxocrinus ungula M. & G.
Flexibilia. Mississip-
pian (Keokuk), Indiana

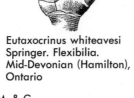

Eutaxocrinus whiteavesi
Springer. Flexibilia.
Mid-Devonian (Hamilton),
Ontario

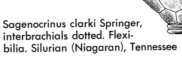
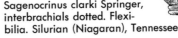

Sagenocrinus clarki Springer,
interbrachials dotted. Flexibilia. Silurian (Niagaran), Tennessee

Inadunate, articulate, camerate, and flexible crinoids

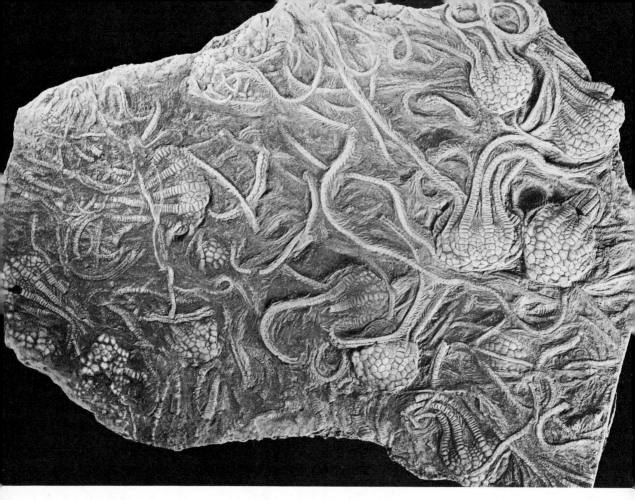

Uintacrinus socialis Grinnell, a stemless articulate crinoid that floated in late Cretaceous seas. This slab was found near Elkader, Kansas.

This crinoid also is supposed to have lived amid strong currents or where waves reached the bottom.

Some peculiarities involve both calyx and tegmen. In *Eucalyptocrinites,* for example, the calyx has a deep concavity at its lower end, so that the stalk is attached in an inverted cup. The tegmen forms a tube and then spreads out; around it are ten partitions that form compartments, each of which holds two branched arms.

Arms. The arms of crinoids vary almost as much as the calyx. In relatively primitive types, such as *Merocrinus,* the arms branch only once and are formed by single rows of jointed plates known as brachials. In *Carabocrinus* these arms became short; in *Petalocrinus* each degenerated into one plate which grew so large that it resembles a petal curved backward toward the base. Other changes may be summarized as follows; numbers refer to the accompanying illustration.

1. Many crinoids kept a single row of brachials but added greatly to their length. Such uniserial arms must have been relatively stiff, without much power of movement.

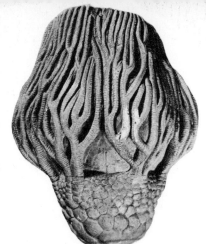

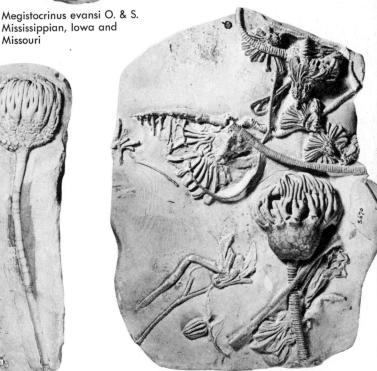

Cactocrinus imperator Laudon,
a camerate. Mississippian, Iowa

Aesiocrinus magnificus M. & G.
Late Pennsylvanian, Missouri

Megistocrinus evansi O. & S.
Mississippian, Iowa and
Missouri

Cactocrinus nodobrachiatus
W. & S. Mississippian, Iowa

Forbesiocrinus multibrachiatus
L. & C. Mississippian, Indiana

Megistocrinus nobilis W. & S., a camerate.
Mississippian. From Le Grand, Iowa

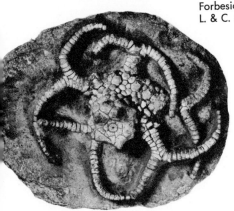

Gilbertsocrinus typus (Hall), a camerate. Mississippian (Burlington),
Iowa and Missouri

Dorycrinus mississippiensis Roemer, a long-spined camerate.
Mississippian (Keokuk), Mississippi Valley

Typical crinoids

Cupressocrinus elongatus Goldf., an inadunate. Devonian, Germany

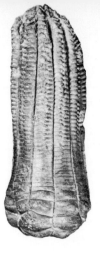

Encrinus liliiformis Lamarck, an articulate. Triassic, Germany

Cyathocrinites multibrachiatus (L. & C.), an inadunate. Mississippian, Indiana

Onychocrinus ulrichi M. & G. Flexibilia. Mississippian (Keokuk), Indiana

Onychocrinus ramulosus (L. & C.). Mississippian (Keokuk), Indiana

Ichthyocrinus laevis Conrad. Flexibilia. Silurian, New York and Ontario

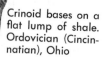

Crinoid bases on a flat lump of shale. Ordovician (Cincinnatian), Ohio

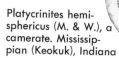

Platycrinites hemisphericus (M. & W.), a camerate. Mississippian (Keokuk), Indiana

Inadunate, articulate, and flexible crinoids

2–3. In other uniserial arms the brachial plates became wedge-shaped. Further shortening and narrowing allowed them to lie side by side with only their edges alternating. Such biserial arms, however, always have uniserial bases.

4. Both uniserial and biserial arms repeatedly developed side branches, or pinnules, comparable to those we have seen in *Comarocystites.* Most Paleozoic and all later crinoids have pinnulate arms.

5. The arms of some crinoids ceased to branch and developed long, slender plates.

6–8. Many crinoids developed arms that branched again and again, becoming both large and complex. Examples of this type include the many-branched pentacrinids of Mesozoic and modern seas. In *Crotalocrinites,* of Silurian age, the abundant branches are linked in flexible nets that either form broad, fanlike fronds or partially enfold each other. Still more extreme is *Barrandeocrinus,* from the Silurian of northern Europe. Its pinnules are free only at the tips; below this they consist of flattened plates that interlock, forming ten structures that curve downward and suggest the sections of an orange. The mouth was buried in a pit amid these overdeveloped arms.

9. *Cornucrinus* lost its free arms, retaining only ambulacra and food grooves that really were parts of the cup.

Spines. Crinoids were the first echinoderms to deserve the name "spiny skins." Many genera have thick, rough plates in the cup; in others the plates extend into spines that project from cup, tegmen, arms, stalk, and even from long anal tubes. *Ancyrocrinus,* as we have seen, also developed basal spines that served as prongs of an anchor.

Still more spiny was *Scyphocrinites spinifer,* of early Devonian age. Its spines are attached to rough plates of the calyx and to the lower brachials. Some of these spines taper to points; others thicken toward their outer ends; still others thicken, divide, and then become pointed. Spines of *Arthroacantha* also are attached by joints, but they do not thicken or divide.

MAIN GROUPS OF CRINOIDS

There are about 5,000 species of fossil crinoids. They as well as species now living may be grouped into four well-marked subclasses:

Inadunata. These are relatively simple crinoids which include the oldest known members of the class. The plates of the calyx are firmly fastened together, the tegmen covers the mouth and lower food grooves, and interradial plates appear on only one side of the cup. The arms are uniserial or biserial and nonpinnulate or pinnulate; in most genera they are free above the radial plates. Early Ordovician to late Permian.

Flexibilia. Joints between plates of both cup and tegmen show that these structures were flexible during life. The lower brachials form part of the cup; interradials range from few to many. The tegmen bears both mouth and open food grooves; the arms are uniserial and have no pinnules. These crinoids supposedly evolved from simple and very ancient members of the Inadunata. Middle Ordovician to late Permian.

Camerata. All plates of the calyx are rigidly united and commonly are thick. The tegmen covers both mouth and lower food grooves. The lower brachial plates form part of the cup, and so—in most genera—do the interradials. The arms are uniserial or biserial and are pinnulate. Middle Ordovician to late Permian; especially abundant during the Mississippian.

Articulata. In this extremely varied group of stalked and stalkless crinoids the cups commonly are small and contain few plates. Plates of the cup are united by slightly flexible joints; the tegmen is a leathery affair that bears the mouth and open food grooves and may be studded with small plates. Early Triassic to Recent.

The articulates must have evolved during the Permian period, though their oldest known members did not appear until other orders were extinct. There also are hints that they form two orders, not one, some having come from inadunates while others are descendants of the Flexibilia. Be that as it may, the articulates achieved little variety during the Mesozoic and early Tertiary, though species such as *Uintacrinus socialis* existed in vast numbers. Expansion began during the Pliocene epoch, and the articulates now number 800 or more widely differing species. Ranging from shallows to abysses and from tropical to near-polar seas, they compare in importance with the camerates of Mississippian times.

CHAPTER XI

Sea Stars, Urchins, and Cucumbers

Wₑ ʜᴀᴠᴇ ʟɪᴋᴇɴᴇᴅ crinoids to starfish resting upon jointed stalks with the mouth directed upward. We now come to two classes in which the mouth is on the under side, and a third in which it lies at one end of a sausage-shaped body.

SEA STARS AND THEIR ORIGIN

Books about living animals generally describe two great groups of star-shaped echinoderms, one of which includes true starfish (asteroids) while the other is made up of brittle and serpent stars (ophiuroids). Paleontologists add a third group, the somasters, and place them all in a class termed the Steller-oidea, or "starlike ones." A useful English equivalent is "sea stars," leaving "starfish" for the animals technically called asteroids.

Somasters ranged from early Ordovician to late Devonian, especially in western Europe. They have short thick arms and large openings that once contained the mouth, surrounded by tough skin. Plates with large pores that accommodated tube feet appear at the edge of this opening and run in two adjacent series along the middle of each arm. Many rows of rodlike plates called virgalia branch off at each side, completing a structure that suggests the arms and pinnules of a crinoid. Exceptionally good specimens show that the upper surface was covered with tough skin studded with little spicules. Skin also covered the under surface between virgalia.

If these fossils mean what they seem to, sea stars are descendants of un-known Cambrian crinoids that lost their stalks, lay mouth downward, and began to crawl with tube feet which their ancestors had used only for breathing.

The leathery skins and spicules of Ordovician somasters probably are specializations, since the oldest starfish have plates resembling those of crinoids.

This resemblance appears only in Paleozoic starfish; the plates of most
later types interlock and generally are rough or spiny. Typical asteroids have
thick arms that contain lobes of the stomach, digestive glands, and reproductive organs. Water can be absorbed and then forced out through the skin, but
it also is taken into the body through a porous plate (madreporite) that lies
on the upper surface, near the point where two arms join. Water goes from
this plate to the tube feet through canals which suggest those of crinoids and
edrioasters.

How Starfish Feed. A starfish feels for food or tastes it by means of specialized tube feet near the tips of its arms. Shorter feet, which line the well-
developed ambulacra, are used mainly for clinging or for crawling at speeds
that vary from an inch or two to almost a foot per minute. Often, however,
the animal lies in one place for hours, scarcely moving an arm.

Starfish use foods of several kinds and devour them in various ways. Some
species eat dead stuff that drifts across the sea bottom, catching it in sheets
of slime which then are swallowed and digested. When such carrion becomes
scarce the secretion of slime is halted and the stomach, which is a sac of soft
membrane, begins to flow out of the mouth. There it dissolves seaweeds,
small algae that grow on rocks, or even astringent sponges. A similar method
is used to devour sea urchins and chitons, though starfish that feed on snails
usually swallow them whole by pushing them into the mouth with their tube
feet. Mussels, clams, and oysters are pulled open by means of the tube feet,
after which the stomach surrounds the victim and rapidly digests its flesh.

Fossil Starfish. Such are the ways of living starfish; fossils seem to have had
similar habits. They begin with such creatures as *Hudsonaster,* of middle to
late Ordovician age. *Hudsonaster* is less than an inch wide and has stubby arms.
Its upper surface is covered with smooth, thick plates that are arranged in
regular order suggesting that of a crinoid cup. *Palaeaster* and *Devonaster* have
longer, more slender arms and small plates between rows of large ones.
Though the latter still form definite patterns, the small plates between them
do not.

Some basically primitive starfish developed unusual forms. *Stürzaster,* for
example, had broad, petal-shaped arms and a bulbous body that suggests the
mushrooms called earth stars. *Cheiropteraster* was even more aberrant; it had
a very large opening for the mouth but no arms, its ambulacra being directly
attached to a baglike body of skin without plates or spicules. *Loriolaster* had
a small mouth and well-developed ambulacra that did form arms, though the

rest of the body was encased in skin. Like *Cheiropteraster* and several other unusual starfish, this genus is found in hard Devonian shales (often miscalled slates) of Bundenbach, Germany.

Starfish are rare in the Paleozoic and are even less plentiful in Mesozoic and Cenozoic formations. Most of the fossils belong to genera that developed large, thick plates that were either smooth or spiny; they include living genera as well as others that are extinct. *Metopaster,* for example, is a Cretaceous genus which, like its modern relatives, has massive plates and arms that are not much more than angles on the sides of the body. *Oreaster* is a modern genus that appeared in Jurassic seas. Fossils have rather slender arms, but the most familiar living species has short arms and a thick, well-armored body whose color may be red, yellow, or blue.

BRITTLE STARS; THE OPHIUROIDS

The Ophiuroidea ("snakelike tails") are so called because most of them have thin, snaky arms; their popular name refers to the fact that those organs are easily broken. Types whose arms branch again and again are called basket stars.

Brittle stars are specialized descendants of somasters whose bodies became disk-shaped and whose arms grew slender. The stomach does not extend into the arms, and the mouth is star-shaped and narrow. Instead of being hollow, the arms contain plates that are fastened together like vertebrae in a backbone. In living species these so-called vertebrae are encased in tough skin set with wide plates and spines, and skin covers plates that strengthen the body. The creatures crawl by pulling with some arms and pushing with others, in a complex of wriggling movements. The arms also are used to hold large pieces of food and take them to the mouth. Small particles are passed along by the tube feet. *Onychaster,* of Mississippian age, clung to the arms or anal tubes of crinoids, apparently feeding on waste materials. These may have been gathered in slime like that secreted and then swallowed by some modern starfish.

Brittle stars first appear in early Ordovician strata and are sparingly found in deposits of later ages and epochs. Though the best specimens come from early Devonian black shales of Europe, good examples have been found in middle Ordovician rocks of eastern North America.

ECHINOIDS, OR SEA URCHINS

The word *urchin* once meant "hedgehog"—a plump, spiny mammal that ranges from western Europe to China. Sea urchins, or Echinoidea, are echinoderms that have neither stalks nor arms and commonly are much more spiny than the mammals for which they are named. They also have a greater range, being found in seas around the world and in formations as old as the late Devonian and as young as the Pleistocene. Good, though not plentiful, fossil sea urchins are found in Silurian and Ordovician strata.

Armor and Anatomy. This long geologic record reveals the development of armor that became increasingly sturdy and so was readily petrified. The most primitive echinoids had tests—they should not be called shells—made of smallish plates that overlapped, were movable, and often fell apart after death. In progressive types the plates are firmly fastened and commonly are thick or are reinforced by secondary deposits that fill as much as half of the test. Several genera whose plates remain relatively thin possess clublike or massive spines. Though their internal structure is lacy or netlike, many of them are strong enough to survive burial and petrifaction.

The oldest and most primitive echinoids are spheroidal; later types may be flattened at top and bottom, subconical, discoidal, or so irregular that only pictures can describe their shapes. The ventral surface commonly is flattened and has a central opening, the peristome ("around the mouth"), which in life is covered by tough skin studded with calcareous plates. The dorsal surface is moderately to steeply arched; in all regular echinoids (Regularia) its central portion is occupied by two sets of plates termed the apical system. One set, the periproct, surrounds the anus; the other, or oculogenital ring, includes five plates at the tips of the ambulacra and five more containing large pores through which reproductive cells pass out of the body.

In irregular echinoids (Irregularia) the apical system is divided. The oculogenital ring remains at or near the center of the upper surface, but the anus and periproct move to the rear. They may even lie on the ventral surface, a short distance back of the mouth.

Both regular and irregular echinoids agree in having one genital plate that is a sievelike madreporite, through which water is taken into canals leading to the tube feet. They reach out from the ambulacra, as they do in crinoids, starfish, and other echinoderms. Each starfish foot, however, comes from one pore and is filled with liquid from one muscular, contractile sac. An urchin's foot starts out as two sacs which send tubes through a pair of pores. The tubes then join and form a single organ, which may be very long.

Ambulacra vary almost as much as the entire test. Some are narrow and almost straight; some are flexuous; others are petal-shaped. They may run from peristome to apical system or may be limited to part of the dorsal surface. In primitive genera they contain two rows of large plates, but some Paleozoic fossils have eight to twenty rows of small ones. Mesozoic and Cenozoic sea urchins combined small plates and rearranged them until as many as six or seven formed a single large compound plate.

All sea urchin tests bear tubercles, which may be large and conspicuous or may be too small to be seen without a magnifying glass. During life the test

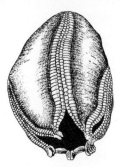

Cheiropteraster giganteus Stürtz, an asteroid. Devonian, Germany

Spicules of varied holothurians, or sea cucumbers, from Europe and North America. Their ages are indicated by letters: M, Mississippian; J, Jurassic; T, Tertiary

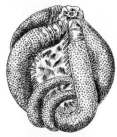

Onychaster flexilis M. & W., a brittle star. Mississippian (Keokuk), Indiana

Metopaster uncatus Forbes, an asteroid. Late Cretaceous, England

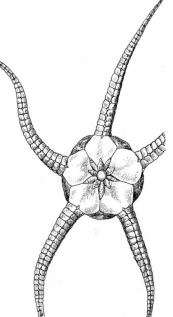

Aganaster gregarius M. & G., an asteroid. Mississippian (Keokuk), Indiana

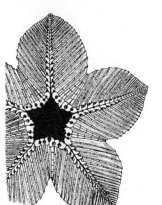

Villebrunaster thorali Spencer, a somaster. Ordovician, France

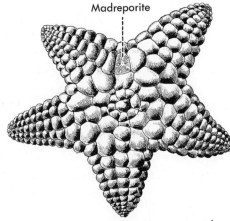

Madreporite

Hudsonaster incomptus (Meek), an asteroid. Late Ordovician (Cincinnatian), Ohio

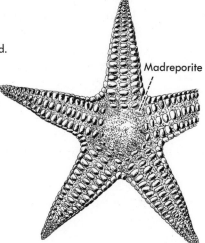

Madreporite

Devonaster eucharis (Hall), an asteroid. Middle Devonian (Hamilton), New York and Ontario

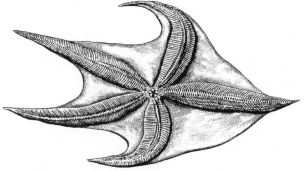

Loriolaster mirabilis Stürtz, an asteroid. Devonian (Bundenbach "slate"), Germany

Sea stars and spicules of sea cucumbers

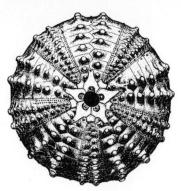

Goniopygus zitteli Clark.
Late Cretaceous (Fredericksburg),
south-central Texas

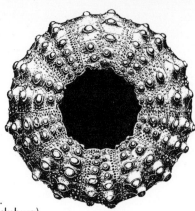

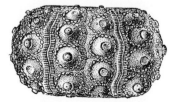

Cidaris splendens (Morton).
Eocene (Vincentown),
New Jersey

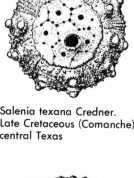

Salenia texana Credner.
Late Cretaceous (Comanche),
central Texas

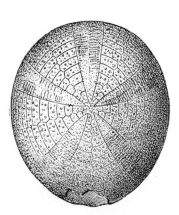

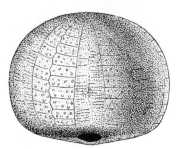

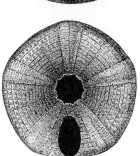

Holaster simplex Shumard.
Early Cretaceous (Washita),
Oklahoma and Texas

Diplopodia taffi Cragin.
Late Cretaceous (Fredericksburg),
north-central Texas

Holectypus planatus Roemer.
Late Cretaceous, Texas

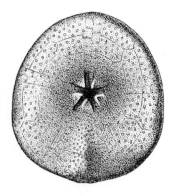

Cassidulus micrococcus Gabb.
Late Cretaceous (Ripley),
Alabama

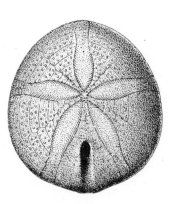

Typical sea urchins, or echinoids (after Clark & Twitchell)

is covered with skin, while the tubercles serve as attachments for spines that are held in place by ligaments and moved by cordlike muscles. In primitive genera these spines are borne only on plates between the ambulacra, but they appear on the ambulacral plates of Mesozoic and Cenozoic urchins.

Echinoids have to eat, and most of them do so with a complex device called the lantern or Aristotle's lantern. It contains five pointed teeth and as many as thirty-five bonelike plates, all operated by some sixty muscles. The plates form five identical sets which serve as sheaths and guides for the teeth as well as attachments for muscles. As teeth wear at one end they grow at the other and are slowly pushed downward through notches in the lantern.

Two other groups of structures demand attention, since they are fairly common fossils. First come the pedicellariae, tiny nipperlike or jawlike structures that move to and fro, capturing or removing things that settle upon the skin. The other structures are plates, rods, and hooks of calcite that are found in the intestine, reproductive glands, and several other structures. Like pedicellariae, they are so small that they must be examined through a microscope.

REGULAR SEA URCHINS

We already have divided echinoderms into Regularia and Irregularia. Members of the former subclass are characterized by a periproct at the center of the dorsal surface and by ambulacra that radiate uniformly so that the test has five equal portions. Division into right and left sides is not conspicuous.

Lepidocentroids. These are the least specialized of sea urchins and may be ancestral to all other members of the class. Early types, from the late Ordovician of Europe, are characterized by spheroidal crowns, by two rows of plates in each ambulacrum, and by interambulacral plates with overlapping edges and no uniformity of arrangement. As ages passed, new types evolved, some with many rows of plates in each ambulacrum, and others whose compound plates were built up of several small ones. The Jurassic *Pelanechinus* went still further, uniting compound plates into "supercompound" ones.

Though most lepidocentroids are extinct, two genera survive in both deep and shallow waters. Their crowns reach diameters of 6 inches and are covered with short but poisonous spines. Though dried specimens are thin and flat, living ones are globular and often are brightly colored.

Melonechinoids. The "melon urchins" are found only in Mississippian strata, in which they may be so abundant as to form layers of limestone. They have thick, rigidly united plates arranged in interlocking rows that number two to ten in each ambulacrum and two to eight in interambulacra. Spines are small and thin.

Cidaroids. This long-lived order appeared in Devonian times and is common in modern seas. Its members have two rows of plates in each ambulacrum and two or more in the interambulacra. Each interambulacral plate bears one broad tubercle to which a large spine is attached, a smooth ring (areole), and a circle of small tubercles that carry secondary spines. If there is room, still smaller tubercles and spines are scattered over the rest of the plate.

Paleozoic cidaroids have flexible crowns and as many as fourteen rows of plates in the ambulacra. Spines may be thin or thick; some have flattened ends that fit together, forming a coat of armor outside the crown. Rigid cidaroids appeared in the Triassic; they and later genera have only two rows of plates in each interambulacrum, but the primary spines remain large. Those of one Jurassic genus are 5 inches long and are covered with rows of smaller spikes.

Stirodonts. These echinoids, which range from Triassic to Recent, are plump or almost spheroidal. Stirodonts seem to be Mesozoic descendants of early cidaroids, with plates and spines much like those of their ancestors. The anus, however, is slightly off center, and modern forms do most of their breathing with specialized gills at the edge of the peristome. In some genera the spines become very long and thick in proportion to the crown, and in *Pseudocidaris* they are egg-shaped. Members of this genus supposedly lived among breakers near the shore and used their massive spines as weights that kept them from being washed about.

Aulodonts. These urchins range from Triassic to Recent and have just twenty rows of plates in the test. Early members evidently were flexible, with simple ambulacral plates; later genera become rigid and developed compound plates. Spines generally are thin and may be hollow, two characters that help distinguish these urchins from stirodonts and cidaroids.

Camarodonts. This order ranges from Jurassic to Recent. Its members have twenty rows of plates that are rigidly united. The most familiar member of this order is *Strongylocentrotus,* one species of which is the green sea urchin found on the northern coasts of Europe and North America. Another Pacific species is much larger, with tests 6 to 10 inches in diameter and long, slender spines.

IRREGULAR SEA URCHINS

In irregular echinoids the anus and periproct are located off center and to the rear, giving the crown right and left sides. This is true even when the periproct moves to the ventral surface and comes near the mouth. Right and left, front and rear may also be distinguished in shape, arrangement, and size of the ambulacra.

Holectypoids. These are the most primitive order of irregular echinoids. They have lanterns—some Irregularia do not; the ambulacra run from oculogenital ring to peristome and generally contain compound plates. Holectypoids range from early Jurassic to Recent, but are larger and more plentiful in Europe than in America.

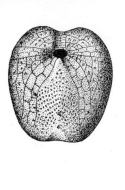
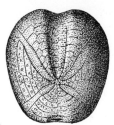
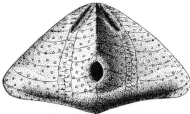

Enallaster texanus (Roemer).
Early Cretaceous (Comanche),
Texas and New Mexico

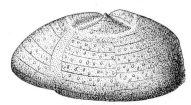

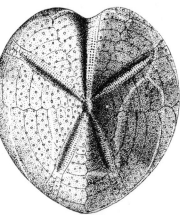

Linthia tumidula Clark.
Eocene (Vincentown),
New Jersey

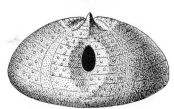

Hemiaster texanus Roemer.
Late Cretaceous (Austin),
south-central Texas

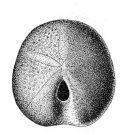
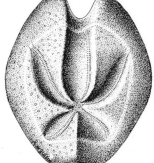

Hemiaster dalli Clark.
Late Cretaceous (Washita),
south-central Texas

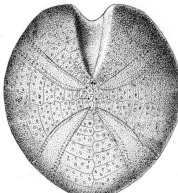

Trematopygus cruciferus (Morton).
Eocene (Vincentown),
New Jersey

Echinobrissus expansus Clark.
Late Cretaceous (Ripley),
Alabama, Mississippi

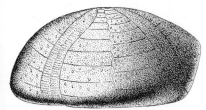

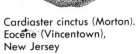

Cardiaster cinctus (Morton).
Eocene (Vincentown),
New Jersey

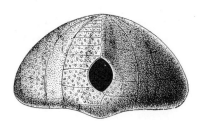

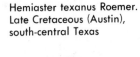

Late Cretaceous and Eocene sea urchins, or echinoids (after Clark & Twitchell)

Pedinopsis pondi Clark, x 0.5.
Late Cretaceous (Austin Chalk),
Travis County, Texas

Scutaster andersoni Pack, x 0.5.
Miocene, southern California

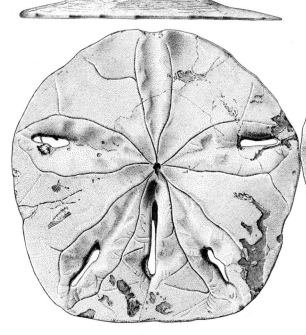
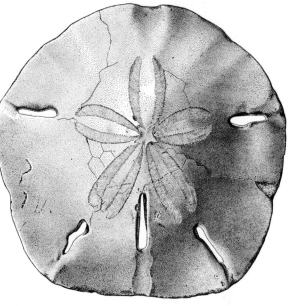

Mellita pentapora (Gmelin), a sand dollar, x 0.5.
Pleistocene ("Ice Age"), South Carolina and Georgia to Texas

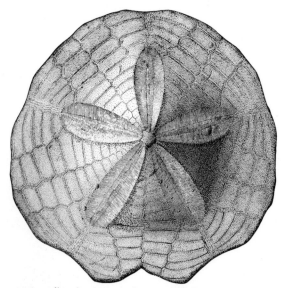

Scutella aberti Conrad, a sand dollar, x 0.5.
Middle Miocene (Choptank), Maryland

Clypeaster bowersi Weaver, x 0.6.
Pliocene, southern California and Lower California

Sea urchins and sand dollars, or echinoids

Cassiduloids. This order is as old as the preceding, for it appeared in early Jurassic times and exists today. In spite of this it is not primitive, for its ambulacra have lost their compound plates, are limited to the dorsal surface, and are bluntly petal-shaped. A double ring of flowerlike plates surrounds the mouth—a structure that exists in no other group of urchins. Fossil cassiduloids are widespread in Mesozoic and Cenozoic formations of North America.

Spatangoids, or Heart Urchins. These echinoids, which are shaped like domes and biscuits as well as hearts, range from early Cretaceous to Recent. Their ambulacra are petal-shaped and may number four instead of five; the mouth is forward from the center, and there is no lantern. The periproct lies in an almost vertical area which really is part of the dorsal surface. Spines are delicate and silky and are either short or very long. Several genera are marked by grooves (fascioles) in which tubercles are microscopic and the spines correspondingly small.

Clypeasteroids. These were the last order of echinoids to appear, their range being late Cretaceous to Recent. In most respects they are highly specialized, since the oculogenital ring is fused, the test assumes unusual shapes and is generally strengthened by internal ribs, plates, and pillars of calcite. The lantern also is fastened directly to the test instead of being attached by muscles.

Early clypeasteroids are tiny and egg-shaped, with ambulacra that are not quite petals. Several later genera, including *Clypeaster* itself, are large and thick, with well-developed petals and the mouth at the top of an inverted funnel. Most clypeasteroids, however, are cake urchins or sand dollars: depressed creatures with a flattened under surface crossed by grooves that commonly branch. Spines are so short and delicate that they may look like fur.

Since clypeasteroids have sturdy tests, they are abundant fossils. In some places they almost fill beds of soft limestone; in others they litter the ground as rain wears away deposits of soft marl or shale.

HOMES AND HABITS OF URCHINS

Sea urchins have many habitats, from reefs and sandy shoals to deep water that is seldom disturbed by waves. Some even live in shallow bays whose bottoms are exposed at low tide.

Regularia. In such varied surroundings, echinoids live in a variety of ways. Almost all are gregarious, forming swarms or schools that number dozens, hundreds, or even thousands of individuals. Many regular species cling tightly to rocks or brace themselves in cracks and crevices by means of spines and tube feet that end in sucking disks. Others excavate burrows, not merely in limestone and shale, but in granite, basalt, and hard, gritty sandstone. Such rock is much more resistant than calcite, and no one knows just how urchins wear it away.

Other regular urchins lie on mud among rocks and corals or upon smooth, firm bottoms. There they crawl by means of their tube feet or by using their spines as stilts. Since the spines fit on ball-and-socket joints, they can be moved in almost any direction.

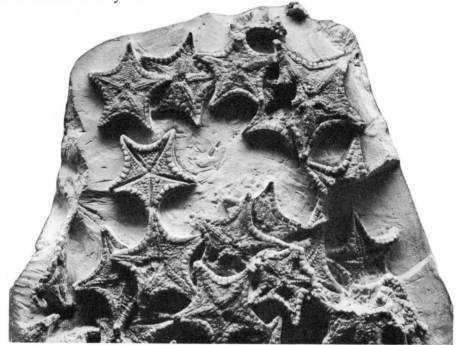

Part of a slab of starfish; Austinaster mccarteri Hakins, in the University of Okla-homa Museum. From the Cretaceous Austin Chalk, near Austin, Texas (Photograph by Hubert Gotthold)

The foods of these regular urchins fit their habits and habitats. Some eat small algae that cover the surface of rocks, but others catch pieces of seaweed on their spines and pass them down to the mouth by means of tube feet. Rock-dwelling urchins devour sponges, hydroids, bryozoans, and tube worms when they can get them, but species that live in crevices or burrows are limited to foods that crawl or drift into their niches. Pedicellariae seize tiny creatures and pass them along to the mouth, and some bottom-dwelling urchins swallow mud and digest whatever food it contains.

Irregularia. Irregular echinoids inhabit muddy or sandy bottoms, where they crawl or burrow. Many heart urchins plow along slowly, scooping mud into their mouths and digesting its organic content. Others lie in burrows 4 to 6 inches deep, getting water for breathing through a chimney that extends to the surface. Long tube feet also reach up through this chimney, picking up food and pulling it down where it can be passed to the mouth.

Many sand dollars crawl under a very thin coating of sediment. But species that live in estuaries rest on edge, partly in water and partly below it, but always across the direction of tidal flow. When the tide recedes they dig in, cover themselves with sand, and either rest quietly or creep to new feeding grounds. They also burrow at the approach of starfish that eat echinoids, but are not disturbed by other species.

Feeding, for a sand dollar, is a complex process. Its spines, of course, are covered with skin; those on the upper surface also secrete mucus and carry cilia that beat to and fro. They produce currents that flow toward the rear, making eddies that wash tiny organisms against the mucus, in which they are trapped. The mucus, in turn, is driven to the under surface, where it collects in grooves and is taken to the mouth. Not until the teeth cut it to pieces does the sand dollar actually eat.

It seems clear that ancient sand dollars fed like their modern descendants, that most fossil heart urchins plowed through mud, and that reef-dwellers devoured both plants and small animals. Beyond this, however, there is little to tell about the feeding habits of specific echinoids.

SEA CUCUMBERS, OR HOLOTHUROIDEA

Sea cucumbers are soft-bodied creatures with leathery skin, whose appearance is well suggested by their name. The mouth lies at one end of the body and is surrounded by tentacles; rows of tube feet run along the body in most species, and tiny porous plates of calcite or iron phosphate are scattered through the skin. Most sea cucumbers lie or crawl on sea bottoms, swallowing mud or trapping small animals with their tentacles. One group consists of burrowers, however, and a single modern genus swims with an umbrella-shaped web of skin that is stretched between elongate tentacles.

The oldest known sea cucumbers are carbonized films found in the Burgess shale. The animals apparently crawled, for fossils once thought to belong to a swimming species now seem to be coelenterates. Separate plates are found in Mississippian and many later formations, but they are so small that few collectors notice them. Impressions of entire animals, from the Jurassic lithographic limestones of Germany, may be seen in a few museums.

CHAPTER XII

Snails and Their Kin

Snails belong to the mollusks—phylum Mollusca—whose name comes from the Latin word for "soft nut." In everyday language mollusks are "shells," edible types often being "shellfish." Actually, many animals that have shells are not mollusks, and some mollusks have either lost their shells or have tucked them away where they cannot be seen. To learn what the phylum really is we must emphasize bodies and give secondary attention to shells.

The molluscan body is soft; its lower part has become a muscular structure that is generally used for locomotion and therefore is called a foot. The upper part of the body is spread out into a mantle that folds downward over the rest of the creature. Since the mantle builds the shell, if there is one, the latter does not completely cover the body, as does the shell of a crab or lobster. The molluscan shell may be limy, chitinous, or both. Limy shells are largely calcite, but they may contain layers of a related mineral called aragonite, which dissolves readily. Such shells are likely to form casts or molds, not petrified fossils.

CHITONS AND TUSK SHELLS

The earliest, simplest mollusks are unknown, for they were part of the horde of soft-bodied creatures that evolved, died out, and disappeared during Precambrian times. But we can get a fair picture of those pioneers by looking at the simplest of living mollusks, the chitons.

Chitons, or Amphineura. The technical name of chitons, Amphineura, refers to their nervous system, which forms a double series around the mouth, in the head, and through the body. A living chiton is an oval creature with an indistinct head and a foot that is merely the flattened under side of the body. The mouth contains a rough tongue, or radula, in the form of a ribbonlike

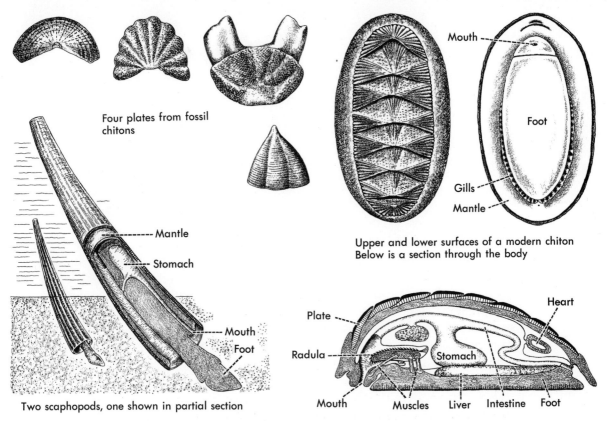

Four plates from fossil chitons

Mouth

Foot

Gills

Mantle

Upper and lower surfaces of a modern chiton
Below is a section through the body

Mantle

Stomach

Mouth

Foot

Two scaphopods, one shown in partial section

Heart

Plate

Radula

Stomach

Mouth   Muscles   Liver   Intestine   Foot

Anatomy of chitons and scaphopods

structure with rows of sharp, horny teeth. Muscles thrust the radula forward and pull it back and forth over a base, thus scraping algae from rocks over which the animal crawls. The digestive system is simple, and the shell (which some species have lost) consists of eight plates, one behind another on the back. They seem to be secretions added to an original structure that was curved like a saucer.

Though chitons are very primitive mollusks, their fossils have not been found in rocks older than Ordovician. Paleozoic species can be recognized by the fact that their plates fitted end to end; those of Mesozoic and later types overlapped like movable shingles, just as they do in modern species.

Scaphopods, or Tusk Shells. Modern members of this group were often used as beads by Indians. They are strangely specialized mollusks whose shells are slender, curved cones that are open at both ends; most species are less than 3 inches long, but one from the Pennsylvanian of Texas reached the amazing length of 2 feet. Living scaphopods burrow in the sea bottom at depths ranging from the level of low tide to at least 15,000 feet. The shell is carried obliquely and extends into the water, the foot is used for creeping and digging, and short tentacles around the mouth capture food in the form of small animals. Fossils range from the Silurian onward but are most common in Cenozoic strata.

SNAILS AND THEIR ALLIES; THE GASTROPODS

The word *gastropod* means "stomach-foot," but a stomach that lies in the foot is a character which these mollusks share with the lowly chiton. Gastropods are better characterized as snails and their kin, whose shells (unless they have been lost) consist of one main structure which bears the deceptive name of valve.

The Gastropod Body. Most fossil gastropods are shells, but to understand them we must picture the creatures to which they belonged. A typical gastropod has a foot that can be spread out very broadly or pulled back into the shell. The body is either tumid or coiled and is covered by the sheetlike mantle. The head has two tentacles, each with an eye on its outer surface about midway between the base and the tip. The mantle is thickened at the edge and at one place forms a pocketlike cavity between itself and the body. In most aquatic species this cavity contains one or two gills, to which water comes through a tube-shaped fold, the siphon. After the gills have taken oxygen from it, this water passes out through the slit that separates body and mantle.

Gastropod Shells. Gastropod shells vary greatly, but all are secreted by the mantle. At the surface is a thin coat, the periostracum, which consists of horny material that protects the shell from wear. It is seldom if ever preserved in fossils and is not developed by gastropods whose shells are so small that they are covered by broad folds of the mantle.

Most of the shell is made up of calcite, aragonite, or both, in the form of layers or fibers. The innermost layers commonly are aragonite and are smoothly "polished" or pearly. Shells that contain much aragonite often dissolve before they can be preserved. Others, whose calcite forms coarse fibers and prisms, crumble when their fossils are weathered out of limestone, marl, or shale. An example of this is illustrated in Chapter I.

Most snail shells are coiled, but many are not, and these characteristics alone tell nothing about relationships. The reason is that some uncoiled snails are primitive, while others have evolved from coiled ancestors. Coiled shells consist of whorls, the outer one being called the body whorl because it covers the part of the body that can be seen when the snail is active. Actually, however, the body may extend through other whorls, almost to the tip of the shell.

The Operculum. The gastropod shell forms a sturdy and ever-ready coat of armor into which the builder can tuck its soft and compressible body. In some groups no further protection is needed; cowries and cone-shells, for example, have such narrow apertures that almost nothing can reach into them. But limpets, abalones, and other conical or slightly coiled snails have apertures as large as their shells. To secure protection these mollusks cling

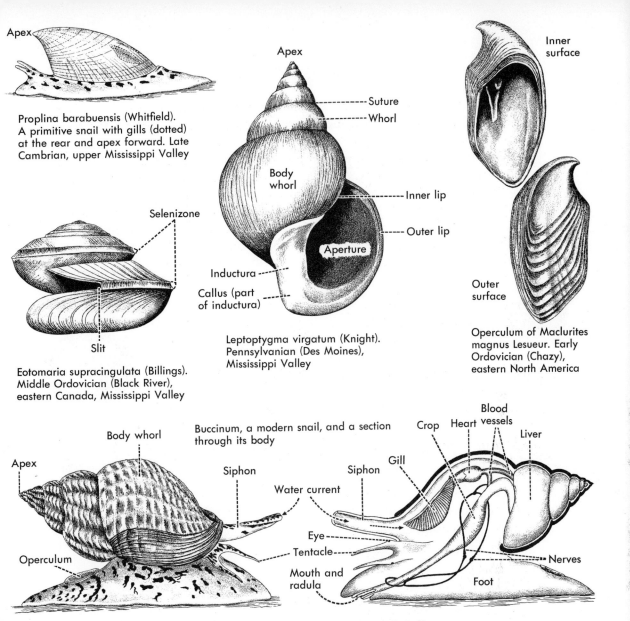

Apex

Proplina barabuensis (Whitfield).
A primitive snail with gills (dotted)
at the rear and apex forward. Late
Cambrian, upper Mississippi Valley

Apex

Suture

Whorl

Body
whorl

Inner lip

Outer lip

Aperture

Inductura

Callus (part
of inductura)

Leptoptygma virgatum (Knight).
Pennsylvanian (Des Moines),
Mississippi Valley

Inner
surface

Outer
surface

Operculum of Maclurites
magnus Lesueur. Early
Ordovician (Chazy),
eastern North America

Selenizone

Slit

Eotomaria supracingulata (Billings).
Middle Ordovician (Black River),
eastern Canada, Mississippi Valley

Body whorl

Buccinum, a modern snail, and a section
through its body

Crop   Heart   Blood
vessels

Liver

Apex

Siphon

Gill

Operculum

Water current

Siphon

Eye

Tentacle

Mouth and
radula

Nerves

Foot

Terms used to describe snail bodies and shells

tightly to rocks and other objects with their broad, muscular feet. The rough
area in an abalone shell shows the size and suggests the strength of the muscle
that contracts, turning the animal's flat foot into a vacuum cup.

Most snails have apertures that are wider than those of cowries but lack
the abalone's powerful foot. Such snails protect themselves by means of an
operculum, which is a horny or calcareous plate secreted by glands above the
hind part of the foot. Though this plate looks absurdly small on an expanded
snail, it fits tightly against the shell when the animal draws far back into the
body whorl.

Horny opercula are seldom if ever preserved as fossils, but those that are strengthened by calcite may be thicker and sturdier than the shells into which they fit. Some of the thickest and commonest fossil opercula belonged to snails called *Maclurites,* of middle to late Ordovician age.

Growth and Length of Life. Many snails grow to large size; one modern species becomes 2 feet long. Many others, both fossil and modern, are covered with growth lines, or wrinkles, which make them look very old. The fact is that snails grow rapidly and have rather short lives. Tube snails reach lengths of 4 to 5 inches in only two or three years; a thick-shelled murex added a frill one fourth to one half inch wide in only three days. Though some snails are known to live twenty years, one to five years is the rule.

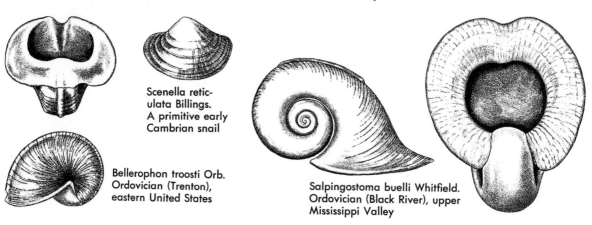

Scenella reticulata Billings. A primitive early Cambrian snail

Bellerophon troosti Orb. Ordovician (Trenton), eastern United States

Salpingostoma buelli Whitfield. Ordovician (Black River), upper Mississippi Valley

A primitive snail and two bellerophonts

AMPHIGASTROPODS AND BELLEROPHONTS

Snails doubtless evolved during Precambrian times, but their oldest known shells are found in early Cambrian rocks. They belong to the amphigastropods, a primitive class characterized by shells that either failed to coil or coiled in one plane, but not in a "twist," or spiral. Marks, or scars, to which muscles were attached show that the body filled the forward part of the shell while two leaf-shaped gills lay to the rear, in a pocket covered by the mantle. The tip, or apex, of the shell therefore pointed forward, and growth was toward the rear. Amphigastropods apparently crawled on muddy sea bottoms, "inching" along from side to side and feeding upon small algae. One early Cambrian genus, *Scenella,* had such a broad shell that it resembles a clam.

In Greek mythology, Bellerophon was a hero who rode to battle on Pegasus, the winged horse. Among fossils, *Bellerophon* is a snail whose shell coils symmetrically in one plane instead of in a spiral. The outer lip flares at both sides and has a central notch, or slit, that becomes a ridge when it is closed. Several related genera are not closely coiled, have still more widely flaring lips, and show other peculiarities.

Lack of muscle scars inside the shell leaves us in doubt as to where bellerophonts belong in molluscan classification. Some paleontologists consider them amphigastropods, directing their coils forward and their apertures toward the rear. Other authorities think bellerophonts were much more specialized creatures whose gills and mantle cavity had moved forward to a place just behind the head. The problem will not be solved until some careful collector finds a shell with distinct muscle scars showing where body and shell were attached.

THE PROSPEROUS PROSOBRANCHS

If bellerophonts are amphigastropods, that primitive group lived throughout the Paleozoic era, or about 300,000,000 years. If bellerophonts had gills near the head, then this life span is shortened by 140,000,000 years, running only from early Cambrian to late Silurian. In either case, amphigastropods were outlived and outnumbered by prosobranchs, the class in which gills and mantle cavity lie near the head, the aperture is directed forward, and the shell's apex points toward the rear. The digestive tract also has become so abruptly and deeply curved that the anus opens above the head. In amphigastropods the tract runs from front to rear.

Undoubted prosobranchs appeared in Cambrian seas and are abundant today. Even though muscle scars may be invisible, most members of this class can be recognized as marine snails that coil spirally. They range from *Maclurites,* whose shell goes into a reversed spiral that is flat on one side and sunken on the other, to tall, slender spires such as *Ectomaria* and *Turritella.* Some are as smooth as well-glazed china; others are wrinkled, ridged, elaborately spiny, or ornamented with dead odds and ends cemented into the shell. Colors of living species range from white or gray to red, green, and purple.

Habits of Some Prosobranchs. Habits vary as greatly as shapes, ornamentation, and colors. Modern periwinkles (*Littorina*) and dog-whelks (*Thais*) dwell on rocks that lie bare and dry at every low tide and are pounded by waves during storms. Olive shells crawl beneath the surface of loose sand, producing markings almost identical with some that are found in Pennsylvanian strata. Many other snails crawl on sandy or muddy bottoms, cling to submerged rocks, or creep over coral reefs. Creeping generally is done with the sole of the foot, which may also be covered with fine channels that serve as suckers with which the snail holds fast to shells or rocks. But *Strombus* and a few other prosobranchs have clawlike opercula that are thrust forward and hooked into sand or mud. Foot muscles then contract, pulling the animals forward.

Platyceras niagarense (Hall). Silurian, central United States

Gyrodes supraplicatus (Conrad). Late Cretaceous, New Jersey to Texas and Utah

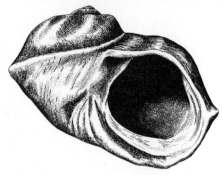

Turbonopsis shumardi (Hall). Middle Devonian (Onondaga), Mississippi Valley

Vermicularia spirata (Philippi). Miocene to Recent, eastern North and South America

Holopea symmetrica Hall. Mid-Ordovician (Trenton), eastern North America

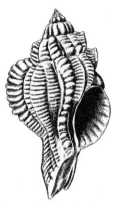

Murex mississippiensis Conrad, x 1.5. Oligocene (Vicksburg), Mississippi

Helminthozyga vermicula Knight. Pennsylvanian, Mississippi Valley

Straparolus pernodosus Meek & Worthen. Pennsylvanian, Mississippi Valley

Turritella vertebroides Morton. Internal mold. Cretaceous, New Jersey to Texas

Turritella mortoni Conrad. Paleocene and Eocene, Maryland to Texas

Lunatia lewisi (Gould), x 0.7. Miocene to Recent, Pacific coast of North America

Hormotoma whiteavesi Clarke & Rued. Middle Silurian, New York

A variety of fossil snails

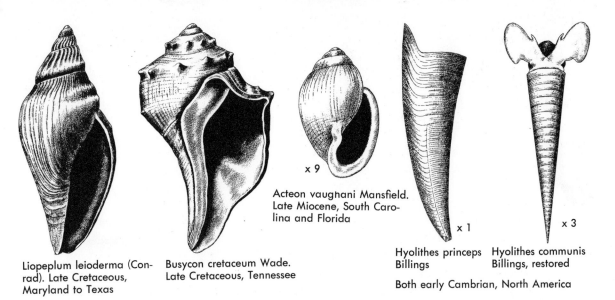

x 9

Acteon vaughani Mansfield.
Late Miocene, South Caro-
lina and Florida

x 1

Hyolithes princeps
Billings

x 3

Hyolithes communis
Billings, restored

Liopeplum leioderma (Con-
rad). Late Cretaceous,
Maryland to Texas

Busycon cretaceum Wade.
Late Cretaceous, Tennessee

Both early Cambrian, North America

Three snails and two pteropods

Most prosobranchs now feed on algae, which they scrape from rocks or the sea bottom with their radulae. Moon snails and oyster drills, however, bore into other mollusks whose flesh is then devoured. This, too, is a long-established habit, for bored mollusks are found in many Tertiary and Mesozoic formations, while bored brachiopods go back to the late Ordovician. They suggest that Paleozoic carnivores preferred lamp-shells to clams, but we cannot be sure. Most early pelecypods are too poorly preserved to show borings even if the latter once were common.

Several carnivorous snails pry into pelecypods or barnacles by means of a tooth or spine on the outer lip of the shell. *Strombus* and others are scavengers that feed on dead fish and invertebrates.

Many limpets, which are prosobranchs whose shells no longer coil, spend most of their lives in special resting places, creeping forth at night to feed upon algae but returning before morning. After settling down, the snails cling so tightly that their shells grow to fit the spots in which they rest.

Fossil limpets may or may not have had this habit, but there is no doubt that some other prosobranchs had definite resting places. Several species of *Platyceras* and *Cyclonema,* for example, clung to the sides or tops of crinoids so tightly that the snails fitted the contours of their hosts and even left marks upon them. Since these snails could not push through the barrier formed by the crinoids' arms and creep about eating algae, we conclude that the mollusks fed upon waste material discharged by their hosts.

When *Vermicularia* is young, its shell is a slender spire resembling *Turritella.* Then the mollusk ceases to coil and builds an irregular, twisted tube that is often mistaken for that of an annelid. *Vermicularia* tubes may be free or attached to other shells or rocks, and they often form tangled masses. *Helminthozyga* is a Pennsylvanian fossil that also became very loosely coiled.

OPISTHOBRANCHS; PROGRESS BY DEGENERATION

Acteon is an egg-shaped or slender snail whose varied species range from the Pierre and Bearpaw formations (Chapter II) to modern temperate seas. They also typify the opisthobranchs, a class that has progressed largely by degeneration. Some, such as *Acteon,* retain a well-developed shell, a mantle, and one gill, though it has twisted around to the rear. In sea hares the shell has become very small, and that of nudibranchs has vanished except from the embryo. Nudibranchs are unknown as fossils, but the group to which *Acteon* belongs appears in the Mississippian and continues through later formations. Several species are useful index fossils in late Cretaceous and Tertiary deposits.

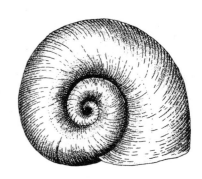

Helisoma trivolvis (Say), twice natural size. This fresh-water snail now ranges from the Atlantic Coast to the Pacific and northward to Alaska. Helisoma also is a Pleistocene and Pliocene fossil.

The Free-swimming Pteropods. Some pteropods are as bare and soft as nudibranchs, but others have thin coiled or conical shells. The head has become indistinct, but the foot is spread out in a pair of winglike fins (*pteropod* means "wing-foot") with which the animals swim. Fossil pteropods are thin-shelled and slender; some have opercula to close their apertures. Doubtful specimens have been collected from Eozoic (Belt) rocks; others have been described from early and middle Cambrian rocks of Newfoundland and British Columbia, as well as from many later formations. Unfortunately most of these fossils are so simple that their true nature remains uncertain. We need only recall that *Conularia* has become a jellyfish and that *Tentaculites* has been transferred from gastropods to annelids in order to realize the need for caution in interpreting these fossils.

PULMONATES; AIR-BREATHING MOLLUSKS

Anyone who has collected in a damp woodland knows that some snails live on land and breathe air. Fresh-water snails share the latter habit, securing bubbles of air at the surface and using it when they submerge. In both groups breathing is done with a lunglike organ developed from the mantle cavity.

Fresh-water pulmonates have shells, though the latter vary greatly in shape. There also are four tentacles on the head, with simple eyes at the base of the hinder pair. These snails may have evolved during the Paleozoic, but their known record begins with Jurassic genera (not species) that survive today. Several are index fossils of late Cretaceous formations, and one characterizes the Morrison beds, in which North America's largest dinosaurs have been found.

Many land snails retain their shells, which may be high-spired or low, thick or thin and brittle. A few slugs, however, have lost their shells, and in others they are reduced to thin plates that are hidden by the mantle. Shell-bearing types date back to the Pennsylvanian period. Though much less common than their aquatic relatives, a few species are index fossils of late Cretaceous and Tertiary formations.

CHAPTER XIII

Pelecypods—Clams, Mussels, and Oysters

Gastropods are the most widely distributed class among mollusks and the only ones that live upon land. Pelecypods are more familiar, however, for they include such edible "shellfish" as oysters, scallops, and clams.

Here again names become troublesome, for the mollusks called pelecypods in Canada and the United States are lamellibranchs in Europe and many other parts of the world. The former name means "hatchet-foot" and refers to the characteristic shape of that organ. Lamellibranch, or "plate gill," aptly describes the structures with which many of these mollusks respire.

WHAT IS A PELECYPOD?

Pelecypods—we use the American name—are built on a plan that is both simpler and more complex than that of a primitive snail or chiton. Simplicity appears in the body, which has lost the head with its tentacles, eyes, and rasping radula. Complexity appears in the shell, which consists of two parts, or valves, which may resemble one another or may differ in function and shape.

The body has two sides, right and left, and is neither coiled like a typical snail nor spread out like a limpet. The foot still is the under part of the body, but in all except some highly specialized forms it has become narrow and hatchet-shaped or wedgelike rather than broad and flat. The gills lie below the body proper, not above it, and range from leaf-shaped organs to folded sheets or even flattened rods. They are covered by two broad flaps of the mantle, which is pierced by holes for the muscles that are attached to the shell.

Varied Methods of Feeding. Since pelecypods cannot devour large creatures, they dine on microscopic organisms in the water from which their gills take oxygen. This means that each animal must bring water into the cavity covered by its mantle, must trap food and reject sand or mud, and must take the food

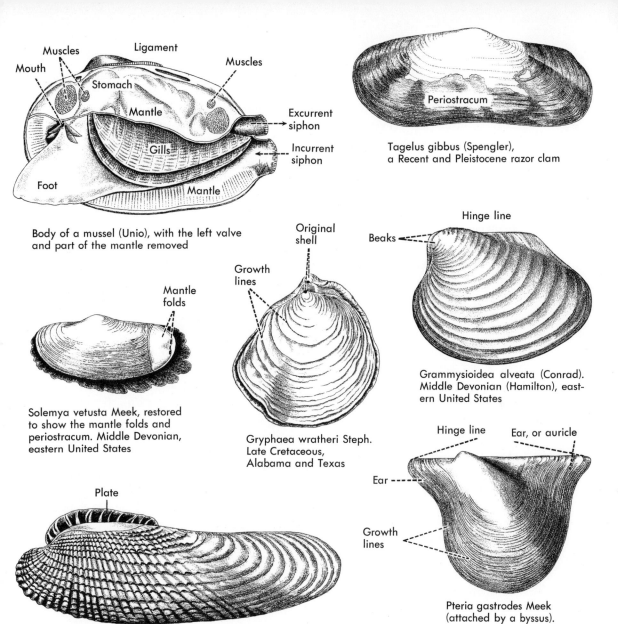

Body of a mussel (Unio), with the left valve
and part of the mantle removed

Tagelus gibbus (Spengler),
a Recent and Pleistocene razor clam

Solemya vetusta Meek, restored
to show the mantle folds and
periostracum. Middle Devonian,
eastern United States

Gryphaea wratheri Steph.
Late Cretaceous,
Alabama and Texas

Grammysioidea alveata (Conrad).
Middle Devonian (Hamilton), eastern United States

Pholas producta (Conrad).
Miocene (Choptank), Atlantic Coastal Plain

Pteria gastrodes Meek
(attached by a byssus).
Late Cretaceous, western U.S.

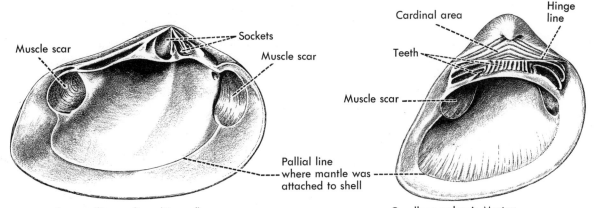

Crassatellites melinus (Conrad).
Miocene (Calvert), Atlantic
Coastal Plain

Cucullaea vulgaris Morton.
Late Cretaceous (Matawan-Monmouth),
New Jersey and Maryland

Structures of pelecypods

to its mouth while it gets rid of rubbish, waste, and water from which oxygen has been removed. These tasks are performed by organs that vary with the habits of different pelecypods.

We see these organs at their simplest in *Solemya* and its primitive relatives, of Devonian to Recent age. The mantle is folded into two indistinct channels inside the hinder part of the shell. Beating cilia produce a current that brings water into the lower, or incurrent, channel and takes it over the gills. There the blood absorbs oxygen and gives up waste, both of which pass easily through the thin gill membranes. At the same time, food is caught on sticky mucus that covers the gills and is carried to the mouth. Another current takes sand, mud, waste, and "used" water into the upper (excurrent) channel and so back to the sea.

In more advanced pelecypods, and especially in those that burrow, the channels become tubes called siphons, which may be separate or covered by a tough sheath of skin. Lengthwise muscles shorten the siphons or pull them into the shell when danger threatens; other muscles can close the tubes and so keep mud or sand out of the mantle cavity. Further protection is given by the mantle itself, whose muscular edges may close its two lobes much as muscles close our lips. The edges may also fuse, forming an envelope whose only openings are the siphons and a slit through which the foot can project.

The giant clam (*Tridacna*) lives on coral reefs where low tides expose most of its shell, though high tides cover it. As water returns, the valves open and the mantle spreads out in thick multicolored folds containing algae that grow in the flesh and use energy from sunlight to make food. These algae are then digested by the clam, which also gets some food in the ordinary manner.

Tridacna is found in Tertiary rocks; the fossil mollusks may or may not have grown algae in their mantles. But there is no doubt about the feeding habits of ancient clams that burrowed in wood, like modern "shipworms." As they burrowed they scraped the wood into powder, which would have filled their holes had it not been devoured. We may safely assume that the fossils digested cellulose, as their relatives do today.

THE PELECYPOD SHELL

Most fossil pelecypods are shells, though casts and internal molds are common. Modern shells, like those of gastropods, generally contain three layers. The periostracum ranges from thin to thick; it covers a limy layer that generally consists of needles and angular prisms of calcite which may look like coarse fibers in weathered fossils such as the thick-shelled *Inoceramus*. The inner layer contains thin sheets of calcite or aragonite which may alternate with material that resembles the periostracum. If the limy sheets are thick and smooth they resemble china; if they are thin and crumpled they appear lus-

Ostrea sellaeformis Conrad.
Eocene (Claiborne), Maryland
to Texas

Trigonia thoracica Morton.
Late Cretaceous, Oregon

Unio gibbosus Whitfield.
Late Cretaceous (Lance),
Montana

Ostrea (Alectryonia) falcata Morton.
Late Cretaceous, Atlantic and Gulf
coastal plains

Venus tridacnoides Lamarck.
Interior of left valve

Venus tridacnoides Lamarck.
Miocene, Atlantic Coastal Plain

Ostrea titan Conrad,
length to 50 inches.
Miocene, California

Lyropecten jeffersonius (Say).
Miocene, Virginia to Florida
and in California

Some fresh-water and salt-water pelecypods

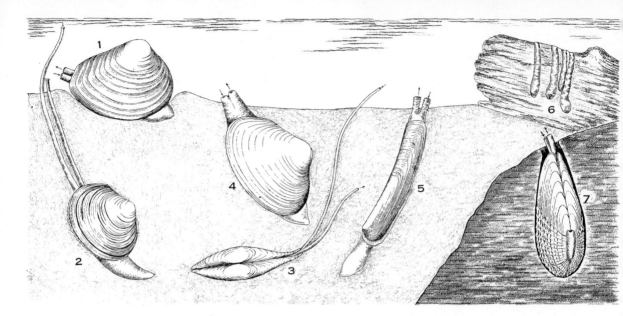

Types of burrowing pelecypods. All are fossils, restored to correspond to related living species. **1.** *Crassatellites.* **2.** *Tellina.* **3.** *Macoma.* **4.** *Mactra.* **5.** *Ensis.* **6.** *Martesia.* **7.** *Pholas. Incurrent and excurrent siphons are marked by arrows showing directions in which currents flow.*

trous and are known as mother-of-pearl. Though pearly luster is sometimes found in fossils, neither it nor the chinalike appearance usually survives petrifaction.

Shell Changes and Structures. The pelecypod shell begins as a convex plate that divides into two smooth and almost circular valves. If growth were uniform this shape would persist, but growth takes place at different rates and in different directions. Because of this the valves generally become convex, forming umbos that stand out prominently when curvature is reduced and the shell begins to spread. Each umbo terminates in a beak whose tip would be the original shell were the latter not worn away.

The beak may come close to the hinge line, along which the two valves are joined. On the other hand, each valve may have an intervening cardinal area that is either flat or convex. The general surface may be smooth except for growth lines, which mark "resting periods" determined by low temperature, lack of food, or reproductive activity. Generally, however, growth lines are combined with radial ridges or wrinkles, concentric ridges, frills, or spines. The hinge line may also be prolonged by ears, or auricles, which are specially well developed in scallop shells, or pectens.

Shells vary greatly in size; some are no larger than a pinhead, but others are very large. The most massive is *Tridacna,* which reaches a width of 54 inches and a weight of 500 pounds. *Haploscapha,* from the late Cretaceous of Kansas, is not so heavy but is as much as 3.3 feet wide and 5 feet long. The life span of these giants is unknown, but many modern clams of moderate size live eight to eighteen years.

Internal Markings. The pelecypod shell, like that of any other shell-bearing mollusk, is built up by the mantle. This is firmly attached to the inner surface of both valves, but its edges are always free. Attachment ends at the pallial line, which shows plainly in most modern and fossil species but is indistinct in some. If there are siphons, the pallial line curves round them, and the depth of the curve (called the pallial sinus) shows whether the siphons are small or large. Since long siphons go with burrowing life, the sinus gives a clue to the habits of many fossils. This clue, however, should be supported by shape of shell, relationships, and other evidence.

Most pelecypod valves also show one or two rough scars that serve as attachment for muscles that close the shell. Since they do this by pulling the valves together, the muscles are called adductors. The scallops we eat are adductor muscles of pelecypods belonging to the genus *Pecten,* which has already been mentioned because of its auricles.

Hinges, Teeth, and Opening Devices. A shell with loosely joined valves can be useful; we have found shells of just that sort in *Lingula* and other primi-

Some free-moving and attached pelecypods, restored. **1.** *Lima swimming [L. reticulata Forbes, Miocene, Maryland].* **2.** *Cardium thrusting out its foot to pull itself forward [C. coosense Dall, Miocene-Recent, Pacific coast].* **3.** *Cornellites lying on the bottom [C. flabella (Con.), Devonian, eastern U.S.A.].* **4.** *Anomia attached to a shell [A. micronema Meek, late Cretaceous, western North America].* **5.** *Mytilus attached by a cluster of threads, or byssus [M. conradinus Orbigny, Miocene, New Jersey to Texas].* **6.** *Byssonychia attached by byssus [B. radiata (Hall), late Ordovician, eastern U.S.A.].* **7–8.** *Two twisted forms cemented to dead shells [***7.** *Toucasia patagiata (White), early Cretaceous, Texas and Mexico;* **8.** *Monopleura texana Roemer, early Cretaceous, Texas and Mexico].*

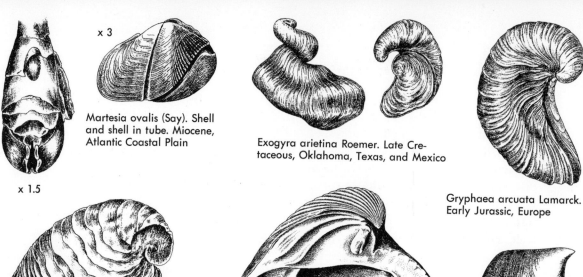

Martesia ovalis (Say). Shell
and shell in tube. Miocene,
Atlantic Coastal Plain

x 3

x 1.5

Exogyra arietina Roemer. Late Cretaceous, Oklahoma, Texas, and Mexico

Gryphaea arcuata Lamarck.
Early Jurassic, Europe

Exogyra ponderosa Roemer. Late Cretaceous, New Jersey to Mexico

x 0.5

Venericardia planicosta Lamarck.
Eocene, world-wide distribution

x 0.5

Myalina subquadrata
Shumard. Pennsylvanian,
southwestern U.S.A.

x 0.5

Some free-living, attached, and tube-building pelecypods

tive brachiopods. But pelecypod valves are hinged, and in most genera the
hinge is strengthened by projecting teeth and sockets into which they fit, thus
locking the valves together when the adductors contract. Both teeth and
sockets are arranged in patterns that differ in the major groups.

Though pelecypod shells must be closed by muscles, most of them are auto-
matically opened by structures called the ligament and resilium. The former
is a tough and sometimes very thick band that runs from valve to valve above
the hinge, but the resilium is a spongy pad between two limy plates inside the
shell. When the latter is closed the pad is compressed; when the muscles relax
the pad expands, forcing the valves to open.

A strange specialization is found in *Pholas* and its kin (piddocks and angel-
wings), whose fossils date back to the early Tertiary. *Pholas* has lost its ligament, and one adductor muscle has moved outside the shell. There it is
attached to plates whose curvature is opposite to that of the valves. When
this muscle contracts it opens the shell instead of closing it.

VARIED HABITS AND HABITATS

Though pelecypods lived during Cambrian times, they did not become common until the middle Ordovician. Their most primitive order, called palae-

oconchs, or "ancient shells," is characterized by thin, elongate valves and hinges in which the teeth are poorly developed or lacking. Modern representatives have small, leaflike gills much like those of gastropods and chitons. Ancient palaeoconchs apparently crept on the muddy bottoms of shallow seas, leaving furrowlike trails that sometimes became fossils.

Shells and Feet for Creeping. Palaeoconchs established a basic pattern from which their successors could and often did diverge. The changes that were most easily made added strength to the shell, improved it as armor, or reduced the labor of crawling. During the Ordovician period several pelecypods shortened and thickened their shells and added teeth to their hinges. Others, of Ordovician to Devonian age, became elongate and wedgelike, with narrow lower margins. Such shells were able to slip through mud with a minimum of friction.

We often think of creeping in terms of pushing, but pelecypods are built to pull. The foot is thrust forward and gets a hold in soft mud or sand; strong muscles then are contracted, pulling the shell forward. The result generally is a slow, halting form of progress, but some creepers can contract their muscles so quickly that they actually jump forward. *Cardium* is able to do this, and so do some burrowers when they are at the surface. Razor clams (*Solen* and *Tagelus*) sometimes leap 10 to 12 inches.

Nestling and Burrowing. Burrowing is a way of life that has developed several times in different groups of pelecypods. We see one early stage in *Crassatellites,* which nestles in a pit that is dug by shifting the shell from one side to the other. The quahogs (*Venus*) go a little further; they dig down until most of the shell is covered, though the hind part and short siphons are exposed. *Mya,* the soft-shelled or sand clam, is completely buried and its siphons are a good deal longer than the shell. As *Mya* burrows, its shell moves from side to side, cutting its way through the sand.

Macoma also burrows in muddy sand. One species, *M. nasuta,* lies on its left side and sends up a long incurrent siphon that moves about over the sand, sucking up slimy food. When no more can be found the siphon is pulled back and thrust up through the sand to a new feeding ground. The excurrent siphon, which is short, discharges its wastes below the surface.

Many clams are able to dig very rapidly. Some of these have thick shells and live in sand; *Venus* is a good example. Razor clams (*Solen, Ensis, Tagelus,* and *Siliqua*) dig almost vertically in sand and have siphons of various lengths. One species of *Siliqua* burrows in sandy beaches along the Pacific coast. When the water is quiet it stays near the surface, but as storm waves crash or ground swells roll in, *Siliqua* pulls itself down below the danger zone.

Boring Clams and "Shipworms." No clam ever bothered its missing head with the difference between burrowing and boring. We take the former to mean digging, chiefly with the foot, in sediment that has not become compact. Borers, however, wear their way through firmly packed clay, stone, shells, or wood.

| A creeping clam pushes its foot through mud or sand. | Then the tip of the foot begins to swell into an anchor. | Muscles in the foot contract, pulling the body forward. | Soon the foot is pushed out and the process begins again. |

Piddocks and angel-wings belong to a family that bores into firm sand or clay and rocks that range from crumbly sandstone to granite. An early stage is seen in *Pholadidea,* which fastens its suckerlike foot to some firm surface and then moves the shell up and down. Its forward portion is covered with ridges that scrape away the surrounding clay or stone. Some members of the family keep on boring and growing throughout their lives. Others reach their full size, cover the sucker foot with shell, and spend the rest of their lives feeding and reproducing.

Lithophaga, the date clam, attaches itself with a cluster of threads and is said to secrete acid that dissolves the rock into which this creature bores. The periostracum is very thick, protecting the shell's layers.

"Shipworms" are not worms at all; they are clams whose valves have become small rasping organs and two little plates that seem to protect the siphons. The young shipworm hatches in the spring, swims for a week or two, and then settles down on a sunken log or some other form of wood. Into this the clam bores, making a tube which it lines with a thin calcareous layer. When shipworms are common they fill large timbers with their borings, making the wood so weak that it crumbles under the impact of waves.

Martesia includes clams related to *Pholas* although they do not resemble it. They have well-developed shells, which are used for boring while the clams

Anthracomya elongata (Dawson). Pennsylvanian, Europe, and Cape Breton to New Mexico

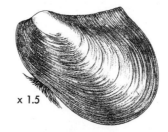

Naiadites carbonarius Dawson, with byssus restored. Pennsylvanian of Nova Scotia

Amnigenia catskillensis (Vanuxem). Middle and late Devonian, Pennsylvania and New York

Three fresh-water mussels of late Paleozoic age

are young. Later the valves are cemented together and to a calcareous tube that is built around the siphons. *Martesia* shells and tubes are found in brackish-water deposits along Two Medicine River of Montana (Chapter II) as well as in other formations.

Scallops and Swimming Clams. Pteropods swim by flapping their feet, and some other gastropods swim or use their expanded feet as rafts. Some pelecypods are swimmers, too, but they propel themselves by opening and closing their shells.

Two related groups invented this process. The family of pectens began in Silurian seas with *Aviculopecten,* which had a straight hinge line, pointed auricles, and a right valve that generally was deeper than the left. Species with equal valves may have crawled, but others lay on the sea bottom. In time some of their descendants began to fasten themselves to seaweeds or shells with threads—the byssus—which emerged from a notch under one auricle. Others took to opening their shells and snapping them shut, thus forcing water out quickly. The result was a jerky type of swimming in which the creatures moved with the hinge line forward. Shell shape indicates that late Paleozoic species of *Aviculopecten* swam in this way, as do *Pecten* and its relatives of Mississippian to Recent seas. Their mantles are fringed with tentacles and bear eye spots that seem to give warning of approaching danger.

Lima, the other swimmer, appeared in Pennsylvanian times and still lives in both the Atlantic and Pacific oceans. Its tentacles are many and long, though the shell seldom reaches 2 inches in length. When some species are not swim-

Plagiopticus partschi Hauer, a rudistid "clam" that grew upright with one valve as a lidlike structure covering the body. Cretaceous of Austria

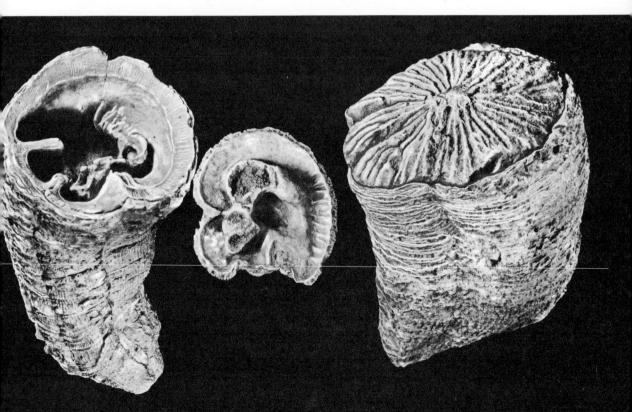

ming they settle down in cavities and secrete tough threads which are tangled into nests, open at both ends. A food-bearing current enters one end and waste goes out at the other.

Attachment by Threads and Cement. Pectens were not the first mollusks to develop a byssus; it appeared in the Ordovician *Byssonychia,* whose anterior margin bears a wide notch through which the threads emerged. A byssus also is found in *Mytilus* and other sea mussels, in jingles (*Anomia*) and in the young of *Tridacna,* and in several other groups. One of these, the Pteriidae, ranges from the Devonian to Recent and includes modern pearl oysters as well as ancient shells that superficially resemble *Aviculopecten.* The Pernidae, also byssus-bearers, include such important Mesozoic genera as *Gervilliopsis* and *Inoceramus.*

Threads of the byssus are spun by a gland on the foot, which is slender and reaches out to fasten each thread into place. Some spinners, such as *Mytilus,* move about by placing one thread far ahead, dissolving the base of the other threads, and then pulling shell and body forward. In *Anomia,* however, the byssus becomes a horny plug or is calcified, and the right valve grows around it. Such shells are firmly attached for the rest of their lives.

Oysters typify the attached, or sessile, pelecypods. After a brief clamlike existence, *Ostrea* attaches itself to rocks, shells, or sunken logs, to which the left valve is cemented. It thereupon becomes longer, wider, and deeper than the right, which sometimes is not much more than a lid covering the cavity filled by the body. *Ostrea* appeared in Triassic seas, became plentiful during Cretaceous times, and is widespread today. Both eastern and Pacific species are found in Pleistocene deposits. The former, *Ostrea virginica,* grew as much as 15 inches long in days before white men began to gather and sell it for food.

ABERRANT BOTTOM-DWELLERS

Oysters are not "normal" pelecypods, since they live on one side and have shells that are much higher than long. Other bivalves become still more abnormal, developing valves that coiled like snails or even assumed the shape of horn corals.

Gryphaea and Exogyra. We first find coiling in *Gryphaea* and *Exogyra,* two members of the oyster family that appeared in shallow Jurassic seas. Like true oysters, they first developed smooth, symmetrical shells that looked as if they were destined to creep or burrow just beneath the surface. Soon, however, these "spat" settled down upon the left valve, which then grew much more rapidly than the right. In early species of *Gryphaea* the left valve first assumed the form of a primitive snail shell but with further growth became massive and coiled. It also broke loose from its attachment and sank into the mud, where weight and shape kept it in its original position. The right valve be-

Exogyra costata Say (left) *and Gryphaea mutabilis* Morton (right), *two late Cretaceous mollusks related to oysters. They are shown as they lived on the sea bottom in what is now McNairy County, Tennessee.*

came a flattened plate that could be raised or lowered to open or close the shell.

During late Cretaceous epochs large species of *Gryphaea* lost most of their tendency to coil and become cup- or bowl-shaped. Some individuals still broke away from the shells to which they had been cemented, but others remained attached throughout life. Shells of both types are plentiful in formations of the Atlantic and Gulf coastal plains, the latter extending as far northward as Tennessee.

Exogyra differs from *Gryphaea* in having an indistinct tooth on the hinge, a very narrow pit for the ligament, and valves that are always spirally coiled. The left valve generally is much larger and thicker than that of *Gryphaea*. In large species—some exceed 6 inches in height—the shell is marked by costae and growth lines that extend into laminae.

The left valves of *Exogyra* range from short or loose spirals to massive structures that are closely coiled at the beak. Most shells seem to have outgrown the bases to which they were cemented, and some evidently broke loose in the manner of *Gryphaea*. Others became so large and so heavy that they sank into the mud, tipping enough to bring their flat right, or upper, valves into a horizontal position. Surprisingly few valves are distorted by contact with other shells. Though *Exogyra* was abundant in many places, it apparently did not grow in such closely packed colonies as those formed by modern oysters.

Double Spirals and Cones. Though both valves of *Exogyra* are spirals, the right one is virtually flat. Other pelecypods developed valves that were spirally coiled and almost equal, so that complete shells look rather like two snails clinging lip to lip. Having achieved this form, some genera went on to turn one valve—either left or right—into a massive spiral, horn-shaped, or conical structure that lay or stood upright on the sea bottom while the other valve became little more than a plate covering the body. Several of these strange shells are important Cretaceous index fossils in Texas, New Mexico, and Mexico.

Most remarkable of all are the rudistids, which lost all trace of coiling. The lower valve became conical—a complex structure composed of plates and layers that looked like a rugose coral and sometimes reached 40 inches in length. The upper valve was reduced to a mere lid whose under surface bore very long teeth that projected into sockets in the lower valve. Rudistids are limited to the Cretaceous and are more plentiful in Europe than in North America.

FROM SALT TO FRESH WATER

Pelecypods appeared in the sea, and throughout the ages most of them have lived in that environment. Some, however, moved into brackish bays and, during Devonian times, adapted themselves to life in fresh water. One well-known genus, *Amnigenia*, contained slender thin-shelled clams about 3 inches long. They lived in streams that crossed the great Catskill delta, which spread across Pennsylvania and New York during middle and late Devonian epochs.

While *Amnigenia* and its offspring crept in streams, related forms called *Naiadites* developed a byssus and fastened themselves to submerged logs. Their shells are found among the famous Pennsylvanian fern nodules of Mazon Creek, Illinois, as well as in Ohio and Nova Scotia. In the last region they are mingled with other genera, one of which (*Anthracomya*) resembles a tiny horse clam.

Most of our modern fresh-water clams, or mussels, belong to the genera *Unio* and *Anodonta*. Fossils from Triassic formations of Massachusetts, Pennsylvania, and the Southwest once were referred to the former genus, but they now seem to belong to other types that survive only in South America. *Unio* apparently developed in Triassic Europe or Asia, reached North America in the late Jurassic, and has thrived on this continent ever since. Fossils are found in beds containing bones of the great Jurassic dinosaurs, as well as in Cretaceous and later formations. Though some shells were preserved, most specimens are only internal molds.

CHAPTER XIV

Feet Before Heads; the Nautiloids

Fishermen in the southwestern Pacific often set woven bamboo traps to catch mollusks of the genus *Nautilus*. They have ivory-white and reddish-brown shells, eyes with pinholes that focus light, and about ninety soft arms that are used in crawling or are stretched out to capture food. Their flesh is boiled or made into soup, and their shells bring good prices from collectors.

NAUTILUS, A SAMPLE CEPHALOPOD

Nautilus is more than an unusual and beautiful shell; it also is a sample of the class of mollusks known as cephalopods. Their name, which means "head-foot," makes sense when we realize that the arms actually are elongate sections of a highly specialized foot. It and the head have come together, so that the arms lie in front of the eyes and cluster around the mouth.

Other features distinguish this cephalopod from mollusks such as snails. Its mouth still contains a radula, but it also is equipped with beaks that are used for biting. The mantle is wrapped around the body and encloses a cavity that contains the anus and four leaflike gills. The arms, or tentacles, are parts of the foot; they stretch out to seize food and pull it to the mouth and are used in crawling. But when *Nautilus* needs to move swiftly it fills the mantle cavity with water and squirts it out through a tube, or funnel, below the body and arms. This funnel also is part of the foot and consists of two fleshy flaps that fold together, forming a tapering tube. Jets of water driven from it enable *Nautilus* to swim jerkily. If the funnel (also called hyponome) points forward its owner swims backward, but when the tube is turned to the rear the creature darts ahead. This is generally done to capture fish or other unwary food.

The Many-chambered Shell. The shell of *Nautilus* suggests a large, narrow snail coiled in one plane, but that resemblance is superficial. Its outer portion

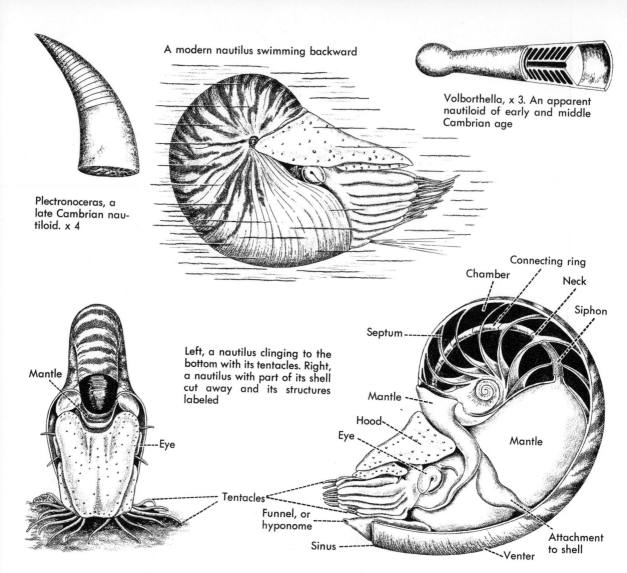

A modern nautilus swimming backward

Volborthella, x 3. An apparent nautiloid of early and middle Cambrian age

Plectronoceras, a late Cambrian nautiloid. x 4

Connecting ring

Chamber

Neck

Siphon

Septum

Mantle

Hood

Mantle

Eye

Left, a nautilus clinging to the bottom with its tentacles. Right, a nautilus with part of its shell cut away and its structures labeled

Mantle

Eye

Tentacles

Funnel, or hyponome

Sinus

Venter

Attachment to shell

Recent and primitive nautiloids. The tentacles are also called arms.

(the wall) has a surface layer that resembles china, a middle layer that is pearly, or nacreous, and an inner one that is clear. The first and second of these layers are formed by the mantle, but the third is secreted by a continuous ring of muscles that fasten body to shell. All three, however, consist of aragonite.

Still greater differences appear in the way the shell is built. A snail's shell is undivided; if we could unroll it, it would form one irregular cone. The shell of *Nautilus,* however, is divided into thirty or more chambers that are separated by pearly partitions called septa. Each septum is secreted by the mantle at the back of the body, cutting off the abandoned part of the shell from the living chamber. As *Nautilus* grows, the mantle builds the living chamber forward while the hind part of the body becomes more and more cramped. At last muscles establish a new line of attachment, the old one is released, and the animal slips forward. This leaves an empty space at the rear, but it is soon closed off by another septum.

Siphon and Siphuncle. We have said that the shell is empty behind the living chamber, but that is not quite true. As the body moves forward, a fleshly stalk, or siphon, remains and the septum is built around it in a backwardly directed neck. This is not very long, but a connecting ring secreted by the siphon continues to the septum behind. Necks and rings together form a tube, the siphuncle, that runs back through chamber after chamber to the very tip of the shell. So does the siphon, which is well supplied with blood vessels and seems to carry gas into the chambers.

The connecting rings of *Nautilus* are thin and disappear when the animal dies. In many fossils, however, they were thickened by deposits of aragonite. The result was siphuncles that often outlasted walls and septa, with shapes that can be used to distinguish genera and species.

FROM SIMPLE SNAIL TO CEPHALOPOD

Doctors often disagree, and those who classify cephalopods are not exceptions to that rule. Yet they seem to be unaminous in saying that the ancestor of these creatures—still undiscovered—differed in no essential respect from a primitive cap-shaped snail. It had a flat creeping foot, a mouth at the front, and gills and anus at the rear. It probably crept over firm but muddy bottoms instead of living on rocks in the manner of modern limpets.

As ages passed, the descendants of this pioneer developed deeper and deeper bodies. This meant that the foot shortened and the digestive tract curved sharply, while the shell became conical or slightly horn-shaped to fit the ever-deepening body. Still later the foot began to curve upward, the mantle secreted a few septa, and part of the body extended through them, forming a primitive siphon. In the final stage of our hypothetical sequence, the digestive tract bent into a V, and the siphon and shell became elongate. The foot continued to grow around the head, dividing into arms and two flaps that curved toward each other. When they met they formed the funnel, with which the newly evolved cephalopod swam when crawling became too slow.

THE VARIED AND LONG-LIVED NAUTILOIDS

Nautilus is both a typical cephalopod and the only surviving member of the subclass Nautiloidea. Though its members differ enormously, nautiloids agree in having relatively simple septa, which generally resemble watch glasses with the concave side forward or are relatively shallow cones. Each septum arches backward below the funnel, forming a hyponomic sinus. Each septum also

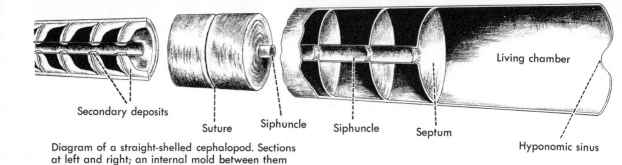

Diagram of a straight-shelled cephalopod. Sections at left and right; an internal mold between them

Secondary deposits · Suture · Siphuncle · Siphuncle · Septum · Living chamber · Hyponomic sinus

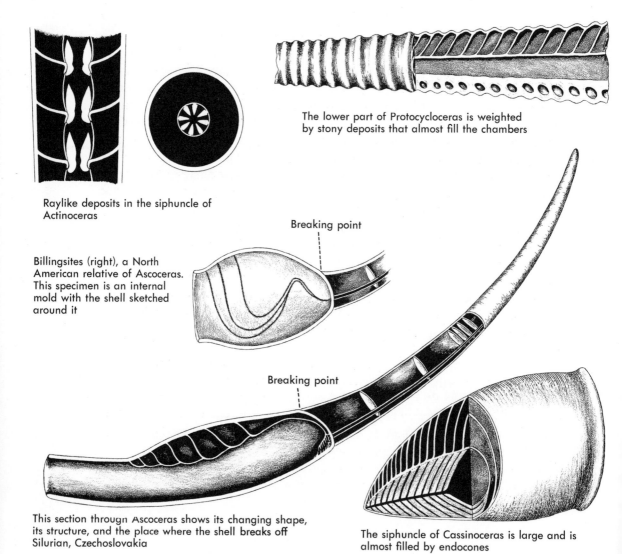

Section through the tip of Endoceras. The siphuncle is almost filled by funnel-shaped deposits known as endocones

Siphuncle

The lower part of Protocycloceras is weighted by stony deposits that almost fill the chambers

Raylike deposits in the siphuncle of Actinoceras

Billingsites (right), a North American relative of Ascoceras. This specimen is an internal mold with the shell sketched around it

Breaking point

Breaking point

This section through Ascoceras shows its changing shape, its structure, and the place where the shell breaks off Silurian, Czechoslovakia

The siphuncle of Cassinoceras is large and is almost filled by endocones

Structures of ancient nautiloids

produces a line, or suture, where it joins the wall. The suture may be straight except for an indentation at the sinus, or it may be variously curved.

The oldest known nautiloid seems to be *Volborthella,* from early Cambrian rocks of Finland and New Brunswick. *Volborthella* had a straight shell a few millimeters long, with a siphuncle near the center and broadly conical septa. Surprisingly, fossils show that this shell began as an egg-shaped capsule that was larger than the tube just in front of it.

Some paleontologists doubt that *Volborthella* is a cephalopod; most of these skeptics accept *Plectronoceras* of the late Cambrian as the oldest and simplest nautiloid. *Plectronoceras* is curved instead of straight, with a deep living chamber and closely spaced septa that are curved like tiny watch glasses. The siphuncle is near the lower side, not at the center of the shell.

The soft parts of these and other early cephalopods are unknown, for none has been found among carbonized films. But we may safely assume that the animals looked much like *Nautilus,* with eyes that had narrow slits ending in pinholes and a tough hood that closed the shell when body, head, and arms were drawn into it. The arms almost certainly had no suckers, but they were longer and less numerous than those of *Nautilus.* Impressions suggest that in some species they numbered only ten.

Why Call Them "Horn-shells"? The names of nautiloids deserve comment, since many of them end with *ceras,* from the Greek word for "horn." Many fossils do resemble curved or coiled horns, and the first use of *ceras* was based upon that resemblance. In time it became a custom that was extended to other cephalopods with external shells. New genera became "Cassin-horns," "Knot-horns," "Moore's-horns," and so on. Although there are a few exceptions, any fossil whose name ends in *ceras* is almost sure to be a cephalopod.

HABITS AND CHANGING SHELLS

Primeval cephalopods may have been straight, like *Volborthella,* but they probably were slightly curved. Since their chambers contained only gas, the shells weighed less than water and much less than the body. Light weight must have made them tip upward, like the shell in the final stage of our supposed evolutionary change from snail to cephalopod.

This probably caused no trouble when shells were small as well as short and were more than counterbalanced by bodies. But as ages passed and shells became large, difficulties appeared. Large shells, much lighter than water, would tip upward and bob to and fro, at the mercy of every wave or current. This would have reduced speed, causing difficulty in steering. It may also have kept cephalopods that built such shells from staying right side up.

These things *may* or *would* have happened, but we cannot be sure that they

Habits of some Paleozoic nautiloids. **1.** *Gonioceras, a flattened bottom-dweller.* **2.** *Gigantoceras, which both crawled and swam; this one is eating a trilobite.* **3.** *Cyrtoceras, which apparently crawled like a snail, using its tentacles.* **4.** *Michelinoceras, a crawler that could swim.* **5.** *Mandaloceras, a drifter with egg-shaped shell*

did. Nautiloids that became unfit to live efficiently probably were weeded out by predators, accidents, or starvation before they departed far from the norm. Their places were taken by relatives that avoided the obstacles we have mentioned, yet increased in size.

Several theories attempt to explain why and how these new and better-adapted nautiloids developed, but each theory contradicts the others. Let us therefore ignore the hows and whys and concentrate upon actual changes in shells and their apparent relationships to orientation and habits.

Ballast and Bottom-dwellers. The first cephalopods were creepers or crawlers, and some of their earliest changes maintained and even increased fitness for bottom-dwelling, or benthonic, life. They are conspicuous in the so-called orthoceracones, whose shells became straight and slender, and sometimes very large. One Ordovician genus, *Endoceras,* reached lengths of 9 to 12 feet.

Such shells, had they been empty, would have drifted with their tips upright and their builders hanging downward at the bottom. But rare specimens with stripes, blotches, and zigzag bands of color on the upper, or dorsal, half of the shell leave no doubt that orthoceracones lived in a horizontal position, with funnel below and head above. This was made possible by stony deposits on the walls and septa and in the siphuncle, which generally lay well below the center of the shell. Deposits on septa and walls also were thickest on the lower side, or venter.

Siphuncular ballast took three forms; some was deposited in rings, some in raylike plates, and some in conical layers called endocones, or "inner cones." The last of these sometimes formed in large siphuncles, which lay very near the venter or in direct contact with it.

Actinoceras is one of the commonest cephalopods that filled the siphuncle with raylike plates. *Endoceras* is a straight-shelled example of shells that possessed endocones, especially near the tips. *Cassinoceras,* on the other hand, was short and thick, with closely spaced chambers that curved part way round the siphuncle and its massive endocones. The aperture is tipped downward just a little, as if the heavily weighted cone raised it well above the mud on which the animal lived.

Strangest of all was the device developed by *Ascoceras* and its relatives, of Ordovician and Silurian age. These creatures began by building slender shells with gentle curvature and no ballast except a siphon that moved closer and closer to the venter. The living chamber also became longer, and during late Ordovician times it began to swell, allowing septa to cut off gas-filled chambers that curved broadly over the dosal region, thus allowing the body to become its own ballast. At last, as the body moved into the enlarged living chamber, it closed the siphuncle and allowed the rest of the shell to drop off. Thus a long, pointed shell became short and better suited to active life than it had been during its youth.

Gonioceras, a Groveler. A very different adaptation to bottom life is seen in *Gonioceras* ("angle-horn") of the Ordovician. Its shell was very wide and low, with a moderately convex central portion and "wings" which thinned to sharp edges that explain the name. The under surface was almost flat; the siphuncle was not very heavy; during adult life the aperture narrowed until the lateral wings were closed. This has been interpreted as a device that kept the creature from pulling itself out of its shell as it crept among seaweeds and corals.

This idea is dubious for two reasons. First, the broad shell and rayed siphuncle gave much better attachment, in proportion to weight, than we find in the massive, straight cones whose apertures were not constricted. Second, *Gonioceras* probably did very little crawling. Its wide shell reminds us of flounders, which lie on the bottom waiting for food but swim from one place to another. *Gonioceras* probably did the same, reaching out for food with its arms and gliding backward through the water when it felt impelled to swim.

Conical and Horn-shaped Crawlers. Both structure and coloration show that long, straight nautiloids crawled and swam in an essentially horizontal position. But some short, wide shells preserve bands of color that went all the way round. These bands, plus shapes and lack of ballast, leave little doubt that the shells were carried upright while their owners crawled.

The simplest of these crawlers are generally called *Rizoceras* and *Cyrtoceras*. One was conical and the other slightly curved, the outer side of the curve being the venter. At least one paleontologist believed that the builders of these shells crawled snailwise, on a flat surface that was a remnant of the original gastropod foot. This would make the creatures the most primitive of cephalopods; archaic relics that managed to survive throughout most of the Paleozoic era. It seems more likely that they were true nautiloids whose shells had shortened and whose bodies were specialized to provide whatever creeping surface was essential to locomotion.

Curved shells were not limited to *Cyrtoceras* and its kin; they appeared in several families and even in another order. They also followed two contrasting plans, one with the siphuncle and venter at the outer side of the curve (exogastric), the other with those parts inside (endogastric). The former offers no new problems, especially if the shells had siphuncles containing deposits that served as ballast. But endogastric shells, with weights or without, are quite different. Did they contain bodies that were heavy enough so the creatures could crawl with the tips of their shells directed downward? Or, since the shells were lighter than water, did they tip upward until their owners drifted with only their arms resting upon the bottom?

Bizarre Crawlers and Drifters. These questions are answered by short, curved shells of Silurian and Devonian age. Some, such as *Protophragmoceras,* had living chambers that were compressed but open; their builders must have lived in the manner of *Cyrtoceras.*

Straight-shelled and coiled nautiloids. Eutrephoceras was closely related to Nautilus.

Armenoceras clermontense
Foerste. Late Ordovician,
Mississippi Valley

Eutrephoceras dekayi (Morton).
Late Cretaceous, widespread
in North America

Endoceras proteiforme Hall.
Middle and late Ordovician,
North America

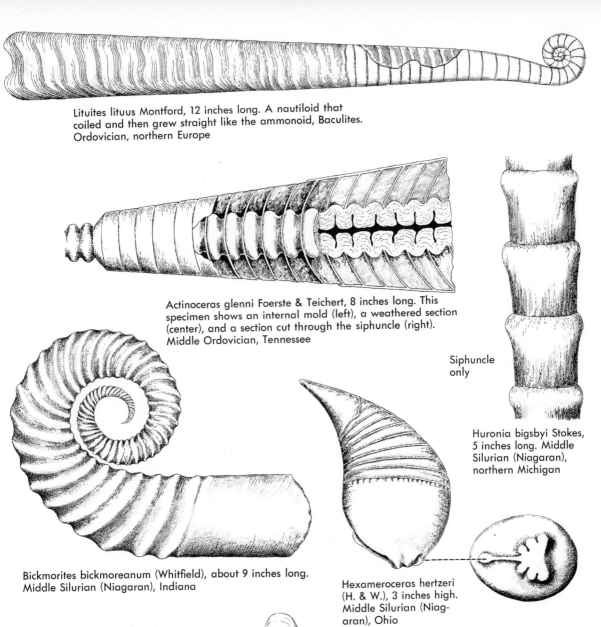

Lituites lituus Montford, 12 inches long. A nautiloid that coiled and then grew straight like the ammonoid, Baculites. Ordovician, northern Europe

Actinoceras glenni Foerste & Teichert, 8 inches long. This specimen shows an internal mold (left), a weathered section (center), and a section cut through the siphuncle (right). Middle Ordovician, Tennessee

Siphuncle only

Huronia bigsbyi Stokes, 5 inches long. Middle Silurian (Niagaran), northern Michigan

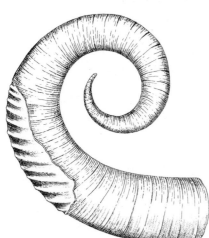

Bickmorites bickmoreanum (Whitfield), about 9 inches long. Middle Silurian (Niagaran), Indiana

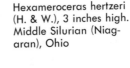

Hexameroceras hertzeri (H. & W.), 3 inches high. Middle Silurian (Niagaran), Ohio

Ryticeras trivolve (Conrad), height 4.5 inches. Devonian (Onondagan), Ont.–N.Y.

Phragmoceras broderipi Barrande, 5 inches high. A short, open coil with a narrow aperture. Silurian, Czechoslovakia

Straight and coiled nautiloids

Genera such as *Phragmoceras* are shorter, and the shell expands rapidly to a large but greatly compressed living chamber. The aperture also is constricted —not merely made narrower, but pinched greatly here and not so much there until it is roughly I-shaped or even more elaborate. Even when the siphuncle is weighted, it is not very heavy. In *Phragmoceras* it must have tipped the shell slightly to the rear but left the task of stabilization primarily to the body. *Phragmoceras* apparently crawled most of the time, with its eyes and arms projecting from the large part of its aperture and its funnel at the rear. The empty chambers provided buoyancy, which was most useful when the animal swam. This it did in a forward direction, not backward, since its funnel was turned to the rear.

Forms such as *Hexameroceras* were not so narrow or so abruptly coiled. They almost certainly drifted, and the shape of the living chamber suggests that the place where eyes and arms emerged was lower than the funnel. It too gave a forward motion, though the shell was relatively wider than that of *Phragmoceras.*

Another type of adaptation to drifting life is found in short-shelled nautiloids such as *Mandaloceras* and *Ovoceras,* of Ordovician to Devonian age. Their shells became both short and wide, with scarcely a trace of curvature and Y- or T-shaped apertures. Crossbars of the Y or T accommodated the eyes, and the rear (really the ventral) extension provided an opening for the funnel, with the arms emerging between. These animals apparently drifted head downward, sinking to the bottom at times but rising by forcing water through the funnel when it was directed downward. By slanting it to the rear they were able to move obliquely forward.

Neither movement could have been very rapid, and the drifting position indicates that food was found on the bottom. The slitlike aperture led an Austrian paleontologist to conclude that these and other constricted cephalopods ate only very small food. He is opposed by others who argue that the beaks could project from even narrow slits, biting into any victim which the arms were able to hold. Actual eating was done by the radula, which probably could extend farther and work more efficiently than that of *Nautilus.*

Coiled Crawlers and Swimmers. Theory says that certain early cephalopods curved like *Cyrtoceras* but did not become short or constrict their apertures. Next they began to coil; first loosely, but then more and more tightly, until the last whorls overlapped and even hid their predecessors.

There is nothing wrong with this theory, but it has not yet been supported by actual series of fossils. It is true that the early Cambrian *Volborthella* is almost straight and that the late Cambrian *Plectronoceras* is fairly long and moderately curved. But early Cambrian seas also contained two groups of closely coiled shells, without intermediate stages. Three other groups, or orders, that appeared during Devonian and Mississippian times seem to have had ancestors that already were closely coiled. How they got that way remains a subject for speculation.

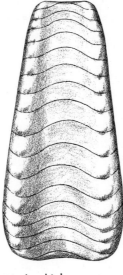

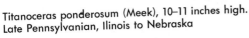
Titanoceras ponderosum (Meek), 10–11 inches high.
Late Pennsylvanian, Ilinois to Nebraska

Solenochilus collectus M. & W., 2 inches
high. Mississippian, Indiana and Illinois; Pennsylvanian, Texas

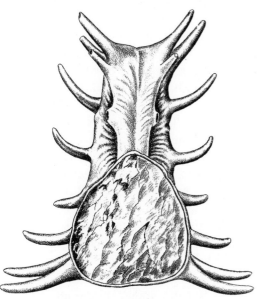
Cooperoceras texanum Miller, about 5 inches
high. Permian, Glass Mountains, Texas

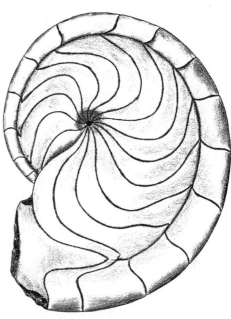
Aturia vanuxemi Conrad, about 6
inches high. Eocene, New Jersey

Endolobus forbesianus (McChesney), 2 inches
high. Pennsylvanian, Ohio to Missouri, Texas

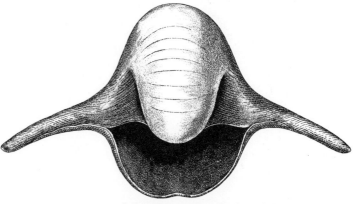
Acanthonautilus cornutus (Golovinsky),
about 4 inches high. Permian, Russia

Coiled nautiloids, some with long spines

Coiled shells are given various names, depending upon the closeness of coiling. More important, so far as habits are concerned, are the size of the body, the width of the shell, and its general shape. Cephalopods such as *Titanoceras* and *Solenocheilus,* which had wide shells and relatively large, heavy bodies, must have spent most of their time crawling, swimming only short distances and then mostly when they were alarmed. Tight or open coiling of shell had little effect upon these habits.

Forms such as *Eurystomites* built discoidal shells that were light in weight and had long but not large living chambers which finally became almost straight. The body evidently was heavy enough to serve as ballast, but the shell must have been so buoyant that the aperture pointed obliquely downward. These animals half crawled and half drifted and could swim more easily than *Titanoceras.* Still, their high, empty shells must have been difficult to guide.

Nautilus typifies coiled cephalopods that developed stubby bodies and compact shells that still were not very narrow. A grown *Nautilus* is just a little heavier than water; so little that it can crawl without much effort and can drift or hover above the bottom with only the slightest use of its funnel. A strong current from that organ sends *Nautilus* swimming shell first. Modern species stay in deep water (as much as 1,785 feet) during the day but often swim toward the surface at night, and fossils may have shared this habit. Since water would crush the shell at a depth of 1,180 feet, *Nautilus* apparently is able to force gas into its chambers, enabling them to withstand the pressures at greater depths. There is no evidence, however, that gas becomes dense enough to help the animals sink or is reduced so much as to make them rise.

Still better suited to swimming were coiled nautiloids with very narrow shells. Some of these appeared in Pennsylvanian seas, but others evolved during the Mesozoic and Cenozoic eras. Many of these creatures had smooth shells, and their septa were deeply curved or folded, producing complex sutures.

Some Aberrant Nautiloids. Most ancient nautiloids had smooth shells bearing faint lines and wrinkles marking brief interruptions in growth. Others developed ridges or annular costae, and a few built grids of ridges. The Rotoceratida went still further, for their shells were ornamented by frills, nodes, spines, and grooves. Some of these must have made swimming almost impossible and apparently interfered with crawling. It is hard to believe that the spines of *Cooperoceras* did not become entangled in seaweeds, or that the frills of *Ryticeras* did not impede creeping and swimming. *Ryticeras* also had to stay away from massive corals, which would have caught and broken those graceful frills.

Several nautiloids whose ancestors had developed coiled shells gave up swimming for drifting or crawling. We see this in such genera as *Schroederoceras,* of Ordovician age. At first its shell was tightly coiled; then it became only silghtly curved, suggesting that its builder compromised between drifting and crawling. The Silurian *Lituites* went much further, for most of its shell was straight and its aperture was constricted. Since neither siphuncle nor walls were weighted, *Lituites* must have drifted head downward like an elongate *Mandaloceras.*

Another Silurian genus, *Mitroceras,* typifies nautiloids that coiled spirally, as if they were snails, though some Devonian genera also uncoiled during maturity. These nautiloids must have crawled with the shell half-floating above them, though nothing suggests that the body had any broad, flat structure analogous to the foot of a snail.

NAUTILOIDS AS FOSSILS

Since the nautiloid shell consists of aragonite, which dissolves readily, most fossils belonging to this group are internal molds. They show the shape of the shell and its varied chambers as well as its siphuncle. Septa appear as curved surfaces or lines across broken specimens or as other lines (the sutures) that show where septa joined the walls.

There are many exceptions, of course, to this rule that shells disappeared while fillings were preserved. The most important are silicified fossils, in which aragonite was replaced by silica colored by impurities such as iron oxide. These remains stand out prominently on weathered slabs of limestone and may be removed by dissolving the latter in commercial hydrochloric ("muriatic") or acetic acid.

For full understanding of fossil nautiloids we need specimens showing how the shell developed from early stages to maturity. Yet much can be learned from incomplete specimens. Casts are enough to distinguish most genera and species, and others can be determined from bits of siphuncle. Weathered sections in rock are useful, too, though they almost never reveal surface ornamentation.

Much more difficult than identifying species is the task of determining genera. Before 1925, many straight or curved nautiloids were placed in the genus *Orthoceras* ("straight horn"), whose siphuncle was near the center and whose shell was smooth except for growth wrinkles and lines. *Nautilus* included a great variety of coiled shells whose siphuncle started out near the center but moved toward the venter. *Gomphoceras* denoted short curved shells that were not much flattened, and so on.

Such genera were simple, but most of them were based on superficial resemblances. When *Orthoceras* was critically studied, only a few species were found to deserve that name, which is now spelled *Orthoceros.* Many species went into new genera, such as *Michelinoceras* and *Geisenocerina.* Other catchall groups suffered a similar fate, so that nautiloids are now divided into a bewildering number of genera distributed through seventy-five families and thirteen or fourteen orders.

There is nothing wrong with this; classification must correspond to differences and relationships, even though they are complex. But it does pose a problem for collectors, who can use up-to-date names only for nautiloids illustrated here, in available textbooks, and in the ever-useful *Index Fossils of North America,* by Shimer and Shrock. Others must be identified as to species, using old generic names until their modern equivalents are found in museums or technical publications.

CHAPTER XV

"Ammon's Stones" and Naked Cephalopods

T HE WORD *Ammonites* means "Ammon's stones"; it was given to fossil shells whose wrinkled whorls suggest rams' horns, which often appeared on the Egyptian god, Ammon. Today we recognize ammonoids—*Ammonites* is a genus—as a subclass of cephalopods that developed increasingly complex septa. Shells ranged from thick to thin, from broad to narrow, and from smooth to almost incredibly ornate. Many members of the group, and perhaps all, could close the shell with a horny plate (anaptychus) or a double calcareous structure (aptychus) when the body was completely drawn into the living chamber. Body, eyes, and arms probably resembled those of nautiloids.

CRUMPLED SEPTA AND SUTURES

Ammonoids apparently were descended from straight-shelled Ordovician nautiloids, but the new group did not become well established until mid-Devonian times. Called goniatites ("angle-stones"), these Devonian forms had smooth shells that ranged from wide to narrow and were compactly coiled. Their name is explained by angular zigzags in their sutures.

How Septa Crumpled. Primitive septa, as we know, were only a little larger than the shell and produced straight or gently curved sutures. In ammonoids, as well as in such nautiloids as *Aturia,* the septa grew so large that they were forced to become fluted or deeply lobed. The process is analogous to that of forcing pieces of paper into a glass tumbler. A little bending will make the paper fit if it is not much larger than the available space. But when the paper is much too large it crumples as it goes into the glass.

This is only an analogy, for it ignores two facts. First, septa were not pushed into cephalopod shells; they were built there by the mantle and correspond to its surface. Second, crumpling is a hit-or-miss process; no two papers

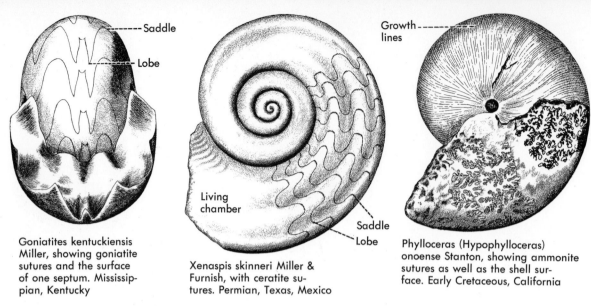

Goniatites kentuckiensis Miller, showing goniatite sutures and the surface of one septum. Mississippian, Kentucky

Xenaspis skinneri Miller & Furnish, with ceratite sutures. Permian, Texas, Mexico

Phylloceras (Hypophylloceras) onoense Stanton, showing ammonite sutures as well as the shell surface. Early Cretaceous, California

Cephalopods with goniatite, ceratite, and ammonite sutures

pushed into a tumbler bend in identical ways. But folds and furrows in cephalopod mantles were definite characters and follow definite patterns that reveal themselves in the sutures. The latter are divided into saddles, which extend forward, and lobes, which are directed backward. For study they generally are drawn flat on cards. If the sutures are long, as they are in large fossils, only half is shown.

Three Types of Sutures. Goniatites lived and prospered for 120,000,000 years, for they appeared in middle Devonian times and lived through the Triassic. During that time members of the group changed greatly, some becoming so wide that they were almost spheroidal. At least one aberrant type became roughly triangular; another resembled a vastly overgrown foraminifer. Goniatites also increased the size of their septa, thereby adding to the saddles and lobes in their sutures. Neither saddles nor lobes were divided, however, and their simplicity distinguishes the type of suture called goniatite.

Ceratite sutures have divided lobes, though the saddles are undivided. Sutures of this type appeared during the Mississippian and continued to the end of the Triassic period. Cephalopods possessing them then died out, but ceratite sutures were developed anew by late Cretaceous genera that simplified their septa.

Ammonite sutures appeared early in the Permian period. In it both saddles and lobes are divided and subdivided, producing patterns that suggest the tracings of frost on windowpanes or the outlines of ferns with unbelievably delicate leaves. With these changes went others in shape and ornamentation which led to shells more elaborate and often more grotesque than the strangest of nautiloids.

Highly specialized ammonoids of the Triassic died out as that period closed, leaving conservative types to carry on. Their descendants, however, soon evolved even more elaborate sutures. Later came secondary simplification, so

Lytoceras batesi Trask.
Early Cretaceous, California

Lioceras concavum Sowerby,
filled with calcite crystals.
Jurassic, England

Scaphites cheyennensis (Owen).
Late Cretaceous, western United
States

Baculites "ovatus Say,"
showing pearly layer.
Late Cretaceous, North
America

Dipoloceras belknapi (Marcou);
the keel does not show in this internal mold. Early Cretaceous,
Oklahoma and Texas

Baculites "ovatus Say," showing sutures. Late Cretaceous,
North America

(Left) Aptychus from the
aperture of an ammonoid.
Jurassic limestone, Solenhofen, Germany

Nipponites mirabilis Yabe.
Cretaceous, Hokkaido, Japan

Some typical ammonoids

that descendants of genera whose sutures had grown increasingly complex reverted to the ceratite type. Some, in fact, developed sutures that were almost as simple as those of early goniatites.

Why Did Sutures Become Ornate? Many writers have tried to explain why ammonoid septa crumpled, making more and more ornate sutures. One theory calls this an orthogenetic trend, a tendency to one type of variation that became established and then continued even though its results ceased to have discernible value. Opposed to this is the theory of selection, which holds that cephalopods with elaborate septa enjoyed a selective advantage because crumpled septa increased the strength of shells. This idea finds support in the fact that many smooth, thin shells of ammonoids that lived in relatively deep water show elaborately crumpled septa, while those of some thin shells in shallow-water deposits are much simpler. Many smooth shells also have more elaborate septa than ornate contemporaries that were strengthened by ribs and bosses. On the other hand, we know of no ammonoids that lived in water deep enough to crush shells with the smoothest of nautiloid septa. Moreover, some well-ribbed shells of shallows have more elaborate sutures than do smooth deep-water genera.

Further difficulty comes from the fact that ammonoids did not change all their septa and sutures each time a new pattern developed. Instead, the new character appeared only after a series of stages that repeated the adult sutures of earlier, ancestral genera. If the final character was advantageous and had triumphed over its predecessors, how did the growing ammonoid manage to live through those preliminary stages?

SHAPES, ORNAMENTS, AND HABITS

Early ammonoids were coiled, though some did not have the whorls in contact. Paleozoic and Mesozoic members of the group developed typical swimming and crawling forms. Many of the former looked and probably lived like *Nautilus;* others had streamlined shells so narrow that we wonder how they remained upright while at rest. Their arms must have spread out as props that kept the creatures from toppling over.

Crawlers appeared as broad, smooth goniatites in Mississippian seas. During the Pennsylvanian and Jurassic periods several genera developed wide shells with flattened sides, like the sluggish pond snail *Helisoma,* once known as *Planorbis.* Several Permian crawlers were almost spheroidal, as were some of late Triassic and Jurassic age. Other types that must have crawled were egg-shaped, triangular, or resembled enormously overgrown Foraminifera. The second and third of these appeared in late Devonian seas.

Frills and Other Ornaments. We recall that some nautiloids covered their loosely coiled shells with frills built as mantles spread out. When each frill

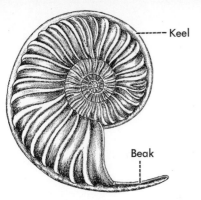

Schloenbachia cristata
(Deluc), with keel and
beak. Early Cretaceous,
Europe

Lytoceras immane Oppel,
showing ornamentation.
Late Jurassic, Europe

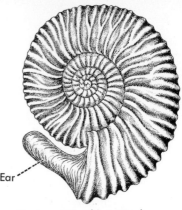

Normannites orbignyi Buckman,
showing the prominent ear.
Middle Jurassic, Europe

Dufrenoya justinae (Hill),
a narrow ammonoid with
coarse ribs. Early Creta-
ceous, Colombia to Texas,
and Africa

Arcestes pacificus
H. & S., a rounded
crawler. Late
Triassic, California

Prodromites gorbyi
(Miller). Early
Mississippian, cen-
tral United States

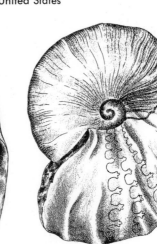

Zemistephanus richardsoni
(Whiteaves), a crawler that
resembled some snails.
Jurassic, British Columbia

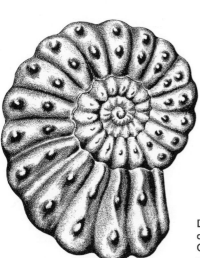

Mortoniceras shoshonense Meek.
Late Cretaceous, Texas

Dipoloceras, a narrow
ammonoid with a keel.
Cretaceous. Compare
with D. belknapi (Marcou)

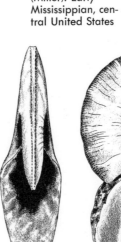

Engonoceras pierdenale (Buch). Early
Cretaceous (Fredericksburg), Texas

Ammonoids of varied shapes

reached full size the mantle contracted, built a short length of ordinary wall, and then flared outward again. Ammonoids such as *Lytoceras* duplicated this process, though fossils seldom show more than broken bases of frills.

An enormous number of ammonoids developed ridges and furrows that ran lengthwise or around the whorls, as well as knoblike bosses and even spines. Most of these structures strengthened the shell, just as corrugations make sheet steel rigid and repoussé decorations give strength to a silver coffeepot or bowl. Many genera so ornamented and strengthened resembled *Nautilus* in over-all shape and apparently had similar habits. Other genera became streamlined, with keels which show that they were relatively rapid swimmers. Many more, however, had features that go with a sluggish crawling life. *Zemistephanus,* for example, looked like an abnormally broad, squat, *Helisoma,* and *Arcestes* had an almost globose shell. Not merely did such shapes reduce speed; they seem to mean that the creatures almost always crawled.

Beaks, Ears, and Funnels. Again like nautiloids, many ammonoids narrowed their apertures during maturity. Others developed beaks (rostra) that grew forward from keels, or ears (auricles) that were added at each side of the aperture. One theory says that constricted apertures kept the body from being torn from its shell—an explanation which assumes that many young animals were pulled out through their wide apertures, or that mature animals became less and less firmly attached to the walls of their shells. Unfortunately there is no evidence in favor of either assumption and some evidence that all ammonoids, both old and young, had very sturdy attachments.

Beaks and ears have been said to mean that their owners seldom or never swam. This theory robs keels of their function as water-cutters and stabilizers and gives beaks and ears a nuisance value which they seemingly did not possess. If these structures were troublesome, they were so when their owners crawled forward, not when they swam backward with their arms trailing as rudders. Narrow, keeled ammonoids such as *Dipoloceras* "make sense" only as swimmers.

Uncoiled Ammonoids. We have seen two nonswimmers, the triangular *Soliclymenia* and *Parawocklumeria,* whose shell was no less grotesque than its name. Others may be found in genera that gave up regular coiling and assumed a variety of shapes which we may summarize as follows:

High-spired types appeared in the late Triassic and in middle to late Cretaceous times. They looked and probably crawled like snails, doing little if any swimming.

Open-coiled ammonoids are found in early Jurassic deposits and throughout the Cretaceous. Some merely have whorls that do not touch; others are considerably shortened; a few form open curves. The first two groups could either crawl or swim, and so could some members of the third. Others may have drifted near the bottom, but that is only a guess.

Baculites took the place *Lituites* had held among ammonoids. After coiling

Soliclymenia paradoxa (Muenster), x 2. Late Devonian, Germany

Parawocklumeria, x 1.5. Devonian

Oecoptychius, x 1.5. Jurassic

Three "aberrant" cephalopods of small size

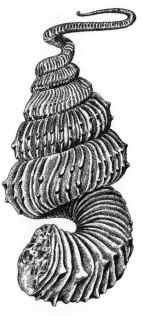

Baculites compressus Say. Very young shell with coil (x 10), and surface of a septum. Late Cretaceous, North America

Pictetia astieri Orb. x 2. Mid-Cretaceous, western Europe

Helicoceras stevensi Whitfield, 6.5 inches high. Cretaceous (Pierre), Great Plains of the U.S.A.

Uncoiled and aberrantly coiled ammonoids of Devonian to late Cretaceous age

for a few whorls it built a straight, compressed shell that ended in an unusually wide beak. Some experts think it drifted head downward; others say it crawled. Fragments with pearly nacre or excellent sutures are common fossils in the late Cretaceous Pierre shale.

Hamulina and its kin, of early Cretaceous age, grew straight forward for a while, made a sharp turn, and then grew straight to the rear. We can picture young and fully grown individuals as creepers and occasional swimmers; in maturity the tip of the shell projected above and beyond their arms. But what did the animals do while they were making that hairpin turn?

Equally puzzling are *Hamites* and *Macroscaphites,* of Cretaceous age. All have been regarded as drifters, with heads and arms hanging downward at some stages but directed upward during old age. They have also been called aberrant crawlers, but neither interpretation is convincing.

Scaphites is little more than a very short *Macroscaphites,* with the same problems of habit and orientation. In youth it could have lived like *Nautilus,* but in maturity and old age it was poorly adapted to crawling and quite as poorly fitted for swimming. If it drifted with mouth and arms upward, it could not pursue its food. Yet it prospered and became an abundant fossil in the Pierre shale and other late Cretaceous formations.

The ultimate in bizarre form is found in *Nipponites* and certain species of *Helicoceras.* The former became an irregular tangle which could not swim and may not have been able even to crawl about. *Helicoceras* included both open loops and species that began by coiling, then built their shells into hair-pin U's, coiled spirally for a few whorls, stopped coiling, and began to bend back toward the apices of their spirals. After a little of that, death put an end to their eccentricities.

HABITATS OF CRETACEOUS AMMONOIDS

Cretaceous rocks of Texas and northeastern Mexico range from soft sand-stones to shales and limestones, and settled in situations ranging from deltas and tidal flats to reefs, extensive shoals, and waters more than 600 feet deep. These formations also contain enormous numbers of ammonoids, with shells so little broken and worn that they plainly were buried close to the places in which they had lived. With them are snails, clams, oysters, sea urchins, fora-minifers, and many other remains. Fossils and formations give the following record of conditions under which ammonoids lived and creatures with which they associated:

1. Ammonoids did not inhabit the ponds, streams, and brackish bays of deltas. This is not surprising, since no cephalopod of any sort has been found in fresh water or in fresh-water deposits.

2. Ammonoids seldom lived in shallow near-shore waters where sand was deposited. Such waters probably were too shallow for these mollusks, became too nearly brackish after hard rains, and grew too warm during the summer. The eggs of many modern cephalopods die very quickly when the water around them becomes warm.

3. Ammonoids also avoided the extensive shallows in which large dinosaurs sometimes waded. There the water ranged from 8 or 10 to perhaps 20 feet in depth and waves often reached the bottom, piling up small ripple marks. Some-times, indeed, the sea water vanished, leaving mud flats to dry and crack under the blazing sun or to be pitted by drops of rain. Large snails and thick-shelled clams found this habitat inviting, as did sea urchins and uncountable billions of the "foram" *Orbitolina*. Ammonoids probably were kept out by the same factors that excluded them from sandy shoals.

4. Few ammonoids thrived where empty clamshells covered the bottom, forming beds of coquina. Still, the narrow but thick-ribbed *Dufrenoya* is com-mon in one coquina deposit.

5. Ammonoids also avoided reefs built by corals and rudistids, where the water was both shallow and rough. Banks of *Gryphaea* and *Exogyra* formed more favorable habitats; narrow ammonoids such as *Engonoceras* and *Dipo-loceras* thrived there, though other types were rare.

6. These same narrow ammonoids reached enormous numbers in seas 30 or 40 to as much as 120 feet deep. There temperature and salinity did not

change much, the muddy bottom was never exposed, and the largest waves produced only oscillations that piled oyster shells into "giant ripples." Other mollusks and sea urchins also were plentiful.

7. Ammonoids reached their greatest abundance and variety in waters 120 to about 600 feet deep, but various kinds apparently needed different bottoms or the conditions that went with them. Sandy limestones and shales contain ornate shells of several types, as well as the narrow ones found in deposits of shallower water. Partly uncoiled forms, such as *Scaphites,* are rare.

Fine-grained shales and soft, marly limestones contain an enormous variety of ammonoids—smooth and rough, squat and narrow, closely coiled, spiral, and partly uncoiled. If there was an ideal habitat for Cretaceous ammonoids, it was a marly bottom under water more than 120 feet deep, with abundant algae that provided food for varied animals, including those eaten by ammonoids.

8. Seas more than 600 feet deep filled a trench, or geosyncline, that extended westward from what now is the Gulf of Mexico. There water was too deep and too dark for seaweeds, and snails and clams were rare or absent. Near the edges of the trough, smooth-shelled ammonoids were suprisingly plentiful. At greater depths the water was cold and contained little oxygen, a factor unfavorable to normal animal life. Snails could not live in such depths, and pelecypods were rare, thin-shelled creatures very different from those of

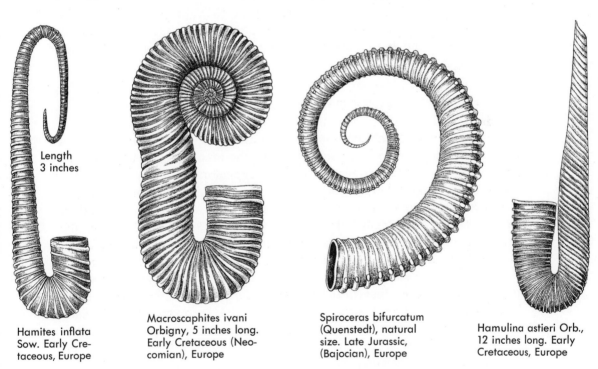

Length
3 inches

Hamites inflata Sow. Early Cretaceous, Europe

Macroscaphites ivani Orbigny, 5 inches long. Early Cretaceous (Neocomian), Europe

Spiroceras bifurcatum (Quenstedt), natural size. Late Jurassic, (Bajocian), Europe

Hamulina astieri Orb., 12 inches long. Early Cretaceous, Europe

Four European ammonoids that uncoiled. All except Hamulina were small.

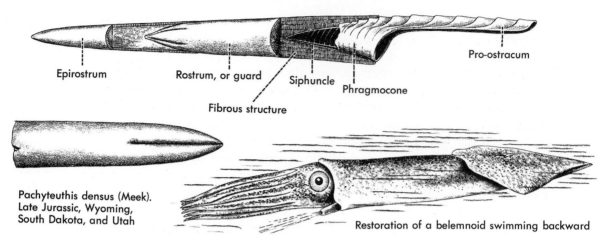

Epirostrum Rostrum, or guard Siphuncle Phragmocone Pro-ostracum

Fibrous structure

Pachyteuthis densus (Meek).
Late Jurassic, Wyoming,
South Dakota, and Utah

Restoration of a belemnoid swimming backward

Shape and structure of typical belemnoids

shallows. Ammonoids were more successful; species with wide, smooth shells were almost the only animals whose remains became fossils. Most of them are preserved in pyrite, good specimens being very attractive.

One more fact appears in this record: ammonoids were gregarious and, except in hostile habitats, they lived and hunted in large schools. They shared this habit with most other cephalopods, from *Volborthella* to the modern *Nautilus* and squids. Only the octopus and cuttlefish are solitary. Both prowl for food alone, and both tuck their soft unprotected bodies into crevices between rocks.

DARTLIKE SWIMMERS—THE BELEMNOIDS

While ammonoids were developing elaborate shells, some of their relatives reduced the shell until it was hidden under the mantle. Thus they became belemnoids, the first rapid swimmers among cephalopods.

Belemnoid Anatomy and Habits. A few fossils preserving impressions of flesh show that belemnoids looked and presumably acted like the modern squid. The body had become torpedo-shaped and was surrounded by a mantle that spread out into two lateral fins that kept the body right side up and could be moved to guide it upward or downward. There was a constricted "neck" behind the head; the eyes were large, round, and dark and apparently focused light with lenses rather than through pinholes. The ten arms were not smooth, like those of *Nautilus*, but were set with hooks that increased their efficiency in catching and holding food. Fossils tell nothing about the diet, but resemblance to squids suggests that it included small fish plus tidbits such as crabs, prawns, and injured belemnoids.

Like most other cephalopods, belemnoids swam by taking water into the mantle cavity and forcing it out through the funnel. When the latter pointed forward its owner swam backward; when the funnel was turned to the rear the belemnoid darted ahead. Alarm caused the creature to release a thick dark liquid from an ink sac that opened into the cavity and through the funnel. The ink spead out in an opaque cloud which supposedly blinded any enemy while the belemnoid darted away. But the ink of modern squids paralyzes the organs of smell, with which predaceous fishes (the squids' chief enemies) do their hunting. Fishes blunder about aimlessly long after they have swum out of the blinding clouds. Belemnoid ink probably had the same effect.

Shells Inside Bodies. Belemnoids apparently evolved when some descendant of early nautiloids outgrew its living chamber and wrapped its mantle round the inadequate shell. That shell, now called a phragmocone, was fairly long at first but was built up more and more slowly as generation followed generation. Thus the phragmocone became smaller and smaller, both actually and in proportion to the body. Only in the upper, or dorsal, region did the shell grow at anything like a normal rate. There it became an elongate shield, the proostracum, which supported and perhaps protected the forward portion of the body.

The long empty shells of early belemnoids enabled them to float their bodies with a minimum of effort. But phragmocones were delicate, and as the creatures gained speed there were many collisions. There also was need for some ballast at the tip of the body so it could cut the water without turning or wobbling.

Both requirements were met by the guard, or rostrum, a solid structure built behind and partly around the shell. It consists of radial fibers arranged in alternating light and dark layers. The latter contain large amounts of or-

Belemnitella americana (Morton). Late Cretaceous, New Jersey to Texas

Sphenodiscus lobatus (Tuomey). Late Cretaceous, Atlantic and Gulf coastal plains

Plesioteuthis, a Jurassic squid from Germany. *B* is the ink bag, *P*, the pen.

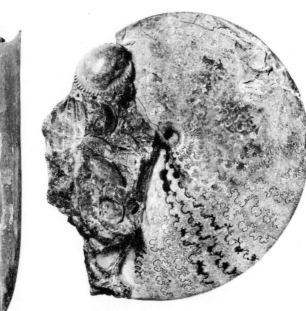

ganic material, but the former are almost pure calcite. Both show plainly in broken or polished sections, which also trace changes in shape as guards became larger and longer. Many also reveal fractures and dislocations—ample proof that belemnoids often bumped into other objects as they darted backward.

Some belemnoids added a fourth internal structure, attached to the guard much as the latter capped the tip of the phragmocone. This epirostrum contained no fibrous layers and was easily destroyed after death. It is known in only a few Jurassic genera.

Belemnoids appeared in Mississippian seas but did not become plentiful until the late Triassic. Countless billions swam in schools during the Jurassic and Cretaceous, but the creatures declined rapidly at the end of the latter period. Their last fossils—aberrant phragmocones and guards—are rare in Eocene rocks.

FROM CONES TO CUTTLEBONE

Belemnoids had hardly become abundant when some of them produced offspring that evolved into sepioids. As they did so the phragmocone coiled or changed its structure, the guard became small or vanished, and sucking cups replaced hooks on the animals' arms.

These changes, which began in the Jurassic, followed two different paths. In one the shield and guard vanished, the shell coiled like a tiny *Gyroceras*, and both body and arms became short. The result was *Spirula*, a small creature that drifts and swims in modern oceans—the only shelled cephalopod known to be truly pelagic. Some of its predecessors stayed in shallow seas, for their shells and shortened guards have been found in Tertiary rocks of North America and Europe.

The second group of sepioids kept a little of the guard, added a new and very wide dorsal shield, and turned the phragmocone into a spongy mass of aragonite in which the septa and other plates are connected by small rods or pillars. Thus it became "cuttlebone," which is given to canaries and other caged birds as a source of calcium carbonate. Fossil cuttlebones and shields are found in Tertiary rocks of Europe, but the modern cuttlefish (*Sepia*) ranges around the world. It is a short, plump creature with two long arms and eight short ones. It can swim rapidly by means of its funnel and slowly by rippling the finfolds that run along both sides of its body.

SQUIDS AND OCTOPODS

When belemnoids died out their place was taken by the teuthoids, or squids. These creatures lost the phragmocone and guard but kept a horny "pen" that may or may not be a remnant of the belemnoid dorsal shield. Squids also were very rapid swimmers, and their sucking cups were superior to hooks for capturing and holding food. Squids appeared in the early Jurassic, made slow progress for millions of years, and then became the most abundant of cephalopods. Since they lived in the manner of belemnoids, it is probable that they crowded the latter out of the seas soon after the beginning of the Tertiary period. Squids could have done this both by eating food on which belemnoids depended and by actually devouring their less able and active relatives.

Octopods, as their name suggests, reduced the number of their arms from ten to eight, at the same time losing all trace of ancestral guard and shell. Because of this they almost never formed fossils, but one genus with round body and lateral fins has been found in late Cretaceous strata of Lebanon. Another group, the argonauts, developed a new and delicate "shell"—really a brood pouch that held developing eggs—between two of the female's arms. A few of these pouches have been found in Pliocene rocks.

As the name suggests, modern argonauts are swimmers at the surface of warm seas around the world. Thus their habits are very different from octopods that live along rocky shores and from giant squids that inhabit dark, cold depths of the oceans. Among the latter is the great *Architeuthis,* which reaches over-all lengths of 55 to 66 feet and weights of 1,000 to 4,000 pounds. This is one case in which living giants exceed anything of the past.

CHAPTER XVI

Worms, Burrows, and Trails

T HE RAILROAD TOWN of Field, British Columbia, lies between precipitous mountains made up of Cambrian rocks. Northward from Field a trail climbs steeply until it crosses Burgess Pass. Beyond the pass another trail leads to the right, climbing above firs and spruces to beds of blackish mid-Cambrian shale exposed on a barren ridge. The shale was discovered in 1909, after Charles D. Walcott paused to push a stone from the trail. When Dr. Walcott last crossed the pass, many years later, he had collected forty thousand fossils from that one small exposure of Burgess shale. Unknown numbers remain in ledges and frost-broken slabs.

These fossils are impressions and films of carbon that show both outer shapes and internal structures in amazing detail. To collect them is to carry our minds back to an age when the ridge was a quiet, muddy corner of a middle Cambrian sea that extended southward from the Arctic Ocean and reached the Pacific near what now is Lower California. Algae were plentiful: green or blue-green species like tufts of silken threads, gracefully branched red seaweeds, and brown ones whose leaflike blades were pierced by many small holes. Little brachiopods were common, too, and so were vaselike glass sponges described in Chapter VI. Jellyfish swam to and fro, sea cucumbers lay on the mud, and worms crawled across it. Some of those worms were small and plain, but others were showy, with brilliant scales and bristles that shimmered as their owners moved about.

WORMS OF VARIED PHYLA

The varied forms of these mid-Cambrian crawlers show that the word *worm* has only general significance. In everyday language it means almost any wriggling or crawling creature, from a caterpillar to a leech or intestinal parasite.

204

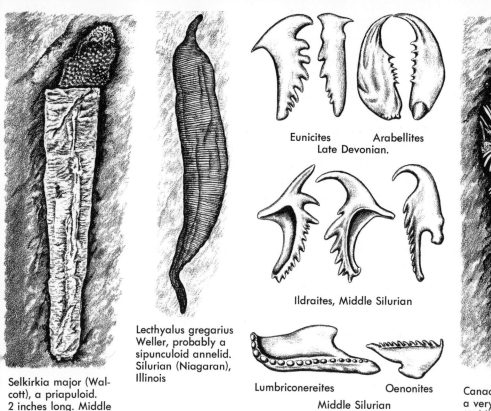

Eunicites   Arabellites
Late Devonian.

Ildraites, Middle Silurian

Lecthyalus gregarius
Weller, probably a
sipunculoid annelid.
Silurian (Niagaran),
Illinois

Lumbriconereites   Oenonites
Middle Silurian

Selkirkia major (Wal-
cott), a priapuloid.
2 inches long. Middle
Cambrian, British
Columbia

Canadia spinosa Walcott,
a very spiny annelid, x 2.
Middle Cambrian, British
Columbia

Priapuloid and annelid worms, and some typical scolecodonts

Many old books about fossils, on the other hand, apply the term to only one or two classes in the phylum that includes earthworms and the most brilliant creatures that lived in the Burgess "pool."

The first of these interpretations is preferable to the second. It is true that caterpillars are young, or larval, insects and should be given their correct name. But even without them, *worm* remains a useful general term that fits a vast number of invertebrate animals that differ in shapes, structure, and relationships and are now distributed among ten or more phyla. Four of these are known from petrified fossils or carbonized films, and at least three more can be traced in solidified burrows and tubes.

Flatworms (Platyhelminthes). Flatworms are the simplest of worms, as well as the simplest animals that have three distinct layers in their bodies instead of the two we have examined in coelenterates. This third layer forms organs such as muscles, as well as others that are lined with sheets of endoderm. Though this three-layered body is simple in flatworms, we have found that it becomes complex and precisely organized in many other phyla.

Since flatworms have no hard parts, they are poorly suited to fossilization. None is found in the Burgess shale; in fact, no free-living flatworms are known as fossils, though a few parasites have been discovered in carbonized insects of Pennsylvanian and Tertiary ages. They show that some flatworms gave up independent life at least 250,000,000 years ago and began to exist as flukes and tapeworms do today.

Roundworms (Nemathelminthes, or Nematoda). Vast numbers of modern roundworms are parasites in plants as well as animals; some, such as trichina and the hookworm, are exceedingly dangerous. Others live in fresh water, soil, sand, and the sea; they are the most abundant of living animals and may outnumber all others combined. Parasitic species have been found in fossil insects, and one free-living form of the Burgess shale is tentatively assigned to this phylum.

Priapuloidea. This is a small group of marine worms that are characterized by a wrinkled body, a straight digestive system, and a proboscis that is covered with spines. They are variously ranked as a phylum, as one class in a phylum called the Gephyrea, and as annelids. The small number of modern species seem to be remnants of an ancient group that includes several fossils from the Burgess shale as well as others from the Silurian of Illinois.

SEGMENTED WORMS (ANNELIDA)

These are the "Vermes" of many old books; they also are often called Annulata. As that name and Annelida imply, these are worms whose bodies are covered with rings which correspond to internal sections in which some parts are repeated over and over again. This characteristic is shown plainly by the common earthworm.

Though annelids are much less abundant than nematodes, most fossil worms belong to this phylum. One reason for this is the fact that annelids are covered with a tough layer, or cuticle, which resists destruction. Many annelids also posses hard, durable jaws or cover themselves with tubes or shells. The former are made of cemented grains or are provided with tough linings, while the latter are quite as sturdy as calcareous shells.

Ancient Marine "Earthworms." The earthworm belongs to a group (the oligochaetes) most of whose members now live on land. A few, however, are marine, as were the only known fossils. The most familiar of these, *Protoscolex,* was a soft-bodied creature with distinct rings which was blunt at the forward end (there was no head) and tapered to the rear. Some specimens seem to possess a clitellum, the bandlike structure that forms a cocoon containing the eggs of a modern oligochaete.

Hunters and Jaws (Scolecodonts). Earthworms and their kin are headless, have bristles instead of legs, and eat small or dead, decaying food. Polychaetes have heads and legs, and many of them are active hunters whose mouths are equipped with two or three types of sharp, horny jaws.

Some carbonized worms of this type have been found, but most of them are known from their jaws, which are termed *scolecodonts,* or "worm-teeth."

Lumbricaria colon Muenster.
Early Jurassic, Solenhofen, Germany

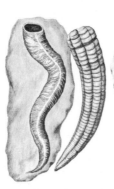

Serpula and Hamulus.
Cretaceous to Recent.
Much enlarged

Arthrophycus allegheniensis Harlan
(annelid burrows often called A.
harlani). Early Silurian (Medina),
eastern North America

Tentaculites richmondensis
Miller. Late Ordovician
(Richmond), Ohio Valley

Cornulites proprius Hall.
Silurian (Niagaran), eastern North America

Ottoia prolifica Walcott, a middle Cambrian annelid (chaetopod)

Trail fillings in shale. Though often
called worms, such traces were commonly
made by other animals

(Above) Two species of Spirorbis,
much enlarged

(Right) Burrows resembling Diplocraterion, but lying horizontally.
Cretaceous, South Dakota

Annelids, burrows, and trails

They range from the early Cambrian to the Recent, and from simple blades or prongs to complex structures with many points. Since scolecodonts are very small, they can be found complete in drill cores, and many are useful index fossils. Others give us a good idea of the abundance and variety of active annelids in seas from which they are otherwise unknown.

Shell-building Worms. Scolecodonts belonged to active worms that crawled, swam, or burrowed in search of prey, as does the modern clamworm, *Nereis.* But annelids that build shells stay in one place, cover themselves with armor of calcite or cemented sand grains, and rely upon small food that can be captured by currents of water or by gills that are covered with sticky mucus.

Fossil shell-builders are easily overlooked, for many of them are small. The commonest probably is *Spirorbis,* which looks like a tiny snail attached to other fossils and ranges from the late Ordovician to the Recent, being very common on the brown seaweeds that often are washed ashore. *Serpula* is either coiled or irregularly twisted; some early species were not attached. *Cornulites* and *Tentaculites* (the latter once called a gastropod) consist of trumpet-shaped tubes with many rings. Some species are tightly fastened to shells or corals, but others either broke loose or grew upon hardened mud. Though most species are less than one half inch long, a few measure 3 to 4 inches.

FOSSIL BURROWS AND CASTINGS

Fossil burrows and tubes were once called "fucoids" on the assumption that they were casts of brown algae. This was followed by an equally uncritical effort to assign them to worms or to dismiss them as problematic affairs of little significance.

The error of this last assumption is shown by *Urechis,* a soft-bodied echiurid, or sausage worm, that lives in elongate U-shaped burrows on the California coast. Fossil sausage worms were unknown until G. E. MacGinitie, who had studied *Urechis* in its present-day home, dug the hardened filling of a typical burrow from the Pliocene Monterey shale. Besides having the characteristic shape, the burrow filling contained a petrified crab, which is a commensal tenant in modern *Urechis* burrows, only a few miles from the place where the fossil was found.

Nemerteans, or ribbon worms, have no hard parts that can be readily preserved and do not appear in lists of fossils. Modern species burrow almost constantly, however, searching for annelids and probably other food. First the worm extends its head forward like a pointed probe; then the head contracts and swells, pulling the body forward. The method is slow and laborious but well fitted to produce the alternately thickened and contracted burrows called *Arthrophycus,* of Silurian age. *Arthrophycus,* however, is generally regarded as the work of annelids which burrowed in this manner.

Many fossil burrows are smooth instead of annulate, and branch less commonly than *Arthrophycus*. Such burrows could have been made by either sipunculids or annelids that swallow sediment, extract food from it, and either cast it into the burrows behind them or discharge it at the surface. The common lugworm, *Arenicola*, does this; since food and sediment are collected on a sticky proboscis, grains that pass through the animal's intestine are smaller than those in the muddy sand around it.

Arenicola discharges its castings at the surface and sometimes lies in U-shaped burrows much smaller than those of *Urechis*. Similar burrows, called *Arenicolites*, often show that the worms looped their way upward or downward, making a series of U-shaped marks that extend through beds of sandstone. They are quite different from *Taonurus*, which may have a similar form but lies on the surface of strata.

Some ancient castings resemble those of *Arenicola*, but others are much larger and longer. This may mean that they were made by bigger worms, but those called *Lumbricaria* closely resemble the castings made by modern burrowing sea cucumbers, which belong to the echinoderms.

Filled burrows are common in fine-grained sandstones, shales, and limestones; when they are plentiful, other fossils generally are scarce. The reason for this is not clear, since small burrowers could hardly destroy corals, shells, and other hard remains.

Scolithus is a common fossil in rocks that range from Cambrian to late Devonian age. It consists of filled tubes in beds of sandstone; tubes that are surprisingly straight and seldom form tangles or intertwine. They have been compared to modern "sand corals," which consist of tubes built by an annelid, *Sabellaria*, that is related to worms with shells. Actually *Scolithus* more closely resembles the tubes of phoronids, which are worms related to brachiopods. *Monocraterion*, which has a funnel around the mouth of its tube, may also be the work of phoronids.

Burrowers Other Than Worms. Although many burrows were made by worms, some were produced by other animals. Some sponges, for example, have rootlike growths that extend downward into mud and serve as holdfasts. Several sea anemones dig cup-shaped holes, but others make vertical tubes or even push their way through mud as they search for food. Some sea cucumbers are accomplished burrowers; that is how they get the mud for castings resembling *Lumbricaria*. Others lie in a U-shaped position, with both mouth and anus at the surface. Some crustaceans dig permanent holes, while others burrow through sand or mud and sift it to secure food. Some clams make holes 12 to as much as 30 inches deep and either travel up and down their burrows or lie at the bottom and send their siphons to the surface. Snails such as *Olivella* crawl just beneath the surface, with the siphon projecting. The result is trails, or collapsed burrows, which can easily be recognized when they appear as fossils.

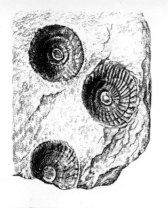

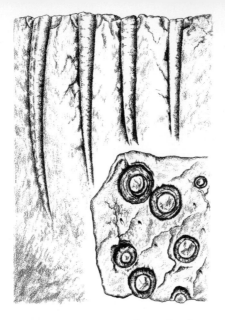

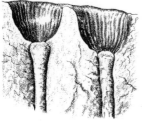

Diplocraterion lyelli Torell.
Early Cambrian, Sweden

Monocraterion tentaculatum Torell.
Early Cambrian, Sweden

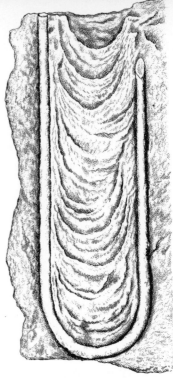

Diplocraterion parallelum Torell.
Early Cambrian, Sweden

A living Spirorbis with its
tentacles extended

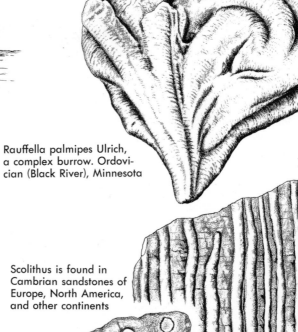

Rauffella palmipes Ulrich,
a complex burrow. Ordovi-
cian (Black River), Minnesota

Scolithus is found in
Cambrian sandstones of
Europe, North America,
and other continents

Scolithus linearis Haldeman.
Slender type, x 0.5

Scolithus linearis Haldeman.
Thick type, x 0.5

Tubes, burrows, and a modern shell-building annelid

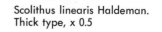

TRAILS—FEW MADE BY WORMS

Many formations, from early Cambrian to Pleistocene, contain fossil trails and other marks or impressions which at one time or another have been credited to worms.

Some supposed trails prove to be burrows: compressed mud or sand which filled burrows that were made just below the surface or along bedding planes between layers of sediment, where food probably was more plentiful than it was above or below. Other "trails" are marks made by shells that were dragged over the bottom by currents or by waves that reached to the floors of shallow seas. Many are preserved as hardened fillings that appear on the surface of beds that covered the marked layers. To see the original pits and scratches, one must make impressions in plaster of paris or plasticine.

Even when these pseudo-trails are removed, we still have a large and interesting array of actual fossil trails. Some may have been made by large, heavy annelids that crept on soft bottoms and left marks made by their "legs," or parapods. But few annelids leave such marks today, and few fossil trails seem to have had this origin. Most of them, instead, belong to six types that may be credited to several groups other than worms:

1. Flat-bottomed furrows with ridges at each side, as well as cross ridges or wrinkles. They commonly end in pits or flattened impressions and were made by crawling snails that plowed into the soft bottom. Some ancient snails even left streaks of slime when they crawled, as slugs do today.

2. Marks that wind to and fro in closely spaced loops. They were made by snails that crawled about, eating films of plants that grew on mud.

3. Deep furrows that end in pits or short burrows. Some of the latter contain fossil clams; these and similar marks made by modern bivalves show that such trails were made by clams that lived in ancient seas.

4. Trails that show marks of two series of jointed legs, one at each side of an apparently elongate body. There may also be marks made by dragging spines, and the trails may end in irregular burrows. Most of these fossils were made by trilobites (Chapter XVII), though some probably are the work of eurypterids (Chapter XIX).

5. Somewhat less regular trails; the impressions of legs are sharper and less uniform. Some of these trails were made by ancient horseshoe crabs (Chapter XIX) and others by eurypterids.

6. Tracks that resemble the preceding but lack traces of dragging spines. Found in Pennsylvanian and later rocks, most of them seem to have been made by crabs and other modernized crustaceans.

This list is not complete, and it raises as many problems as it solves. Still, it is enough to indicate that fossil trails are much more than mere curios or hypothetical worms. They deserve careful collection and study, which will include experiments with modern bottom-dwellers whose trails in soft mud and sand can be preserved by casting them in plaster. An example of such work is K. E. Caster's study of *Paramphibius,* reported in the *Journal of Paleontology,* vol. 12, pages 3–60, for 1938. Besides explaining some very interesting trails, Professor Caster proved that a supposed amphibian really was a fossil king crab.

CHAPTER XVII

When Trilobites Roamed

N<small>O ONE CAN TELL</small> a simple, continuous story of fossils, especially those that lack backbones. For the world of invertebrates is not simple, and its phyla evolved too long ago to follow each other through Paleozoic and later time. We can only deal with them group by group and, having told the story of one, must go back to remote antiquity to begin the record of another. In complex phyla, whose classes differ widely, we are forced to do this several times.

JOINTS AND SKIN-CRUSTS; THE ARTHROPODS

This is specially true of arthropods, a phylum so old and so varied that it is divided into five subphyla and an ever-increasing number of classes. Several of these apparently were established before the Cambrian period began, and only four have records limited to post-Devonian times.

The name Arthropoda means "jointed feet" but is an understatement. From head to whatever serves as tail, the typical arthropod is a series of segments, or somites, connected by movable joints. More may be traced in grooves and constrictions where segments once movable have been fused into shields or plates.

The Useful Exoskeleton. Joints show plainly because they bend, being soft parts of an exoskeleton that often becomes hard enough to be called a shell. It really is a crust secreted by the skin—a laminated crust made up of three layers. At the surface is a waxy sheet that seems to serve as waterproofing. Below this is a layer that gives stiffness and strength and therefore is fully developed only between the flexible joints. It may be chitinous, but in crabs and their relatives it contains secondary deposits of calcite. Last of all, in direct contact with the skin, is a tough but flexible layer of chitin. It forms

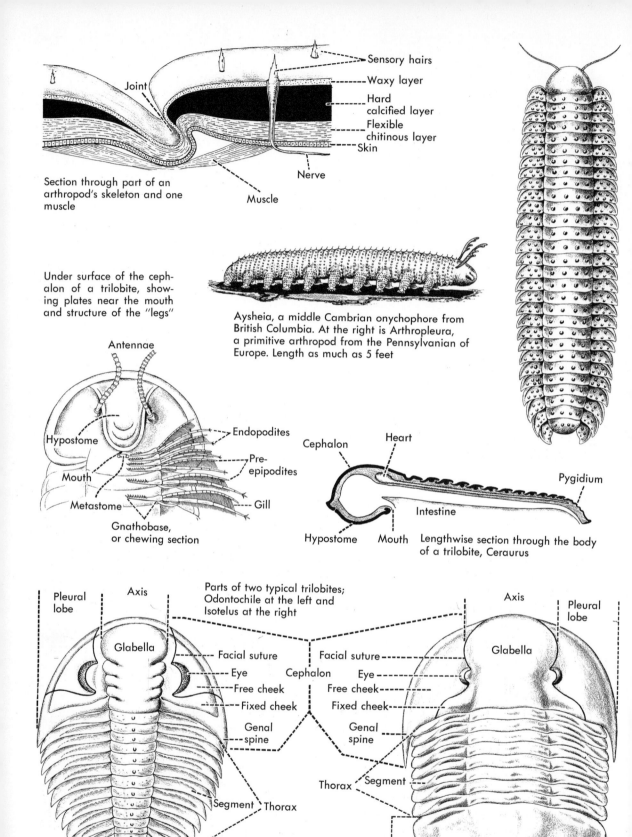

Sensory hairs
Waxy layer
Hard calcified layer
Flexible chitinous layer
Skin
Joint
Nerve
Muscle

Section through part of an arthropod's skeleton and one muscle

Under surface of the cephalon of a trilobite, showing plates near the mouth and structure of the "legs"

Aysheia, a middle Cambrian onychophore from British Columbia. At the right is Arthropleura, a primitive arthropod from the Pennsylvanian of Europe. Length as much as 5 feet

Antennae
Hypostome
Mouth
Metastome
Gnathobase, or chewing section
Endopodites
Pre-epipodites
Gill

Cephalon
Heart
Pygidium
Hypostome
Mouth
Intestine
Lengthwise section through the body of a trilobite, Ceraurus

Parts of two typical trilobites; Odontochile at the left and Isotelus at the right

Pleural lobe
Axis
Glabella
Facial suture
Eye
Free cheek
Fixed cheek
Genal spine
Cephalon
Segment
Thorax
Grooves
Pygidium

Axis
Pleural lobe
Glabella
Facial suture
Eye
Free cheek
Fixed cheek
Genal spine
Segment
Thorax
Pygidium

Aysheia pedunculata Walcott, x 1.4.
A wormlike onychophore.
Middle Cambrian, British Columbia

Opabina regalis Walcott,
a "trilobitomorph." Middle
Cambrian, British Columbia

Ceraurus pleurexanthemus
Green. Ordovician, Eastern N.A.

Phacops iowensis Delo. Note eye facets.
Middle Devonian (Cedar Valley), Iowa

Dipleura dekayi Green, coiled. Middle
Devonian (Hamilton), eastern United States

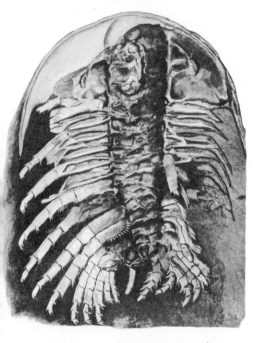

Olenoides serratus (Rominger), natural size.
Retouched to show the legs with their chewing bases and gills. Middle Cambrian (Burgess shale), British Columbia. (After Walcott)

Olenoides serratus (Rominger), with antennae and legs,
x 0.5. Middle Cambrian, British Columbia

An onychophore, some trilobites, and a "trilobitomorph"

most of the crust in soft-bodied insects and on newly molted, or "soft-shell," crabs.

Exoskeletons, as we know, support the soft structures inside them and generally serve as armor. The arthropod crust follows this rule—but, thanks to its joints, it also carries out some of the functions performed by bones in the vertebrate skeleton. Many vertebrate muscles run from bone to bone and by contracting produce movement in arms, legs, jaws, and so on. Arthropod muscles are fastened to skin, which generally is firmly attached to the crust-like exoskeleton. When muscles running from segment to segment contract, they produce movements as rapid and precise as those of most vertebrates.

Molting and the Fossil Record. In two respects, however, a crust is inferior to bones or even to ordinary shells. It is much less flexible than the former; no combination of arthropod organs can produce the variety of movements achieved by the vertebrate arm and hand. Once formed and hardened, the crust also is fixed; it cannot increase in size day by day as its owner grows. The developing arthropod must crowd more and more body into its casing until skin finally separates from crust, the latter splits, and its maker struggles out in a thin, soft covering. Then the body swells, the exoskeleton thickens, and the animal is again in an unyielding crust.

This process of shedding the crust, called molting or ecdysis, takes place four to ten times in many arthropods and as many as thirty times in long-lived, ever-growing types such as lobsters. During early growth, molting also may be accompanied by radical changes in appearance and structure. Young crabs, for example, begin life as tiny, spiny drifters and go through shrimp-like stages before reaching their final form. After that, molting means little except increase in size. Insects, on the other hand, stop growing when they achieve their final form.

Ancient arthropods also molted and changed, or metamorphosed. This vastly increased the number of fossils, for castoff crusts were almost as durable as dead bodies. Thus one animal, with good luck, might leave several fossils, ranging from fragments to perfect exoskeletons. When castoff crusts show progressive changes in shape and structure, they reveal the development of species and larger groups.

LINKS BETWEEN ARTHROPODS AND WORMS

The record of arthropods begins in Eozoic strata of Glacier National Park, Montana, and in South Australia, whence came the very imperfect fossils mentioned in Chapter IV. *Xenusion,* from a glacial boulder found in North Germany, probably is much older but is not a true arthropod. It is generally placed in the Onychophora, a phylum or subphylum of wormlike creatures that seem to be offspring of annelid worms. They lack annelid segmentation, retain wormlike bodies, and have legs that are not yet jointed. Some books call them pararthropods, or "almost arthropods."

Modern onychophores creep in damp tropical or subtropical forests, but *Xenusion* was marine. So was *Aysheia* of the Burgess shale, a wormlike creature with twenty wrinkled legs that ended in claws, and with rings of bristles around its body. The head had one pair of branched antennae and two other projections that probably secreted ill-tasting slime when the creature was attacked. All in all, *Aysheia* was so close to modern onychophores that the latter appear as "living fossils" that apparently have found refuge in surroundings very different from those in which they evolved.

Arthropleura, though a true arthropod, is another primitive creature that lived beyond its time. It had a rather simple head, twenty-nine segments, and a diminutive tail. The exoskeleton covered head, tail, and body segments, each of which carried one pair of jointed legs that divided into two. *Arthropleura* apparently inhabited moist lowlands or swamps, for its remains are found in coal-bearing Pennsylvanian formations from England to Czechoslovakia. The largest species was 5 feet long and must have looked like a huge, broad-bodied centipede.

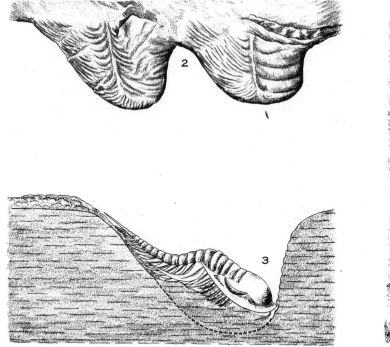
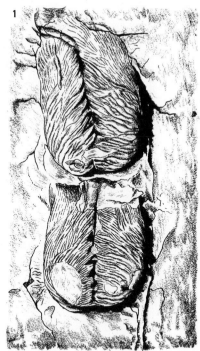

1. *Fillings of two pits apparently dug by an early Cambrian species of Olenellus.* **2.** *Side view of the fillings.* **3.** *restoration of the trilobite digging. The pits seem to have been dug to hold eggs.*

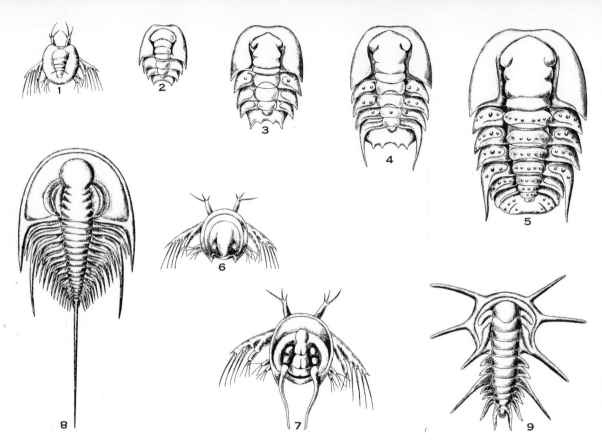

How trilobites changed as they grew. **1–5.** *Stages in the development of Shumardia pusilla (Sars), enlarged 40 times. The appendages have been restored in Stage 1. Although Stage 5 is only half the adult size, it has most of the adult characters.* **6–7.** *Two early stages of Paedumias transitans Walcott, enlarged 20 times, with appendages restored;* **8** *is an adult of this species, natural size.* **9.** *An immature stage of Olenelloides armatus Peach, showing spines on the cephalon. Enlarged about 7 times*

THREE-LOBED BODIES; THE TRILOBITES

Though onychophores and arthropleurids took to land, they did not become abundant. Another group remained in the sea and there produced a bewildering array of families, genera, and species. For almost 300,000,000 years its members were the most plentiful and successful of arthropods.

We call these creatures the Trilobita, or trilobites, a name that means "three-lobed ones." It might be interpreted in terms of a three-part plan that seems to consist of head, body, and tail. The name actually refers to portions that run lengthwise and are separated by furrows, not joints. These grooves divide every trilobite into an axial lobe in the middle and two pleurae—one at each side of the body.

Current theory makes trilobites the descendants of very ancient annelid worms in which the head increased in size by absorbing segments behind it, while the body spread broadly by developing pleurae on both sides of the original segments. On this basis, the most primitive genus of trilobites now known is *Olenellus,* which was discovered in early Cambrian shales of Georgia Center, Vermont, but ranges westward to Nevada and British Columbia. The most primitive species is *O. vermontanus,* a flattened creature with a broad head and spiny segments that are narrowest and most like those of annelids at the hinder part of the body. A spine on the axial lobe of the fifteenth segment extends back to the buttonlike "tail."

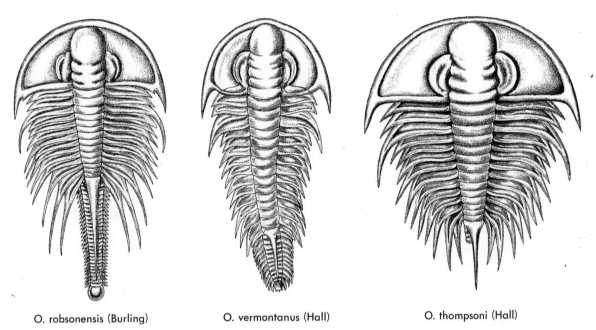

O. robsonensis (Burling)   O. vermontanus (Hall)   O. thompsoni (Hall)

Three species of Olenellus, showing reduction in number of segments after the one with a long spine

Olenellus is old, unprogressive, and none too well preserved. Other genera, more advanced as well as better fossils, enable us to review the anatomy of trilobites and trace some of their most significant changes.

Cephalon. This structure, which is much more than a head, contains six segments that are fused into a single continuous shield. In *Olenellus* it suggests a half moon, with curved margins that extend toward the rear in two genal spines. In other genera it varies so greatly that even pictures can indicate only a few of its shapes. The most bizarre probably is that of the spiny *Terataspis,* though the rounded *Bumastus* also shows an extreme type of specialization.

Like the rest of the trilobite body, the typical cephalon shows three longitudinal lobes: the glabella and the lateral cheeks. Lines or grooves, the facial sutures, divide the fixed cheeks from the free ones. In *Olenellus* and other primitive genera, the sutures follow or even lie below the edge of the cephalon. Migrations to the upper surface of the shield and back again are discussed in connection with classification.

The glabella of *Olenellus* is a raised area that ends in a swollen bulb. Paired grooves at each side are all that remains of joints between segments in the cephalon. The grooves deepened in some later genera but became shallow or even disappeared from others. The glabella itself also changed shape, becoming narrow in some trilobites but very broad and high in others.

The under side of the cephalon seldom shows plainly in fossils. When it does, it reveals a mouth, four pairs of legs, and bases of two jointed antennae. The mouth leads to a stomach that is largest under the glabella and tapers into an intestine running back to the pygidium. Exceptionally well preserved specimens show a simple heart above and behind the stomach. It apparently pumped watery blood into a segmented vessel running through the axial lobe. A "lip" plate (hypostome) lying in front of the mouth is sometimes found as a separate fossil.

Eyes. The primitive trilobite eye is a blunt, raised crescent containing many cups that were lined with sensitive cells, all covered with a clear visual area, or cornea, that is smooth or grooved between the cups. At first the number of these was not large, but in some genera it increased to 12,000 or even 15,000. Others reversed this trend, reducing the number of facets to 600, 200, or as few as fourteen.

Still more extreme was the complete loss of compound eyes, which might or might not be accompanied by the development of two or more new simple eyes on the free cheeks. This trend is seen in *Paraharpes* and some other members of the order to which it belongs.

Eyes differ almost as much in shape as they do in structure. Simple eyes are mere dots or granules. Compound eyes form crescents, lenticular elevations, knobs, or hemispheres at the ends of immovable stalks. A few small genera have relatively huge convex eyes that were able to look downward and to the rear as well as forward, upward, and sidewise.

Thorax. The primitive trilobite thorax contains at least forty-four segments, fourteen or fifteen of which bear broad and well-defined pleural lobes that end in backwardly directed spines. The number of thoracic segments was consistently reduced; even some species of *Olenellus* got along with only eighteen to twenty. The ultimate in reduction was reached by agnostids, whose thoracic segments were very small and numbered only two.

Thoracic segments were reduced both by loss and by fusion into the pygidium. The latter is shown by such genera as *Ogygopsis* and *Trimerus,* whose pygidia contain many segments fused to form a single plate. In *Arctinurus* these segments still keep the spiny tips of their lateral lobes.

Zacanthoides also has spines that once were the tips of free segments, but

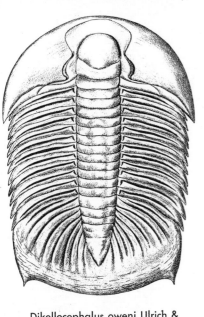

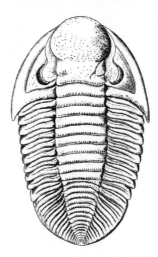

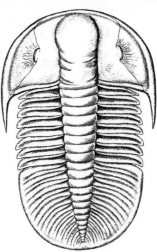

Griffithides bufo (M. & W.), 1.3 inches long. Mississippian (Keokuk), Indiana

Ogygopsis klotzi Rominger, 3.5 inches long. Middle Cambrian, British Columbia

Dikellocephalus oweni Ulrich & Resser, natural size. Late Cambrian, Wisconsin

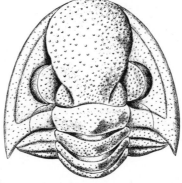

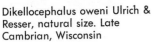

Phillipsia sampsoni Vogdes, cephalon enlarged. Early Mississippian, Missouri

Kaskia chesterensis W. & W., x 4. Mississippian, Pennsylvania to Oklahoma

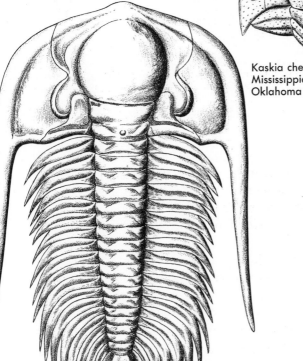

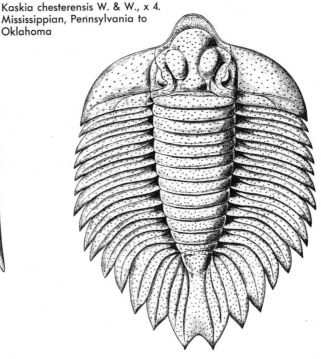

Paradoxides harlani Green, natural size. Middle Cambrian, Massachusetts

Arctinurus boltoni (Bigsby), 5 to 6 inches long. Middle Silurian, New York

Some typical trilobites

Pagetia bootes Walcott.
A mid-Cambrian eodiscid,
x 5. British Columbia

Eodiscus punctatus Salter.
A mid-Cambrian eodiscid,
x 5. Newfoundland

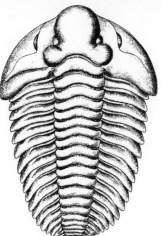

Calymene platys Green.
Middle Devonian, New
York and Indiana

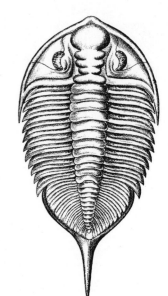

Flexicalymene meeki (Foerste).
Late Ordovician, central and
eastern North America

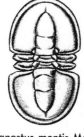

Agnostus montis Matthew.
A mid-Cambrian agnostid,
x 5. British Columbia

Hypagnostus metisensis
Rasetti, x 5. A mid-Cambrian
agnostid from Quebec

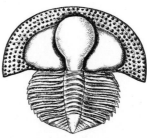

Cryptolithus bellulus (Ulrich).
Mid-Ordovician, central and
eastern United States

Dalmanites limulurus (Green).
Middle Silurian (Niagaran),
eastern United States

Some typical trilobites

our interest centers on segment number eight. Here is a long axial spine that seems to match that on the fifteenth segment of *Olenellus*. If it does, seven segments have disappeared from the anterior part of the thorax. *Redlichia* has lost only five, but no one can tell how many have vanished from species lacking the medial spine.

Several other trilobites kept eight to thirteen thoracic segments but lost all except the faintest traces of division into lobes. *Trimerus* and *Bumastus* are good examples of this trend.

Antennae and Legs. Most fossil trilobites have lost their appendages, but a few specimens retain them. They begin with two jointed antennae that are attached at each side of the hypostome. During life the antennae probably carried small organs of taste and smell, as do the antennae of modern lobsters.

The jointed legs are borne in pairs on the under side of the cephalon, thorax, and pygidium, if the last contains several segments. Each leg divides into a lower branch (endopodite), which was used in walking, and an upper branch (pre-epipodite) with feathery gills, which both breathed oxygen and served as oars for swimming. Though some authorities think trilobites swam upside down, they probably maintained a normal position that allowed them to walk without turning over.

Pygidium. This structure, which may look like a tail, really is the hindmost part of the thoracic region, since it contains part of the intestinal canal and the anus. The pygidium is very small in primitive genera, such as *Olenellus,* but in other early Cambrian forms it has grown by incorporating three or more thoracic segments. This process continued during middle Cambrian and later epochs, until some pygidia became as large as the cephalon and contained eighteen or more segments. The under surface of such pygidia bore some of the legs of segments that had been absorbed.

Many pygidia, as we have just seen, bear grooves marking the segments they have absorbed, as well as other grooves that once ran across the pleurae. In some genera these grooves remained deep and distinct; in others they became indistinct and finally disappeared. In still other genera some grooves were lost and others were kept, and those on pleural lobes of the pygidium do not match grooves of its axial lobe. There seems to be too little room for complete and matching series.

From Egg to Adult. Trilobites must have laid eggs, as most arthropods do today. Having no pouches or other means of carrying her eggs, the female probably left them in some sheltered spot. Filled pits of early Cambrian age suggest that *Olenellus* dug a hole, laid eggs in it, and then went away, leaving the "nest" to be filled by drifting sand. If that is true, the male probably followed the female and waited beside her, ready to fertilize the ova as soon as they were laid. Sand washed into the "nests" was loose enough to let water reach the eggs and provide them with oxygen, and to let newly hatched young escape. At the same time, sand hid the eggs from scavengers and predators, including other trilobites.

Silicified fossils dissolved from limestone trace the development of several trilobites. During the first stage there were only six segments—the same six that were fused to form the cephalon. In the second stage some thoracic segments were added; in the third the pygidium appeared. In the fourth stage the larva possessed the structures it would have as an adult, though it still had to grow and make substantial changes in proportions. These four stages are termed *anaprotaspis, metaprotaspis, meraspis,* and *holaspis*—fine Greek terms for creatures that lived, grew, and died out as much as a half billion years ago.

In one respect all trilobite larvae are deceptive; they lack appendages. Comparison with modern arthropods leaves no doubt that larval trilobites had branched, spiny legs that were used in swimming. These organs have been added to most of our illustrations of trilobite larvae.

At the left, an Arctinurus walks on a muddy sea bottom. At the right, a second Arctinurus is molting and is partly out of its "shell."

SUTURES, MOLTING, AND CLASSIFICATION

Among most trilobites the facial sutures were vitally important in molting, since they formed lines of weakness along which the exoskeleton could break. The gap was wide if the suture was marginal, meaning that it lay at the edge of the cephalon. The gap narrowed as the free cheeks came closer and closer to the glabella. There must have been a great deal of wriggling, twisting, and squeezing before such animals as *Arctinurus* pulled themselves out of their armor. The process probably was carried on amid corals or under sheltering seaweeds, where the "soft-shelled" trilobite could hide while building its new skin-crust.

We say that facial sutures were important to *most* trilobites, because one order lacks them. There also are genera, such as *Acidaspis,* in which the sutures are too faint to be seen. They could hardly have had much value when the molting season arrived.

Protoparia. Facial sutures also help to distinguish five of the six orders into which trilobites are generally divided. The most primitive and oldest are the protoparians, which include the early Cambrian *Olenellus.* Typical protoparians have large cephalons with crescent-shaped eyes, long genal spines, and marginal sutures. The last feature means that the free cheeks are narrow,

Protoparia

Proparia

Opisthoparia

Hypoparia

Position of the facial suture in four orders of trilobites. Sutures are marked by heavy lines.

curved affairs on the under side of the head. There are as many as forty-four thoracic segments, and the pygidium is small. In *Olenellus* the fifteenth thoracic segment bears a very long medial spine and is followed by as many as twenty-nine short and relatively narrow segments that commonly are missing from fossils. In *Paedumias* the spine is almost as long as the rest of the animal; *Elliptocephala* has spines on the fifteenth to nineteenth segment.

Early specimens of *Olenellus* lacked segments behind number fifteen, which was called a telson and was regarded as a highly specialized tail. Complete specimens (which belonged to other species) were called *Mesonacis,* and many years passed before the two were finally associated. Since *Olenellus* is the older name, *Mesonacis* has been discarded.

Holmia has axial spines on thirteen thoracic segments, but the last one is not very long and there are only a few segments behind it. In *Wanneria* the last two medial spines are missing, and all have disappeared from *Nevadia,* a relatively advanced genus.

Proparia. These trilobites appeared in mid-Cambrian times and lived to the end of the Devonian. They are more compact than protoparians, with larger pygidia, fewer thoracic segments, and cephalons that may or may not end in spines. The eyes are relatively large, and the glabellae tend to swell into bulbs that may be covered with knoblike pustules. The facial suture swings upward on each side of the glabella, curves along at the upper edge of each eye, and then curves back to the margin again. This leaves the visual part of the eye attached to the free cheek.

One of the best-known proparians, *Phacops rana,* is common in middle Devonian rocks of the eastern and southern United States. *Dalmanites,* a Silurian genus, has a spine at the end of the pygidium and may have another extending forward from the cephalon. The pygidial spine is a new structure, quite different from the axial spines of *Olenellus* and *Paedumias.*

Opisthoparia. Though less ancient than *Olenellus* and its kin, opisthoparians appeared during early Cambrian times and survived to the end of the Paleozoic. In them the facial suture may be marginal at the forward end or it may appear on the upper surface of the cephalon. In either case, it runs to the posterior edge of that structure, so that the genal spines as well as the eyes are parts of the free cheeks.

Opisthoparians are the largest and most varied of trilobite orders. Early genera, such as *Paradoxides,* closely resemble such protoparians as *Holmia;* later types specialized in various ways. *Isotelus,* for example, became smooth and reduced the number of its thoracic segments by adding them to its "tail"; some species reached lengths of 30 inches, which made them the largest of all known trilobites. Other opisthoparians developed thick, rough crusts, became broad and almost flat, or possessed bulbous cephalons and pygidia. Some genera had long medial spines suggesting those of *Olenellus,* though thoraxes were shortened so much that the spines appeared on the eighth or ninth segment and were followed by only one segment plus pygidium. Other genera bore a bristling array of entirely new spines.

Hypoparia. In this specialized order the cephalon developed a broad, pitted border (the fringe) and the facial sutures returned to the margin, though deep indentations or loops might extend to the dorsal surface. The compound eyes degenerated or were lost, though simple eyes with one lens appeared in several genera. Thoracic segments were as few as six or seven or as many as

A group of Isotelus gigas DeKay in limestone. Ordovician (Trenton), Trenton Falls, New York. The fossils are about 3 inches long.

twenty-eight to thirty-two. Hypoparians appeared in the early Ordovician and died out long before the Devonian period closed.

Eodiscida. These are tiny trilobites 6 to 8 millimeters long whose facial sutures are proparian or marginal, whose eyes are small or more generally are lacking, and whose thoracic segments number only two or three. Both cephalon and pygidium are relatively large. Some genera are spiny. Eodiscids are limited to early and middle Cambrian deposits.

Agnostida. These minute creatures range from early Cambrian to late Ordovician. They lack eyes, have marginal facial sutures, and possess only two thoracic segments. In shape they resemble eodiscids, but they are so different from most trilobites that a few authors place them in a separate class. Excellent specimens are common in the Burgess shale.

Trilobites must have been in existence during a large portion of the Eozoic era, since three very different orders were well established at the dawn of the Cambrian. There is little doubt that opisthoparians also evolved during the Eozoic era, and proparians may be equally ancient. This leaves only the bizarre hypoparians as products of Paleozoic evolution, probably during the latter half of the Cambrian period.

HABITS AND ADAPTATIONS

All trilobites were marine; so far as we know, they did not even venture into brackish estuaries. But within their one environment they swam at the surface or below it, crawled or skimmed over the bottom, lay upon it, and plowed through sand or mud. Many small species burrowed into rubbish, which also provided them with food.

The Ways of Olenellus. Since elongate species of *Olenellus* are primitive, they provide the basic point of departure for other trilobite habits and adaptations. The newly hatched *Olenellus* was a tiny rounded creature that undoubtedly drifted by means of hairlike appendages. It continued to do so during the meraspid stage, but with holaspid life it settled down to bottom-dwelling existence under shallow water and often near the shores of seas.

Though *Olenellus* ranged across North America, there is no better place to study its habits than the valley containing Lake Louise, in western Alberta. There, at the foot of ice-hung cliffs, talus slopes include slabs of lower Cambrian quartzite and dark, micaceous shale. The latter contains crusts and impressions of trilobites, while the former is rich in traces of their activities.

Olenellus was able to swim with its gills or crawl with its endopodites. When swimming it left no trail, but in crawling the jointed endopodites dug into the sand, while spines on the cephalon and thoracic segments occasionally cut sharp furrows. Some of the trails so made became fossils, and so did pits bearing marks of endopodites and spines. Some of those pits were shallow and irregular; they apparently were dug for food, which consisted of small, soft-bodied burrowing worms.

A Variety of Crawlers. Crawling remained the dominant mode of trilobite travel, yet the shapes and sizes of crawlers changed greatly. *Olenellus vermontanus* was long and narow, but the width of *O. thompsoni* almost equalled its length. Middle Cambrian and later times saw the development of many broad, depressed crawlers. Some, such as *Paradoxides,* had small pygidia and many thoracic segments; in others (*Dikellocephalus* and *Eobronteus* are examples) the thorax was reduced and the pygidium large. *Arctinurus,* of the Silurian, combined a very short, broad cephalon that ended in a snout with an exceedingly wide thorax. The snout suggests that *Arctinurus* plowed into drifts of dead animals and plants, either to feed upon them or to capture small animals that did so. The bladelike segments and pygidial sections may have provided a camouflage that made *Arctinurus* blend with dead plants.

From the middle Cambrian onward, the dominant trend among crawling trilobites was toward smaller and more compact crusts that also became thick and strong. Many genera also developed the power to roll up when danger threatened, tucking pygidium under cephalon or—if they were equal—bringing the two together. Thus the relatively weak under surface was hidden while the carapace served as a coat of armor.

Plowers in Mud. Both *Asaphus* and *Dalmanites* had eyes that were raised high above the free cheeks, which may mean that they plowed into mud and decaying litter on the bottom instead of crawling over it and pausing now and then to dig. *Dalmanites* probably used the spine on its pygidium to right itself when some accident turned it onto its back.

Cryptolithus and *Paraharpes* are small hypoparians whose broad fringes spread far beyond the rest of the body when they were enrolled. When feeding they apparently plowed through mud and rubbish, with their fringes push-

A cluster of Phacops rana Green on a limestone nodule found in shale. Middle Devonian (Hamilton), New York. The trilobites are about 1.25 inches long.

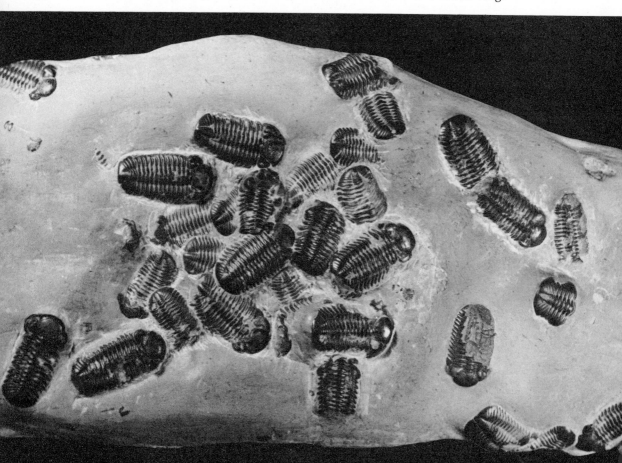

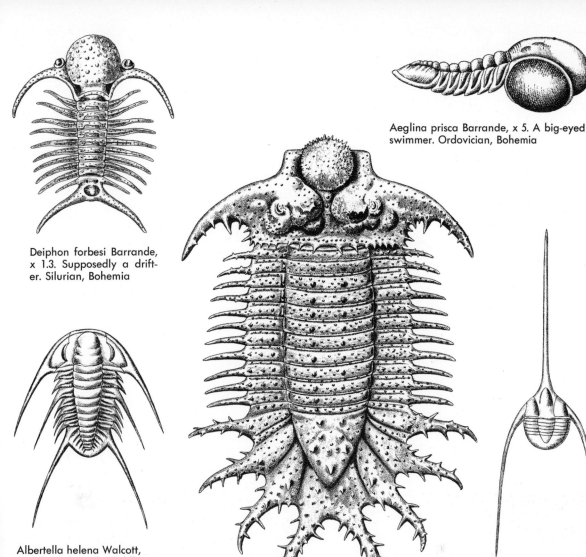

Aeglina prisca Barrande, x 5. A big-eyed swimmer. Ordovician, Bohemia

Deiphon forbesi Barrande, x 1.3. Supposedly a drifter. Silurian, Bohemia

Albertella helena Walcott, slightly enlarged. Middle Cambrian, northern Rockies

Terataspis grandis (Hall), about 18 inches long. Apparently a crawler. Middle Devonian (Onondagan), New York

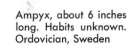

Ampyx, about 6 inches long. Habits unknown. Ordovician, Sweden

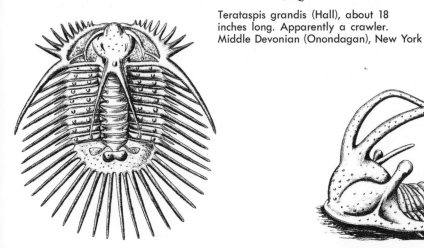

Radiaspis radiata (Goldfuss), 1 inch long. A drifter. Devonian, Germany

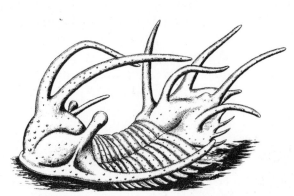

Ceratarges armatus (Goldfuss), 1.5 inches long. Probably a crawler. Middle Devonian, Germany

Six spiny trilobites and a smooth swimmer

A variety of bottom-dwelling trilobites. Trimerus **(1)** *and Ectenaspis* **(2)** *dug their pygidia into the mud and lay in wait for dead food. Bumastus* **(3)** *plowed through the mud and Paraharpes* **(4)** *crept upon it. Flexicalymene* **(5)** *could crawl or swim but rolled up when danger threatened.*

ing both aside much as a snowplow moves snow. The degenerate eyes of hypoparians were no obstacle to this sort of life.

Bumastus and *Illaenus* (both opisthoparians) were much larger, with smooth pygidia and cephalons, and compound eyes that were carried well above rubbish and mud. The animals probably were crawlers that plowed into the bottom only when they were feeding. If the pygidium was thrust into the mud, it provided leverage for thrusting movements of the thorax and cephalon.

Isotelus and its kin may have crawled, but their broad pygidia could dig into the mud, providing leverage for plowing. The long-snouted *Ectenaspis* went much further, for the position of well-preserved fossils shows that it dug tail-first into soft bottoms and lay with only its head at the surface. There it was ready to capture tiny crawlers or dead bodies as they drifted by.

Burrowers. Both eodiscids and agnostids apparently were burrowers. Their small, smooth shells indicate this, and so does degeneration or loss of eyes. In the Burgess shale, moreover, these small trilobites are most abundant and well preserved in drifts of organic fragments. This suggests that the trilobites burrowed into those drifts and there ate what they could find.

Swimmers and Drifters. Free-swimming trilobites are typified by *Aeglina,* the genus with enormous eyes that could see in all directions. The term *enormous* is relative, however; though the eyes are huge in proportion to the body, a full-grown *Aeglina* was less than a half inch long. Some authorities believe that this creature hid during the day and came out at night, making its own light with round organs on its upper surface.

Drifting, or planktonic, trilobites lived in ancient sargasso seas of both North America and Europe. A sargasso sea is one in which seaweeds and other branched organisms float about, providing shelter for fish and a variety of invertebrates. Many of the latter possess long spines which offer resistance to currents and so enable the creatures to float.

Such spines appear on meraspid larvae of *Olenelloides* and adults of *Olenellus fremonti,* both of the early Cambrian. More elaborate, however, are *Deiphon, Radiaspis,* and other genera of Ordovician to Devonian age. Some bear spines upon bodies of normal shape; in others the body is little more than a framework of spines. Among the strangest was the eyeless *Ampyx,* whose cephalon bore three spines that were five times as long as the body. *Ampyx* could hardly have crawled and surely did not burrow. But as a planktonic drifter, how did it get along without eyes?

Trilobite Giants. *Agnostus* is only one fourth of an inch long, and the majority of trilobites are three fourths of an inch to 3 inches in length. Some forms, however, became larger and a few outstripped their relatives so much that we may call them giants.

The first giant was *Paradoxides harlani,* found in early Cambrian strata of Massachusetts; it reached a length of 19 inches, and its cephalon was almost 12 inches wide. The next giant was *Isotelus,* which reached lengths of 27 to 30 inches. More spectacular, however, were *Uralichas* and *Terataspis,* both of which had ornate crusts. The latter, which reached lengths of 19 to perhaps 27 inches, also was the spiniest of all large trilobites.

PROBLEMATIC CAMBRIAN ARTHROPODS

Cambrian formations of Europe, North America, and China contain a variety of arthropods once called crustaceans. A few may actually belong in that class, but the rest seem to be less advanced creatures whose closest relationships seem to be with trilobites. The largest numbers, both of specimens and of species, are found in the Burgess shale.

Hymenocaris, which ranges from British Columbia to Europe, has two pairs of antennae, a jointed thorax that bears eleven pairs of legs, and an abdominal region that lacks them. The thorax is covered by a thin, smooth bivalve shell which is one of the commonest Burgess fossils. It can be readily distinguished from *Tuzoia,* which is larger, has a reticulate surface and a straight upper margin, and generally possesses spines.

Marrella, often called the lace crab, has a very narrow thorax, four very large spines, and many gill-bearing legs. It has been regarded as a newly molted trilobite, but this interpretation seems to be ruled out by two pairs of feathery antennae. Despite its delicate, lacy appearance, *Marrella* also is common in the Burgess shale.

Sidneyia is about 5 inches wide, with a very broad cephalothorax and body, a finlike telson, and feathery antennae. If large, jointed pincers found near it belong to this creature, it probably was an active predator, though the pincers were not nearly so strong as those of a crayfish or lobster.

CHAPTER XVIII

Crustaceans

Trilobites remind us of crayfish, lobsters, and even crabs, for all three have jointed exoskeletons and legs that mark them as arthropods. Yet they belong to different branches of that phylum, for crayfish, lobsters, and crabs are crustaceans—a class that also includes shrimps, barnacles, and several less familiar creatures. Though most of them live in salt or fresh water, a few make their homes on land and some have become parasites.

VARIED CRUSTACEANS

Some authorities call crustaceans a class; others make them a subphylum. The animals, however, do not change; all are distinguished from trilobites by two pairs of antennae—not one—and by three pairs of legs that have become specialized into organs that chew food and push it into the mouth. Though these structures seldom appear in fossils, the latter generally show that the body consists of head, thorax, and abdomen, though the first two commonly are united in the cephalothorax.

Branchiopoda. These creatures, whose name means "gill-feet," are the most primitive crustaceans. Like primitive trilobites, they have a large number of body segments; the jointed legs, which also are numerous, carry gills and are used for both breathing and swimming. At the bottom of the scale stand fairy shrimps and brine shrimps, small creatures with distinct head, stalked eyes, and segmented thorax that is not covered with armor. Modern members of this group, the anostracans, live in normal seas, briny lagoons or salt lakes, and in fresh-water pools fed by rain or melting snow. One Oligocene genus, which lived in lakes, is almost identical with the fairy shrimps of modern fresh-water pools. Fairy shrimps also were abundant in the lake inhabited by Miocene arthropods of the Mojave Desert.

232

Notostracans are more progressive, for they cover the head and thorax with a carapace. The best-known genus, *Apus,* includes Cenozoic, Mesozoic, and even Permian species. Fossils that seem to be closely related have been found in Cambrian rocks. A few specimens preserve traces of a gland that secreted the carapace.

Conchostracans also range from the Cambrian to Recent. They cover their bodies with bivalved shells and so look like small clams unless their gill-bearing legs and antennae can be seen. Some fossil members of this order were marine, but others are found in fresh-water deposits. Several species of *Cyzicus* and related genera, all formerly called *Estheria,* occur in Devonian and later formations and are plentiful in modern ponds. Vast numbers of *Cyzicus* shells were found in fresh-water shales of Triassic age at Princeton, New Jersey. These shale beds also contained many skeletons of the small, bony fish *Diplurus,* which is described in Chapter XXI.

Ostracodes. These crustaceans also have bivalve shells, but their bodies are shorter than those of branchiopods and they have only four legs. The four antennae are used for crawling, swimming and digging; males also employ the first pair to clasp females during mating. Most species have only one eye, though some have two compound eyes. The valves are hinged and overlap. Most species are 0.5 to 4 millimeters long, though one modern form reaches a length of 10 millimeters and some fossils exceeded 20.

Modern ostracodes live in seas, brackish bays, and fresh water, where they swim, crawl, cling to plants, or burrow in mud. Their food consists of algae and diatoms as well as living and dead animals. One fossil sea scorpion (Chapter XIX) contains hundreds of shells of ostracodes that apparently were trapped and covered with mud while they were feeding inside its shell. The sea scorpion had not dined on ostracodes, for shells of the latter are not broken. They also are found in legs as well as in parts of the scorpion's body that once contained the digestive system.

Ostracodes molt, like all other arthropods; some species did so eight times before reaching their final shape and size. Most fossils consist only of valves whose proper position is determined by muscle scars. In general, the thin end is forward and the thick is to the rear, toward which spines and other elevations are directed.

Ostracodes appeared in early Ordovician seas and have been plentiful ever since. Some had smooth shells, but others were marked by ridges, knobs, pits, and furrows, all of which are used in identification. Since many species spread widely but did not live very long, they make excellent index fossils.

Barnacles, or Cirripeds. Until 1830, barnacles were regarded as mollusks, since most of them have thick calcareous shells. Then they were found to be crustaceans that swim or drift about while they are young. After molting one to three times they develop shells much like those of ostracodes; then they settle down on their heads, lose their bivalved shells, and secrete others made up of plates that overlap or are held together by tough skin. Food is brought to the mouth by branched, fringed legs that resemble curved feathers, explaining the group's technical name of Cirripedia, or "fringe-feet." The legs sweep to and fro with rhythmic movements, catching food which then is raked off by comblike organs near the mouth. The statement that the legs produce currents that take food into the mouth has been proved to be an error.

The early history of barnacles is a puzzle. Some authorities say they appeared in Ordovician seas as elongate creatures with alternating plates, and the general look of small, flattened cones. But two British authorities have placed these fossils among the echinoderms. If they are right, the oldest known cirripede is *Hercolepas* from the Silurian, an acorn barnacle. Acorn barnacles got their name from their shape, which is rounded or conical unless they are closely crowded. They have no stalk, and the plates that cover their bodies are firmly cemented, though those that close the shell are freely movable. Excellent specimens are found in some Mesozoic and Cenozoic deposits.

Goose barnacles are so called because they once were supposed to produce young wild geese. Modern species are attached by long stalks that are either scaly or naked, but some fossil genera have short stalks that are completely covered by plates. Plates on the body are separate and movable, being held together by leathery skin. Because of this, fossils generally consist of separate plates. They are limited to Mesozoic and Cenozoic formations.

HARD "SOFT-SHELLS," OR MALACOSTRACA

Branchiopods are the oldest crustaceans, ostracodes are those most abundant as fossils, and barnacles are the most specialized. But malacostracans are the most familiar and the ones we first think of when crustaceans are mentioned.

Malacostraca ("soft-shells") is a poor name for these animals, since it fits them only during short periods that immediately follow molting. At other times most malacostracans are well armored in shells that consist of tough chitin or of chitin hardened and thickened with limy material.

The history of malacostracans, like that of barnacles, is subject to doubt and argument. Before 1935 they were thought to have arisen as small creatures with two wrinkled valves whose fossils are found in early Cambrian rocks of eastern Canada and are named *Bradoria*. These remains and many others then were moved into another group whose members supposedly are not even crustaceans. This made Devonian pill bugs the oldest known malacostracans, though not the most primitive. Some experts now think *Bradoria* should be returned to its original position. If they are right, it takes the history of this group back through the Silurian, Ordovician, and Cambrian periods, almost to the beginning of Paleozoic time.

Bradoria robusta (Matthew),
x 8. An archaeostracan

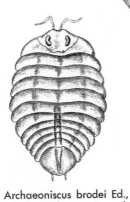

Archaeoniscus brodei Ed.,
x 3. A sow bug, or isopod.
Late Jurassic, England

Caryocaris curvilata Gurley, x 4.
An early malacostracan. Ordovician (graptolite shales), widespread in North America

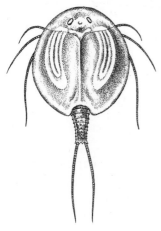

Apus beedei Ruedemann, x 2.
A branchiopod, restored.
Permian (Enid), Oklahoma

Echinocaris punctata (Hall).
A malacostracan, x 1. Middle
to late Devonian, eastern
United States

Mesothyra oceani Hall, x 0.5.
A malacostracan. Late Devonian, New York

Cyzicus ortoni (Clarke), x 10.
A branchiopod, restored. Late
Pennsylvanian, Ohio

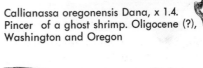

Callianassa oregonensis Dana, x 1.4.
Pincer of a ghost shrimp. Oligocene (?),
Washington and Oregon

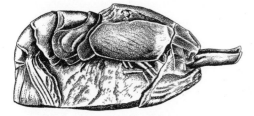

Palaeopalaemon newberryi Whitfield, x 2.
A crayfish-like malacostracan. Late
Devonian of Ohio; early Mississippian
of Iowa

Callianassa mortoni Pilsbry, x 0.75.
Pincer of ghost shrimp. Late Cretaceous,
Coastal Plain from New Jersey
to Texas

Varied crustaceans

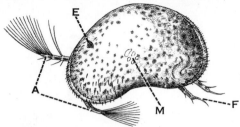

Cypris, a modern ostracod, enlarged. *E*, eye; *A*, antennae, *M*, muscle scars, *F*, foot.

Loxoconcha claibornensis Murray, x 15. Exterior and interior. Eocene (Claiborne), Alabama

Leperditia fabulites (Conrad), x 2. Middle Ordovician, eastern North America

Cytheretta burnsi (Ulrich & Bassler), x 25. Miocene, Virginia, Florida, and Alabama

Ranapeltis trilateralis S. & S., x 30. Devonian (Onondaga), Pennsylvania

Kirkbyella bellipuncta (Van Pelt), x 16. Middle Devonian, central U.S.A.

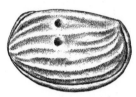

Glyptopleura alvea Cooper, x 30. Mississippian (Chester), Illinois

Hollinella kolmodini (Jones), x 20. Middle Devonian, Ohio Valley

Paraechmina spinosa (Hall), x 20. Middle Silurian, Ontario to Maryland

Kloedenia ventralis (U. & B.), x 20. Late Silurian, Appalachian Mts.

Cytherura cretacea Alex., x 120. Late Cretaceous, Texas

Cytheropteron navarroense Alexander, x 35. Late Cretaceous, Arkansas and Texas

Drepanella crassinoda Ulr., x 15. Ordovician, Virginia to Indiana

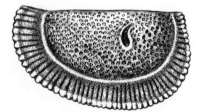

Eurychilina reticulata Ulrich, x 20. Middle Ordovician, eastern U.S.A.

Aparchites canadensis Fritz, x 30. Mid-Devonian (Onondagan), Ontario

Pyricythereis simiensis LeRoy. Pliocene, California

Some typical ostracodes

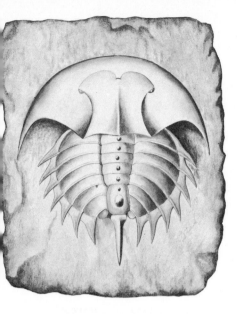

Prestwichianella danae (Meek), a fresh-water xiphosuran. Pennsylvanian, Illinois

Protabalanus hamiltonensis Whitfield, a barnacle, x 10. Middle Devonian, New York

Balanus concavus Bronn, acorn barnacles on a snail. Miocene to Recent, North America and Europe

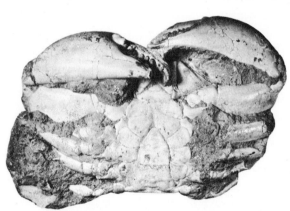

Loricula darwini Woodward, a short-stalked barnacle. Cretaceous, England

Balanus estrellanus Conrad, acorn barnacles. Pliocene, California

Lower and upper surfaces of a swimming crab. An ancestor of the modern Pacific edible crab, Cancer magister Dana. Tertiary, Panama

Panaeus speciosus Oppel, a shrimp, x 0.5. Early Jurassic, Solenhofen, Germany

Crustaceans and a xiphosuran, Prestwichianella

Decapoda. Unquestioned malacostracans include creatures that resemble *Apus,* as well as wood-borers with fourteen legs and strange parasites that live on whales. But most fossil malacostracans are decapods—crustaceans with ten ordinary legs, plus six that are specialized as food handlers, or maxillae. The thorax contains six segments that are joined with the head in an armored cephalothorax, and the eyes are on movable stalks. The abdomen generally contains six clearly marked segments and ends in a tailpiece, or telson.

Shrimps and prawns are primitive decapods, since they lack pincers and their crusts are not calcified. They are rare in Triassic formations, but many different kinds have been found in the Jurassic lithographic limestones of southern Germany. Fossils preserve exoskeleton, antennae, legs, and abdominal appendages used in swimming, along with the fanlike tail.

Ghost shrimps are not true shrimps but are related to hermit crabs. The former are thinly armored burrowers; the latter have naked abdomens which they hide in shells. Pincers of both are found in Cretaceous and Tertiary formations. One ghost shrimp, *Callianassa mortoni,* is an index fossil in late Cretaceous formations from New Jersey to Texas.

Spiny lobsters are sometimes called crayfish; modern species have prickly shells and massive antennae, and all ten legs are used for walking. Some fossils, however, have long, slim pincers; in others the forelegs are very long and the last segment is covered with hairs that seem to have been used as feelers. Most fossil spiny lobsters are found in Mesozoic rocks of Europe, choice specimens coming from the Jurassic lithographic limestones. These also contain early true lobsters (*Eryma*), less than 2 inches long, with pincers shaped like long-nosed pliers. *Astacus,* the fresh-water crayfish, has been found in Miocene and perhaps in Pliocene rocks of Idaho and eastern Oregon.

Crabs are the most modern crustaceans and are least like ancestral types. We see this in the broad, heavy carapace, the short abdomen that is bent under the thorax, the abbreviated antennae, and the lack of a tail fan. They appear in middle Jurassic strata of Europe, in genera allied to modern forms that still bear traces of relationship to crustaceans with tails. Many bizarre crabs lived in seas that covered southern Europe and northern Africa during the Eocene epoch; some (like a few modern crabs) seem to have looked like stony algae. Several genera and species of crabs are index fossils in Tertiary formations of North America, though they are much less common than mollusks. The eastern edible, or blue, crab (*Callinectes sapidus*) is found in Pleistocene deposits of Massachusetts and New Jersey. A relative of western edible crabs, *Cancer fissus,* is a Pliocene fossil of California.

CHAPTER XIX

Arthropods from Shoals to Air

T HOUGH many arthropods now live on land, earliest members of the phylum were aquatic. They apparently remained so until true land plants—not lichens—covered the continents with vegetation. It provided shelter, moisture, and a variety of foods that opened a rich new environment to creatures that could solve the problems of living in air.

The solution of these problems was a gradual and slow process. Before the Cambrian period ended, modified offspring of olenellid trilobites went into estuaries. During the Ordovician, descendants of these animals invaded streams and evolved into chelicerates, or arthropods whose antennae had vanished and whose second pair of appendages had become pincerlike jaws.

Land plants apparently appeared in middle Silurian times, which we may roughly date at 350,000,000 B.C. Before the period closed—that is, within some 25,000,000 years—land-dwelling chelicerates were becoming fossils in Sweden, Scotland, Wales, and New York. Others, not yet terrestrial, were developing features that allowed them to live in shallow, brackish water or on intertidal flats. One of their descendants can still live out of water for days, taking trips that range from a few rods to more than a half mile.

THE PERSISTENT XIPHOSURANS

This modern wanderer, the horseshoe (or king) crab, is famous as a so-called living fossil. Variously called *Limulus* and *Xiphosura*—the latter name has priority—it has survived with only minor changes since early Permian times. For some 210,000,000 years, therefore, the horseshoe crab has had a wide cephalothorax (also called the prosoma) that suggests a horse's hoof in outline and ends in genal spines. Like the cephalon of trilobites, the cephalothorax

239

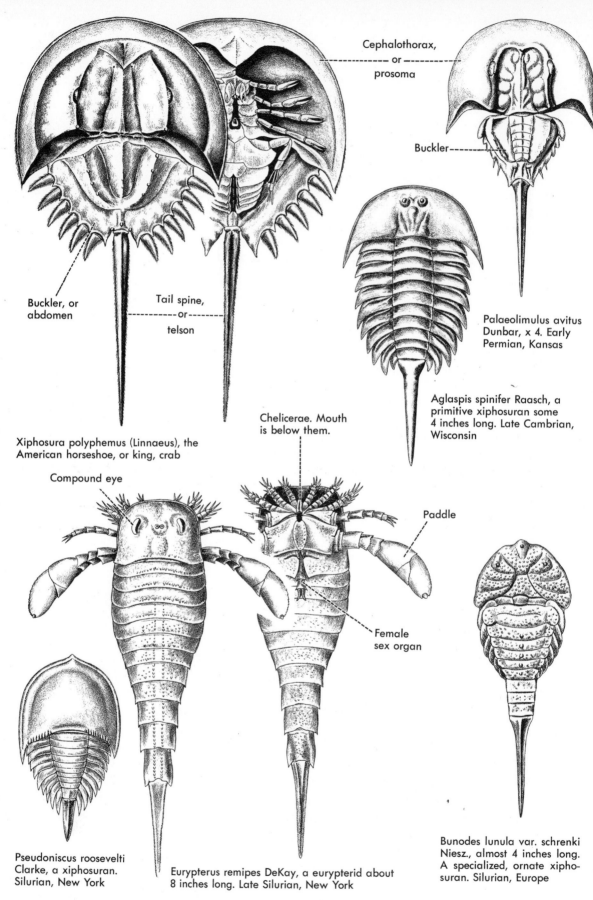

Cephalothorax,
— or —
prosoma

Buckler

Buckler, or
abdomen

Tail spine,
— or —
telson

Palaeolimulus avitus
Dunbar, x 4. Early
Permian, Kansas

Aglaspis spinifer Raasch, a
primitive xiphosuran some
4 inches long. Late Cambrian,
Wisconsin

Chelicerae. Mouth
is below them.

Xiphosura polyphemus (Linnaeus), the
American horseshoe, or king, crab

Compound eye

Paddle

Female
sex organ

Pseudoniscus roosevelti
Clarke, a xiphosuran.
Silurian, New York

Eurypterus remipes DeKay, a eurypterid about
8 inches long. Late Silurian, New York

Bunodes lunula var. schrenki
Niesz., almost 4 inches long.
A specialized, ornate xipho-
suran. Silurian, Europe

Some typical xiphosurans and eurypterids, of the subphylum Chelicerata

contains both head and visceral organs such as liver, stomach, and intestine. These continue into the spine-bordered buckler (also called the abdomen), which is followed by the telson.

There are two compound and two simple eyes; the mouth is centrally located under the cephalothorax; there are six pairs of legs but no antennae. The first two legs are chelicerae; the next eight are used for walking and are tipped with pincers; their spiny bases cut food to pieces before it enters the mouth. A sixth pair of legs is specialized pushers whose principal function is to force the creature forward through mud or sand. The under surface of the buckler bears broad appendages that are flipped to and fro when the animal swims. These appendages also are used in respiration, for they bear "gill books" made up of 150 to 200 very thin leaves through which oxygen from water passes into the blood.

The best-known horseshoe crab, *Xiphosura polyphemus,* lives along the Atlantic coast from Nova Scotia southward and on the Gulf coast of Florida. *Xiphosura* plows and digs for worms and other small creatures, often covering itself with sand. In the spring it comes to very shallow bays, where it mates and deposits its eggs. Trails are easily seen between tides, some made by single animals and some made by pairs of animals—pairs in which the smallish male clings to the telson of his larger mate. These trails may be either shallow or deep; they often wind to and fro for long distances before ending in irregular pits in which the eggs are laid.

Ancient Relatives of Horseshoe Crabs. As the young *Xiphosura* develops it molts, grows, and changes shape at a rapid rate. It also duplicates some of the stages through which the order passed during the Paleozoic. The first stage is reminiscent of *Aglaspis,* a late Cambrian animal with a relatively short cephalon, eleven body segments, and sixteen pairs of legs besides the chelicerae. Then come stages resembling later forms with fewer and fewer segments. The Silurian *Bunodes,* for example, had nine; *Belinurus* (Devonian to Pennsylvanian) possessed eight, and *Prestwichianella* (Pennsylvanian) had seven. *Palaeolimulus,* from Permian rocks of Kansas, had only the buckler, though grooves on its medial lobe are remains of six segments. The lobes themselves indicate descent from some trilobite.

Most ancient xiphosurans were marine, but *Belinurus* and *Prestwichianella* invaded brackish lagoons and even made their way into swamps. *Prestwichianella,* especially, is a rare but characteristic fossil in the Coal Age concretions of Mazon Creek, Illinois, which also contain land plants, and fresh-water fish and mollusks.

As has been said, *Xiphosura* crawls over sandy shores during the mating season. Ancient trails made by xiphosurans have been found in formations ranging from Ordovician to Cretaceous in age. Some of those from the Devonian of Pennsylvania were once regarded as amphibian footprints; others from the Triassic of New Jersey were ascribed to tiny reptiles. Most dramatic are Jurassic trails from Germany, which generally end in remains of creatures that made them. Instead of coming ashore to mate and lay eggs, the German xiphosurans were frantically trying to get back to salt water but were failing in the attempt.

Varied species of *Eurypterus* range from Ordovician to Permian of both North America and Europe. In general they remind us of slender aglaspids with blunt narrow heads, tapering abdomens without pleural spines, and exoskeletons ornamented by knobs, scales, and ridges. Typical American species range from 5 to 17 inches in length, and some are 30 inches long.

Eurypterus has five pairs of legs: four short, spiny pairs that were used for walking and one that had spread out into paddles. The chelicerae had become so small that the walking legs must have been used to hold food, but the bases of the paddles bore teeth used for chewing. Males had clasping organs on the under side; the female genital organs fitted over these claspers. Five abdominal segments had gills on the under surface, where they were covered by plates. The plates probably were used in swimming, especially if the creature turned itself over and skimmed along like a huge fairy shrimp. Still, two large compound eyes and two simple ones, all on the dorsal side of the prosoma, suggest that *Eurypterus* generally traveled with its "back," or dorsal surface, upward.

Eurypterus shows the basic plan of eurypterids. As ages passed, these creatures specialized in varied and often surprising ways. Some developed almost triangular prosomas, while the first six segments of the abdomen became very wide. Others had squarish prosomas, and the first four legs became long, with many slender spines which look as if they were nets for trapping food. An Ordovician genus misnamed *Megalograptus* became spiny and developed pincers instead of a spinelike telson.

Stylonurus combined a long telson and tapering abdomen with a rather small and very rough prosoma on which the compound eyes moved closer and closer to the center. The first two walking legs were short and spiny, the second and third pairs were long, with comblike rows of spines, and the last two pairs were still longer and bore lengthwise ridges. They also looked alike, for the legs that were paddles in other eurypterids had evolved into slender organs tipped by sharp curved claws.

Stylonurus apparently walked on its eight long legs and may have used the spiny ones to hold food, since its chelicerae were short. Silurian species were barely 5 inches long, but one from the middle Devonian of New York grew to 4 feet 6 inches. Even it did not equal *Pterygotus,* which reached lengths of 6 to 7 feet. Its compound eyes were very large, its telson had become a wide plate, and its chelicerae were long, toothed pincers so jointed that they could reach the mouth. *Pterygotus,* which could swim as well as crawl, was an active hunter and the most dangerous arthropod of late Silurian and early Devonian times.

Growth Stages and Habits. Castoff crusts show that eurypterids went through extensive metamorphoses. The very young *Stylonurus myops,* for example, was short and broad, with eyes on raised oval areas and only five

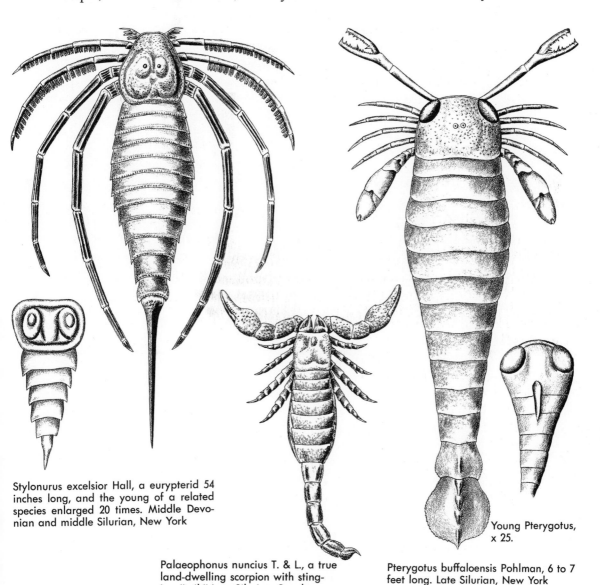

Stylonurus excelsior Hall, a eurypterid 54 inches long, and the young of a related species enlarged 20 times. Middle Devonian and middle Silurian, New York

Palaeophonus nuncius T. & L., a true land-dwelling scorpion with sting-ing "tail." Late Silurian, Sweden

Young Pterygotus, x 25.

Pterygotus buffaloensis Pohlman, 6 to 7 feet long. Late Silurian, New York

Three typical sea scorpions, or eurypterids, and a true scorpion

segments between carapace and telson. In succeeding stages, segments were added, their extremities became spinose, and the telson grew long and slender.

Early eurypterids were marine, but in Silurian times they took up life in wide lagoons or bays in which the water varied from exceedingly salty to brackish. Large numbers of young eurypterids in shaly layers at Otisville, New York, suggest that the area was a sheltered breeding place comparable to the shallow, protected bays in which *Xiphosura polyphemus* now deposits its eggs.

As time passed, more and more eurypterids moved into brackish bays, and from them into rivers and even swamps. Dead animals were buried in shales and limestones interbedded with coal, in regions as far apart as Germany, Nova Scotia, and central Illinois. *Anthraconectes,* from Pennsylvanian strata of Pennsylvania and Illinois, is a scaly form with spiny segments that is only

Eophrynus prestvici (Buckland) a Pennsylvanian spider, from England. At the right is Euphoberia armigera Meek & Worthen, a milliped about 3.5 inches long. Pennsylvanian, Grundy County, Illinois

8 to 9 inches long. It is found among plants of the swampy coal forests, in beds of shale that also contain fresh-water mussels and snails. The last eurypterids, of Permian Europe, are also associated with fossil vines and trees of swampy woodlands.

SCORPIONS AND OTHER ARACHNIDS

Scorpions look as if they had evolved from eurypterids such as *Pterygotus,* whose chelicerae had become long, powerful pincers. Actually, the scorpion's chelicerae are short and inconspicious, its pincers being the first pair of walking legs, enlarged and modified. The fifth pair of legs never forms paddles, as it does in most eurypterids. The scorpion telson also has become a sort of hypodermic needle that can inject poison produced in a large gland at its base. The respiratory organs are book lungs which take oxygen from air, not water.

These features suggest that scorpions are evolutionary nieces and nephews of eurypterids, not direct descendants. They also are respectably ancient, for fully developed specimens are found in late Silurian rocks of New York and Sweden. Other specimens come from Pennsylvanian deposits of Mazon Creek, in Grundy County, Illinois.

Spiders and Daddy Longlegs. Spiders, like scorpions, are air-breathers, though most of them use tubes that branch and run through the body. Spiders also lack pincers and their bodies are short, without telsons. In spite of these differences, both spiders and scorpions belong to one class, the Arachnida, which also includes the spiderlike harvest men, or daddy longlegs, and several other groups. Except in ticks and mites, the body is divided into a plated cephalothorax and jointed abdomen. The former bears six pairs of appendages, four pairs of which are walking legs. There are no antennae.

Both spiders and daddy longlegs are found in Pennsylvanian formations, though their fully developed form and variety indicate that they evolved long before that time. The finest fossil spiders, however, come from Miocene nodules in California and from Tertiary amber deposits in the Baltic region of Europe. The amber, which is fossil resin, reveals even minute hairs on the bodies of these arachnids.

THOUSAND-LEGS AND CENTIPEDES

Millipedes and centipedes are elongate, wormlike crawlers that form the class or subphylum of myriapods. Modern millipedes hide in the ground or under dead sticks and leaves, where they feed on decaying material or roots. They have hard, shiny exoskeletons, one pair of antennae, and two pairs of short legs on each of their many body segments. Their oldest known fossils come from late Silurian rocks of Scotland, and others are found in Pennsylvanian strata. *Euphoberia,* from Mazon Creek, is a spiny form with relatively long legs and segments that seem to divide on the under side of the body. Another form from Mazon Creek reached a length of 8 inches and ranks as the world's largest millipede.

Centipedes have only one pair of legs per segment, and those just behind the head have become poison fangs. There are undoubted centipedes in the Baltic amber, and fossils found at Mazon Creek may belong to this group.

THE AMAZINGLY SUCCESSFUL INSECTS

Insects are the largest and most successful class of arthropods; in fact, they are the most successful group in the entire animal kingdom. Not only do they live in a great variety of habitats—their 900,000 species outnumber those of all other living animals about four to one—they also exist in vast and ever-increasing abundance, which seems not to be curbed by poisons and other devices employed against them by man.

The name *insect* comes from a Latin word meaning "cut into"; it refers to the fact that the insect body is sharply divided into head, thorax, and abdomen. The head is made up of six segments, the thorax of three, and the abdomen contains as few as six or as many as eleven or twelve. Antennae number only two, six legs are attached to the thorax, and the abdomen bears none. Young, or larvae, may be aquatic and breathe with gills, but adults take air into tubes vastly more complex than those possessed by spiders. Most adult insects also have hard, chitinous exoskeletons.

Primitive Wingless Insects. We often picture insects as agile creatures, with two or four wings, that spend much of their time in flight though they may rest or hunt food on the ground. Actually, great numbers of insects are terrestrial and almost flightless, and the class began as wingless creatures that probably did not crawl to heights of more than a few inches. Primitive types still survive in springtails, bristletails, and silverfish. The first of these are very

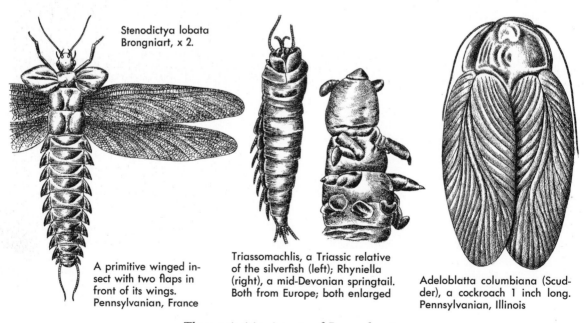

Stenodictya lobata Brongniart, x 2.

A primitive winged insect with two flaps in front of its wings. Pennsylvanian, France

Triassomachlis, a Triassic relative of the silverfish (left); Rhyniella (right), a mid-Devonian springtail. Both from Europe; both enlarged

Adeloblatta columbiana (Scudder), a cockroach 1 inch long. Pennsylvanian, Illinois

Three primitive insects of Pennsylvanian age

small, with short antennae and simple eyes; they run on short legs or jump with forked "tails" attached to the under side of the body. The oldest known springtails lived in a mid-Devonian peat bog of Scotland.

Bristletails, which seem to be more primitive than springtails, have not yet been discovered in rocks older than the Tertiary. Silverfish go back to the Triassic and undoubtedly will be found in older formations. Not only are these creatures ancient; they are outstanding examples of insects' pliancy and success. At a time when silverfish should be living fossils threatened with extinction, they are pushing their range ever northward in man's well-heated buildings. There, removed from their natural foods, silverfish thrive on starched clothing, books and slick-paper magazines, and crumbs that collect in kitchens.

Early "Ancient-wings." Many animal organs are made-overs; legs have turned into pincers, other legs serve as jaws, and so on. Wings, on the other hand, are new, for they developed from four out of six flaps that appeared on

Wing of Typus gracilis Carpenter, an ancestral dragonfly from the Permian of Oklahoma; length 145 mm.

Below is a remarkably perfect fly from Baltic amber. (Photographs by F. M. Carpenter)

Two termites in amber. Both insects are in the winged stage, showing that they were trapped in resin during the spring mating season. (Photograph by P. S. Tice, from Buchsbaum's "Animals without Backbones")

the back of the first three thoracic segments. This is shown by fossils such as *Stenodictya,* from Pennsylvanian deposits of France. *Stenodictya* has two flaps on the first thoracic segment, but true wings on the second and third. Flaps and wings are essentially alike, for both are thin, both have networks of veins, and both possess tiny hairs scattered over the upper surface.

Flaps must have evolved into wings during Mississippian times, since insects fully equipped for flight have been found in Pennsylvanian strata. We call them paleopterans because their vein patterns are archaic though complex, and because the wings themselves could not be folded when their owners were at rest.

Most paleopterans had wingspreads of 1 to 4 inches, but many were a great deal larger. Some species of Protodonata, often called ancestral dragonflies, had wingspreads of 28 to 30 inches and bodies 12 to 15 inches in length. Like true dragonflies, they were swift-flying predators with spiny legs used in capturing prey. The Protodonata range from Pennsylvanian to Triassic and from Europe to Australia; exceptionally fine specimens have been found in thin layers of Permian limestone at Elmo, sixteen miles south of Abilene, Kansas. True dragonflies evolved in late Permian times.

Neopterans with Folding Wings. Wings were life-saving acquisitions which enabled their owners to escape from spiders, scorpions, and small vertebrates that hunted on the ground. Yet the primitive wing was also a nuisance, since by spreading sideways it kept paleopterans from hiding under branches and leaves. New rewards could be won by wings that would fold, permitting ready concealment as well as escape by flight.

Such a chance was much too good to be missed, especially by a young class that was constantly changing. Several insect groups evolved wings that would fold, some in an order whose other features are those of paleopterans. Long before the Pennsylvanian period came to an end, there was a considerable array of neuropterous ("new-winged") insects whose wings folded backward, one pair over another. Among these newly evolved groups were cockroaches, whose fossils may be recognized by their large forewings with characteristic venation, as well as by the broad thorax which in many species almost hides the head. Some Pennsylvanian roaches reached lengths of 3 to 4 inches, but later species were not so large. Since early cockroaches lived on damp ground under swampy forests, their remains were readily buried in mud and therefore are disproportionately common among Paleozoic insects.

Complete Metamorphosis. Early insects, even neopterans, went through an incomplete metamorphosis. This means that their eggs hatched into tiny nymphs which looked and lived very much like their full-grown parents. A cockroach nymph, for example, sheds its skin-crust several times, but it does little more than grow, become mature, and add two pairs of wings that are lacking when it hatches. As countless housewives know, the nymph runs about like its parents, eats as they do, and lives amid the same surroundings.

There is nothing wrong with this; witness the fact that cockroaches remain prosperous and abundant after 230,000,000 years. Still, many insects have found improved chances for life when the young live in one environment and the adults in another. This can be done with incomplete metamorphosis; young dragonflies, for instance, creep at the bottom of pools, but adults take to dry land and hunt or escape enemies in the air. But the range of environments is still greater when young have one form, adults have another, and an intermediate stage makes provision for extensive change. We see this in a butterfly, whose young is a wormlike larva that crawls upon plants and devours their leaves. This larva becomes a chrysalis—legless, mouthless, and encased in armor that gives protection while the body is reorganized. The adult then emerges with four broad wings, legs adapted to clinging, and mouth parts that suck juices such as the nectar of flowers. No butterfly can crowd out its own young ones or take food from them, nor does it need to spend its life in one habitat. The same is true of flies, bees, and a variety of other insects that pass through complete metamorphosis.

These advantages were won during late Pennsylvanian times, for two groups of early Permian insects went through larval, pupal, and adult stages. They

Protolindenia wittei (Giebel), a true dragonfly with a wingspread of more than 4 inches. Jurassic, Solenhofen, Germany (Photograph by Dr. F. M. Carpenter)

accounted for only 5 per cent of the known species then living, but the proportion increased during subsequent ages. Today 88 per cent of the world's insects go through a complete metamorphosis.

Varied Insect Groups. Few insects seem more typical of our modern world than grasshoppers and crickets. Yet the group to which they belong is an old one whose history is being pushed back into Permian and Pennsylvanian times. Some cricketlike insects of the Permian closely resemble living members of this group. The group of insects to which May flies belong also appeared early in the Permian period.

Beetles appeared in the late Permian but did not become abundant until the Mesozoic era. More than 2,300 Tertiary species have been described, and their hard, shelly forewings are abundant in the Pleistocene tar deposits of California.

Modern flies have lost one pair of wings, a fact recognized by their name of Diptera, or "two-wings." Fossil flies share this characteristic, but four-winged ancestors have been found in the Permian of Australia. Mothlike insects found in Permian and Triassic formations actually belong to other groups, but true moths and butterflies appeared in the Eocene epoch. Those found in the Oligocene lake beds of Florissant and elsewhere in Colorado (Chapter XXXI) preserve color markings as well as antennae and the hairlike scales that covered both abdomen and thorax. Bees, wasps, ants, and bugs also are most often found in Tertiary formations, though the group to which cicadas and leaf hoppers belong is present among early Permian insects of Kansas.

In general, fossil insects are significant without being plentiful. They tell a great deal about the evolution of their class, but they are found in only a few regions and formations, and even in those they may be overshadowed by fossil plants. Sometimes, however, the two combine, as they do in carbonized galls or Florissant leaves that were trimmed or perforated by leaf-cutting bees.

Clatrotitan andersoni McKeown. A relative of crickets, with a very large chirping organ. Length 138 mm. Triassic, New South Wales

Raphidia mortua (Rohwer), a snakefly 16.5 mm. long. Oligocene, Florissant, Colorado

Dunbaria fasciipennis Tillyard, showing color pattern on wings. Width 37 mm. Early Permian, Elmo, Kansas

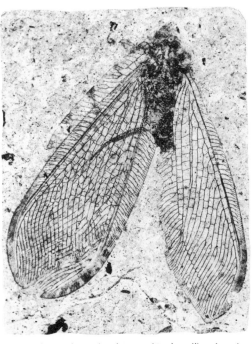

Lithosmylus columbianus (Cockerell), related to dobson flies. Oligocene, Florissant, Colorado. Length 30 mm.

A robber fly (family Asilidae) 25 mm. long. Note hairs on the legs. Oligocene, Florissant, Colorado

Prodryas persephone Scudder, a butterfly showing color pattern. Width 53 mm. Oligocene, Florissant, Colorado

Permian, Triassic, and Miocene insects (Photographs by Dr. F. M. Carpenter)

CHAPTER XX

Nets and Wrigglers to Sharks

MANY early Paleozoic formations contain small carbonized fossils that once were chitinous or horny. Since they resemble pen or pencil marks they were named graptolites, or "written stones."

Though graptolites are plentiful, their nature has long been a puzzle. Linnaeus called them "false fossils"; others mistook them for plants, sponges, coelenterates, and bryozoans. In 1948 a Polish scientist linked them with *Rhabdopleura,* a wormlike modern animal whose fossils have been found in Cretaceous and Tertiary strata.

This was the most surprising interpretation of all; though *Rhabdopleura* looks like a worm, it has a rodlike structure, the notochord, which is the first trace of the internal skeleton found in vertebrates. Since the rod is short—it lies in front of the mouth—*Rhabdopleura* is termed a hemichordate, or "half chordate." The creature builds colonies by budding; a muscular stalk links each animal, or zooid, to a branched, flesh-filled tube (the stolon) that runs through the colony. When undisturbed, *Rhabdopleura* extends its body to feed and breathe with gills, but it can quickly pull itself back into shelter by contracting its stalk.

If graptolites had notochords—some authorities deny this—they were lost before fossilization. Evidence that the creatures were hemichordates consists chiefly of chitinous tubes or cups called thecae, which consist of half rings that join in zigzag patterns. In four of the five graptolite orders, the thecae also are linked by stolon tubes. The entire colony is termed a rhabdosome.

TWO GROUPS OF GRAPTOLITES

Graptolites, as we have said, are divided among five orders. Three of these, however, are so uncommon that we may ignore them.

Dictyonema flabelliforme (Eichwald), of early Ordovician age. The drawing shows how this dendroid graptolite looked when it was alive.

Dendroidea. These are the most primitive graptolites and those most like *Rhabdopleura.* Thin thecae bud in groups of three and are joined by stolons. Characteristically, each colony begins with one tubelike theca (the sicula), from whose base a threadlike nema extends. A chitinous patch served as attachment to the sea bottom or some other object, such as a seaweed or shell.

Dendroids bud in groups of three. The chief function of one bud was to bud again; it is completely enclosed by its theca. The other buds developed open thecae, which means that their occupants ate, breathed, and reproduced sexually. Since one open theca is always large and the other is small, we infer that the former contained a female zooid while the latter enclosed a male.

Dendroids ranged from late Cambrian to Mississippian—a racial life of about 180,000,000 years—but they never became very abundant or attained great variety. Some genera, such as *Inocaulis,* have sometimes been called seaweeds.

Graptoloidea. This advanced order had lost its special budding zooids and retained only one type of open cup or tube. Any zooid, therefore, was able to bud and build up its colony, as well as to reproduce sexually. Stolons also disappeared, and the thecae opened into one long internal cavity, or canal. In many genera there were two canals and two rows of thecae, one on each side of the threadlike nema, here known as the virgula. In other genera there is only one canal, and one row of thecae has been lost. Those that remain, however, may take on a variety of shapes.

Graptoloids are the most abundant, most varied, and most specialized members of their class and are the ones most often found. In spite of this, they are limited to Ordovician and Silurian formations.

SHAPES, HABITS, AND HOMES

The earliest graptolites formed small colonies with slender branches that grew upward from a base attached to shells or firm mud. Before the Cambrian period closed, however, colonies had assumed several different forms. Still others were developed during Ordovician times.

Dendrograptus typifies branched or bushy dendroids. In them the nema was a short stalk or had almost vanished; the colonies were attached to shells or

Graptolites and a modern hemichordate

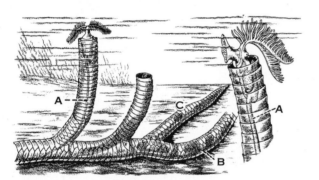

Rhabdopleura, a modern hemichordate. At the left are branched tubes with an animal feeding. At the right, one animal much enlarged. A, stalk; B, stolon; C, developing bud

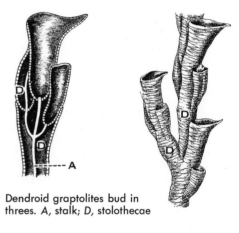

Dendroid graptolites bud in threes. A, stalk; D, stolothecae

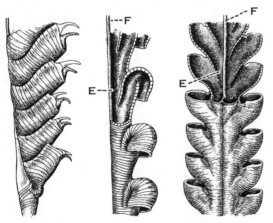

Budding in three genera of graptoloids. E, central canal; F, the nema, also called virgula

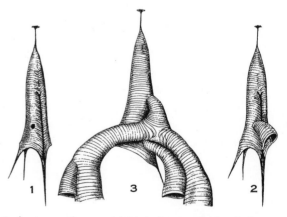

Early stages of a graptoloid. 1, shows only the sicula; 2, the sicula and one bud; 3, the beginning of branching

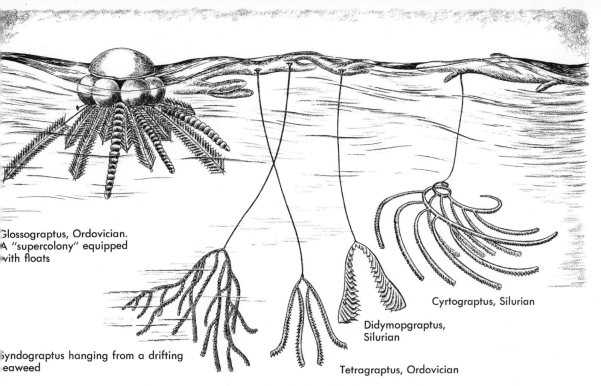

Glossograptus, Ordovician. A "supercolony" equipped with floats

Cyrtograptus, Silurian

Didymopgraptus, Silurian

Syndograptus hanging from a drifting seaweed

Tetragraptus, Ordovician

Restorations of some floating and drifting graptolites

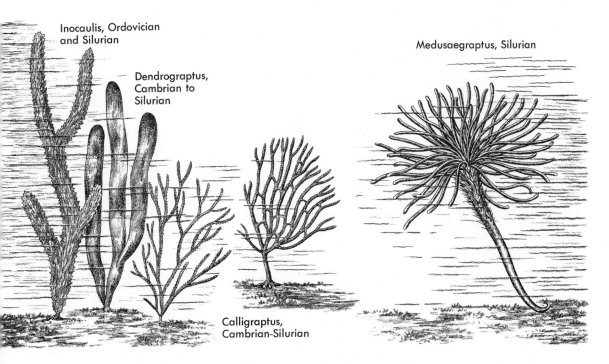

Inocaulis, Ordovician and Silurian

Medusaegraptus, Silurian

Dendrograptus, Cambrian to Silurian

Calligraptus, Cambrian-Silurian

Restorations of some bottom-dwelling graptolites

to hardened mud. Such habits limited the spread of both adults and larvae, and few species of bushy dendroids are widely distributed.

Callograptus and *Dictyonema* show two types of colonies with very different habits. The former is fanlike and consists of branches that divide again and again and are connected by dissepiments, or crossbars. There is either a short stalk or none, with a base attached to the sea bottom. These graptolites lived much like the bushy dendroids, and their species did not spread widely.

Dictyonema was conical when it was alive, though fossils generally are flattened and therefore resemble fans. The base of the cone is attached to a thread-like nema, whose end expands into a disk that plainly was used for attachment. Since the nema is too thin to have held the colony above the sea floor, *Dictyonema* must have fastened itself to floating shells or seaweeds, letting its conical network hang downward. Since seaweeds drift long distances, we are not surprised to learn that such species as *Dictyonema flabelliforme* are found in both Europe and North America, with what seem to be varieties in other parts of the world. Such cosmopolitan distribution is characteristic of floating and drifting organisms.

Most fossils of *Diplograptus* and *Glossograptus* are fragments, but a few fine specimens contain clusters of rhabdosomes whose nemas are fastened to a central disk. This, in turn, was covered by an umbrella-shaped float surrounded by smaller floats of cylindrical shape. The whole structure formed a super-colony, or synrhabdosome, that drifted on Paleozoic seas as the man-of-war jellyfish drifts upon waves and currents today. Zooids may even have been specialized for different functions, as are those in the Recent man-of-war.

We do not know how many other graptoloids built supercolonies, for most fossils are scattered fragments whose arrangement cannot be determined. Several genera, however, formed branched or spiral colonies that hung from floating objects in the manner of *Dictyonema*. Some graptoloids even built conical networks which suggest the skeletons of sponges in their general form.

Habitats and Preservation. Bushy and encrusting graptolites occur in chert; they and short-stalked species of *Dictyonema* are also found in limestone. But most graptolites drifted or floated, apparently in open waters where currents carried them long distances. They kept on drifting after death, finally reaching quiet, deep portions of seas that filled the long basins called geosynclines. There the dead graptolites sank and were covered by mud that hardened into dark gray or black shale.

Another factor helps to explain why most graptolites are found in black shale. Their colonies were so delicate that sand would have soon ground them to bits, and so would trilobites and lesser scavengers that often swarmed where lime mud accumulated. But most black shale settled in stagnant regions where the water contained little oxygen and was poisoned by hydrogen sulfide from slowly decaying rubbish. Since few scavengers lived in such surroundings, dead graptolites lay undisturbed until they were carbonized.

BRAINS, VERTEBRAE, AND BONES

While graptolites sank into poisoned sea water, something new appeared in streams. Although it had no backbone, or vertebral column, we call it a vertebrate.

This contradiction reminds us that technical names often persist long after they have lost their literal meanings. *Vertebrate* is one of those terms. When it first came into use it was applied only to creatures with vertebral columns of

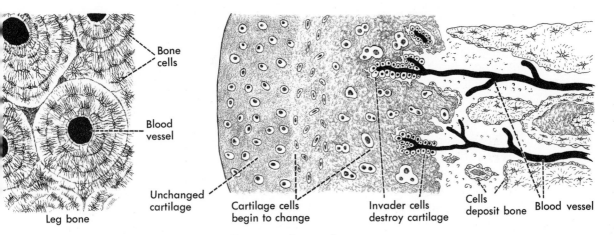

Leg bone — Bone cells — Blood vessel — Unchanged cartilage — Cartilage cells begin to change — Invader cells destroy cartilage — Cells deposit bone — Blood vessel

From cartilage to bone

cartilage or bone—sharks, lizards, cats, and so on. But as time passed, scientists discovered that these creatures shared essential characters with others that either lacked vertebrae or had them only in rudimentary form. Today, therefore, the term *vertebrate* means any animal that meets the following requirements:

1. It must possess a notochord which, unlike that of hemichordates, runs almost the full length of the body. This notochord may persist throughout life or it may be replaced by vertebrae as the animal grows.

2. The forward end of the nerve cord (which lies *above* the notochord) must be enlarged to form a brain.

3. The brain must be surrounded by a cranium, or braincase. This may consist of cartilage, bone, or a combination of both.

4. Other structures, also cartilaginous or bony, provide support for the gills if those organs are present.

To these, such things as vertebrae, ribs, jaws, and skeletal supports for fins or limbs may or may not be added. Since the really critical elements are brain and braincase (cranium), a considerable number of zoologists have abandoned the term *vertebrate* in all except popular usuage, replacing it with *craniate*.

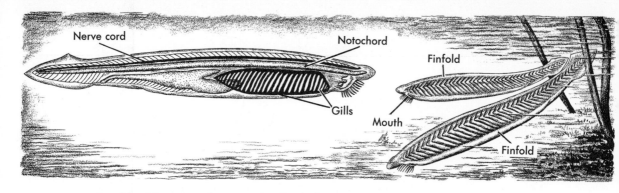

Amphioxids are modern sea-dwelling chordates about 2 inches long. The diagram shows the notochord below the nerve cord.

Most paleontologists keep the older term, with the implied proviso that it does not mean what it says.

Bone and Cartilage. Before going further we must distinguish between cartilage and bone. The former is a tough, translucent substance built up by round cells that can grow, or expand, as they age. Ordinary cartilage is not hard; since it shrivels or decays readily it is seldom preserved in fossils. Exceptions to this rule are found chiefly among fishes, in which cartilage may be hardened by calcium compounds. When that happens, the modified tissue is readily petrified.

Bone consists of fibrous material that is thickened and strengthened by limy deposits. Both substances are formed by branched, irregular cells which are nourished by blood flowing through tubular channels. Since bones are hard, they cannot expand, but grow larger by the addition of layers at or near their surface. Large bones generally are porous or hollow at the center, with marrow cavities and tubelike canals that accommodate blood vessels and nerves. These, as well as cell spaces and layers of deposition, are commonly preserved in fossils.

Cephalaspis, an ostracoderm of the Old Red Sandstone. About 7 inches long. At the right is the head shield of Sclerodus, natural size.

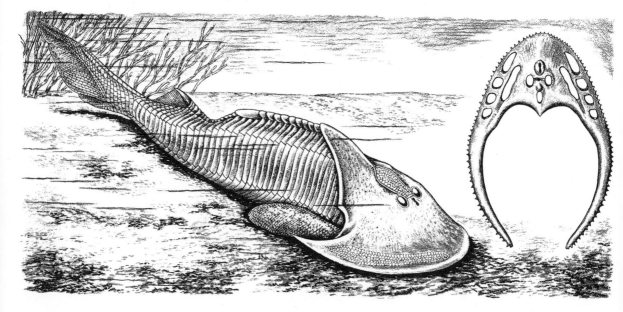

Bones grow in myriad forms; they also belong to two types that differ in origin. Those that developed first during vertebrate (or craniate) evolution are called dermal, since they appear in the skin and either remain there or stay near the surface of the body. They also are bony from the beginning. Replacement bones, on the other hand, start out as cartilaginous structures around the brain or notochord, in the legs, and in other "deep" parts of the body. Then, as their owner grows, the cartilage and its cells are destroyed and bone is built up in their place. If the ability to do this is lost—as it is by some fish and amphibians—replacement "bones" remain cartilaginous.

From "Worms" to Agnaths. No fossils show how vertebrates evolved, for their ancestors apparently were soft-bodied creatures that were not carbonized. We think, however, that the story begins with wormlike hemichordates whose descendants became torpedo-shaped and extended the notochord from head region to tail. Muscles also became horizontal V's, a finfold developed on the back, and gills that opened behind the mouth carried on respiration, or breathing. Thus the creatures became cephalochordates, a phylum whose only surviving members are the lancelets, or amphioxids. They inhabit shallow seas from England to California and Japan, burrowing in sandy shoals where they strain food from water that enters the mouth and is forced through pockets surrounding the gills. There the food particles are caught in slime that goes to the throat and is swallowed. An amphioxid is not a vertebrate, for its nerve cord does not begin with a brain and it has no cranium. We feel sure, however, that some late Precambrian or early Cambrian cephalochordates produced descendants whose nerve cords enlarged into simple brains from which hollow bulbs extended to the skin and there developed into eyes. When cartilage began to cover their brains, these progressive cephalochordates became vertebrates.

We are tempted to call these creatures fish, since they lived in the water, had streamlined bodies, and breathed by means of gills. But true fish have two or more fins arranged in pairs, and their mouths are equipped with jaws. The first vertebrates must have lacked both these characters, and so did many of their descendants. We therefore group them together in a class called the Agnatha, or agnaths, which means "jawless ones."

ARMORED OSTRACODERMS

The first agnaths also left no fossils, though a creature that probably was much like them has been found in Silurian strata of England. The oldest fossil vertebrates, called ostracoderms ("shell-skins") were more advanced animals whose heads, bodies, and even tails were protected by shields, plates, and scales of dermal bone. Several genera also had hard replacement bone in the braincase, and all possessed some form of cartilaginous support for the

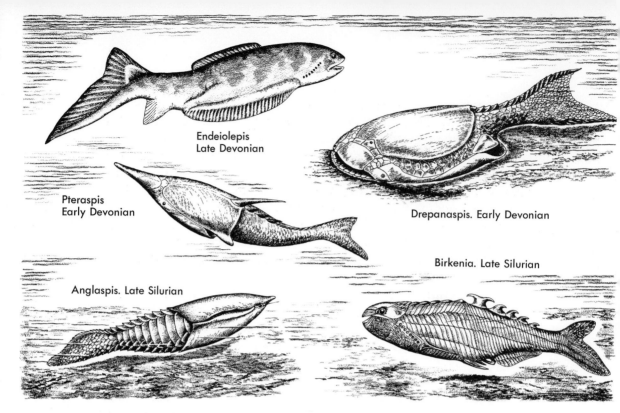

Five agnaths, or jawless "fish." Lengths range from 2.5 to 12 inches.

gills. No trace of a vertebral column has been found, though there may have been two rows of cartilaginous rods that formed upside-down V's over the main nerve cord. Such rods, found in living agnaths, are the first elements of vertebrae.

Ostracoderms may have evolved in streams, but their oldest fossils come from typically marine strata in the Black Hills of South Dakota and the Big Horn Mountains of Wyoming, as well as from shallow-water sandstones near Canyon City, Colorado. Their age is either middle or late Ordovician.

These creatures had hard, ornately sculptured armor, but their fossils are too badly broken to reveal much more. Our first clear picture of ostracoderm life comes from late Silurian (Downtonian) rocks of northwestern Europe and Spitzbergen. A thick series of sandstones and shales, the Downtonian records the upheaval of mountains from England to the Arctic Ocean, with others in Greenland, northern France, and southern Germany. Some ranges were so high that they cast rain shadows, turning lesser ridges and valleys into semi-deserts. When rains did fall they transformed streams into raging floods and filled low basins with shallow lakes into which ostracoderms spread. Returning droughts left many of them stranded, to die under blazing sunshine. Their remains were buried when the next floods left their layers of sediment.

Osteostracans. Downtonian fossils show that ostracoderms had progressed far from their original state, since they belonged to three specialized orders. The best known order, called osteostracans ("bony shells"), includes creatures that were completely encased in plates and scales consisting of bone covered with dentine. In a typical genus, *Cephalaspis,* the plates formed a shield that covered the head and was rounded in front but projected backward in "horns" resembling the spines of many trilobites. The two eyes lay close together and looked upward; a single nostril opened in front of them, and between them lay the pineal body, a structure that seems to have distinguished light from shade. The under side of the head bore an oval mouth near the front and openings for ten pairs of gills. There was a simple brain from which networks of nerves extended to three dorsal areas covered with small plates. Once regarded as electrical organs, these areas are now called sensory fields that were affected by pressure, temperature, and very low sounds.

The body of *Cephalaspis* tapered to the tail, where it bent upward to support a plated fin that contained cartilaginous rays. This type of tail, called heterocercal, is found in many other agnaths and among primitive fish. Narrow plates allowed the body to bend freely, and a dorsal fin kept it from rolling. Two scaly flaps probably served as balancing organs, but they were not true fins.

Cephalaspis seemingly could swim fairly well, though its tail tended to force it downward instead of straight ahead. The creature probably spent most of its time in lakes, rivers, and estuaries, where it fed by sucking mud into its mouth and straining out bits of food as they passed over the gills. These habits were shared by other Downtonian osteostracans. Among them were the ornately spinose *Sclerodus* and *Boreaspis,* which had a forward spine almost as long as the shield. *Tremataspis,* on the other hand, was tadpole-shaped and lacked balancing flaps, since its shield encased most of the body. None of these genera was as long-lived and successful as *Cephalaspis,* which ranged from Spitzbergen to eastern Asia during late Silurian and early Devonian epochs. It then reached eastern Canada, where it survived to the end of Devonian times.

Anaspids. Though related to osteostracans, these creatures were torpedo-shaped and had ventral fins. The eyes lay near the sides of the head; the hind end of the body bent downward, producing a reversed heterocercal tail which drove the animal upward as it swam. Genera such as *Birkenia* were well armored with rough bony plates and had spines on both the back and the belly. Other genera lost much of this armor, and the late Devonian *Endeiolepis* was almost naked. It also possessed a soft dorsal fin, while two finfolds strengthened by scales ran along its sides. *Endeiolepis* probably fed near the surface and was the best swimmer among the ostracoderms.

Heterostracans. This group may include the oldest ostracoderms, since its armor resembles the fragmentary Ordovician plates. Primitive species were torpedo-shaped creatures 2 to 6 inches long, with downturned tails, no fins on the back, and eyes at the sides of the head. Plates of the head and trunk were fused, though two openings allowed water to leave the gills. Overlapping plates or diamond-shaped scales covered the hinder portions and tail. There apparently were two nostrils, which were used to sample, or "smell," the water, not for breathing.

Streamlined heterostracans probably swam near the surface, though the lack of medial fins doubtless allowed them to roll and wobble badly. *Drepanaspis* and its relatives, however, were broad, flattened animals some 12 inches long that must have wriggled on the bottom. There they scooped rubbish into broad, slitlike mouths, extracting particles that were suitable for food.

Why the armor? Most modern animals have armor only if it protects them against their enemies, which may also be relatives. But ostracoderms did not feed upon each other; their jawless mouths were utterly unsuited to predatory life. During most of their existence they possessed no vertebrate enemies, and few species wandered into seas where savage cephalopods abounded. What other animals could attack them, making armor necessary?

This question seems to be answered by deposits in which shells of sea scorpions lie near ostracoderm armor. Although some eurypterids fed on carrion, others were active carnivores equipped with strong pincers. These predators made armor a necessity for sluggish agnaths, which would have been torn to bits had they been naked.

CYCLOSTOMES AND CONODONTS

Ostracoderms became common during late Silurian times but dwindled in numbers and disappeared at the end of the Devonian period. Some experts say they vanished without trace; others suspect that the osteostracans left descendants in the form of lampreys and hagfishes, collectively termed cyclostomes, or "round-mouths." They are eel-shaped, limbless, and jawless creatures that live in both fresh and salt water. Their skin is smooth, they have only one nostril, and they feed by attaching themselves to living fish. There

A modern lamprey and its mouth

Conodonts from Paleozoic formations

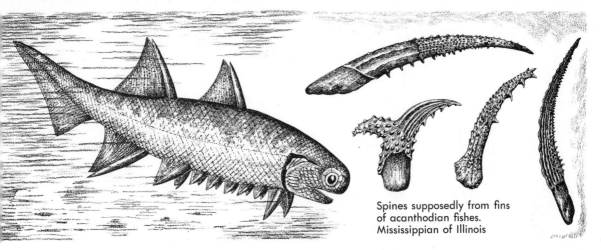

Spines supposedly from fins of acanthodian fishes. Mississippian of Illinois

Climatius, an early Devonian fish about 3 inches long. It had jaws and seven pairs of fins supported by spines.

they tear through skin and flesh until they reach the body cavity, where they feed upon the viscera and juices of their still-living victims.

Conodonts are small toothlike fossils that appear in Cambrian rocks of Utah and Wyoming and continue through the Paleozoic. Many authors regard them as toothlike denticles from the mouths of extinct cyclostomes. Other experts deny that conodonts are either denticles or toothlike scales, but regard them as internal structures of swimming animals that may have belonged to a distinct class of chordates. The actual fossils are often associated with cephalopods, ostracods, and fish, but are rare in reef deposits. Clusters of specimens indicate that conodonts of several types were found in a single animal, whatever it may have been. In spite of this uncertainty, many form-species have been named and are used successfully as index fossils.

FISHES WITH JAWS; THE PLACODERMS

Fishes may be defined as vertebrates with jaws, gills, and paired fins. Jaws apparently began when bars of cartilage supporting the first two pairs of gills disappeared, while the third pair swung forward until they enclosed the mouth. In time the fourth pair of bars also shifted and in part became the hyoid arch. It propped the upper jaws against the braincase.

According to one theory, paired fins started out as longitudinal folds resembling those of *Endeiolepis.* In time parts of these folds ceased to develop, dividing what remained into pairs of fins. Numbering seven or more in early stages, these pairs finally settled down to two, called pelvic and pectoral.

Placoderms were the first fish to possess both paired fins and jaws, though the fourth pair of gill arches had not become supports for the jaws. Backbones were even more primitive, for the notochord persisted throughout life and vertebrae were represented only by Y-shaped spines that developed above

Some late Devonian arthrodires. Dinichthys (left) *reached lengths of 3 to 30 feet, but Coccosteus* (right) *was 14 to 16 inches in length.*

and below it. In many genera these spines were cartilaginous and vanished soon after death, but in some they were hard enough to be preserved in fossils.

Acanthodians. Often miscalled "spiny sharks," these were the least progressive placoderms. Early forms were not much larger than minnows but were most unminnowlike in appearance and anatomy. *Climatius,* for example, was 3 inches long, with a blunt head, a sharklike tail, and hard diamond-shaped scales that covered its entire body. The paired fins numbered fourteen, but ten were little more than spines, and strong spines supported the unpaired dorsal and ventral fins.

Climatius and other early acanthodians lived in fresh water, but many of their descendants went to sea. In doing so they increased in size and lost most of their armor, as well as the small, spinelike paired fins. Other fin spines persisted, however, and in some Carboniferous species were half as long as the entire fish.

Arthrodires. These fish, whose name means "jointed neck," lost most of the body armor but developed a massive head shield that was hinged to plates on the shoulder region. During the late Devonian, some arthrodires also became the largest and most savage vertebrates of their time.

Dinichthys ("terrible fish") was the best-known of these giants, for its remains have been found in late Devonian shales that settled in a shallow sea that once covered northern Ohio. *Dinichthys* had a broad, blunt head, a capacious mouth, and a body whose length is estimated at 24 to 30 feet. The internal skeleton was almost wholly cartilaginous, but the head and thoracic shields consisted of massive bones that have no exact counterparts in fish other than arthrodires. Pointed and beveled plates took the place of teeth, and a hinge allowed the head to rise while the jaws were lowered, giving an enormous bite. Since *Dinichthys* could hardly have been an active swimmer, we assume that it hid among seaweeds, waiting for other fish. When one came within reach the wide mouth snapped shut, shearing the victim between the beveled and serrate jaw plates.

Pterichthyodes, an Antiarch. As old as arthrodires, but more advanced, was a group of armored fishes known as antiarchs. Appearing in middle Devonian pools of Europe, they spread round the world and then died out before the Mississippian period began.

The most famous antiarch is the wingfish, *Pterichthyodes,* also called *Pterichthys.* Found in the Old Red Sandstone of Scotland (Chapter XXI), *Pterichthyodes* was so well armored that it first was mistaken for a crab. Bony plates enclosed its head and trunk, thick scales continued to the tail, and plates covered creeping organs that must have begun as paired fins. Their faint resemblance to wings explains the creature's names.

Being sluggish bottom-dwellers, wingfish were often trapped as temporary ponds dried up after seasonal floods. Exposed to both air and sunshine, the stranded creatures struggled and died. Strata recording these events are strewn with "remains which exhibit unequivocally the marks of violent death. The figures are contorted, contracted, curved; the tail in many instances is bent round to the head; the fins are spread to the full as in fishes that die in convulsions."

Those are the words of Hugh Miller, quarryman, geologist, and author, for whom the finest wingfish is named. Miller supposed that antiarchs were detroyed by volcanic eruptions, not by droughts that dried up pools and streams.

Bothriolepis. Relatives of the wingfish are found in middle and late Devonian rocks in almost all parts of the world. They reached North America near the end of that period, becoming common in streams and lakes of the region that is now the Gaspé Peninsula of Quebec. There fishermen who catch modern

Two armored antiarchs that falsely resembled ostracoderms.

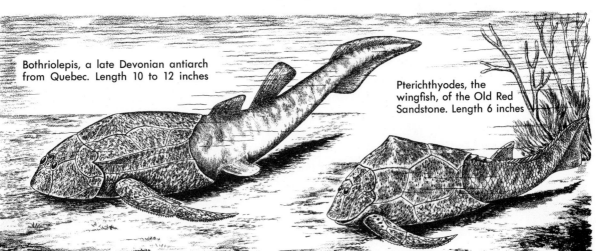

Bothriolepis, a late Devonian antiarch from Quebec. Length 10 to 12 inches

Pterichthyodes, the wingfish, of the Old Red Sandstone. Length 6 inches

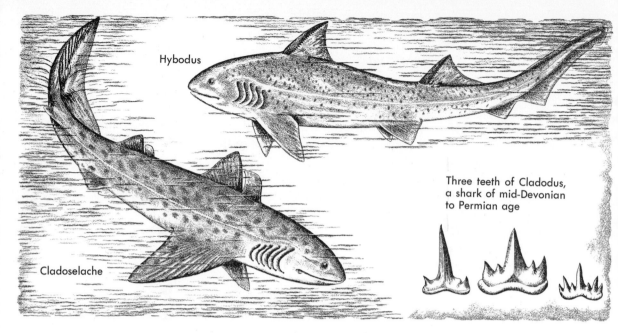

Hybodus

Cladoselache

Three teeth of Cladodus, a shark of mid-Devonian to Permian age

Hybodus was a common Mesozoic shark 7 to 8 feet in length; it is found in North America, Europe, and Asia. Cladoselache, about 4 feet long, is best known from fossils in late Devonian shales near Cleveland, Ohio.

herring also dig petrified antiarchs from beds of gray shale and soft sandstone exposed along the shore. Their commonest find, *Bothriolepis,* was about 10 inches long. The fossils show a blunt head and broad body encased in elaborately pitted plates. The tail and part of the trunk were naked; the creeping organs were relatively long, with rows of short spines along their edges. Sections cut through well-preserved specimens show two pockets that branched off from the pharynx and served as lungs. When *Bothriolepis* was stranded on a tidal flat it escaped destruction by breathing air until water returned.

SHARKS AND THEIR KIN; THE CHONDRICHTHYES

For many years sharks were regarded as primitive fish that had neither developed true bone nor completed their skulls. Like many another time-honored notion, this one has proved to be false. Instead of being primitive, sharks and their kin—the class Chondrichthyes—are descendants of placoderms that lost the power to produce bone and so reverted to skeletons of cartilage. Even when it was hardened by limy deposits, it was not ossified.

Cladoselachians. This interpretation "makes sense" of the fact that shark-like fishes did not appear until mid-Devonian times, some 30,000,000 years after bony placoderms became common. The first fossils of this new group, called *Cladodus,* are pointed teeth whose blunt bases rested in cartilaginous jaws. Next comes *Cladoselache,* a slender fish 2 to 4 feet long, whose shape and broad heterocercal tail show that it was built for speed. Its pectoral fins

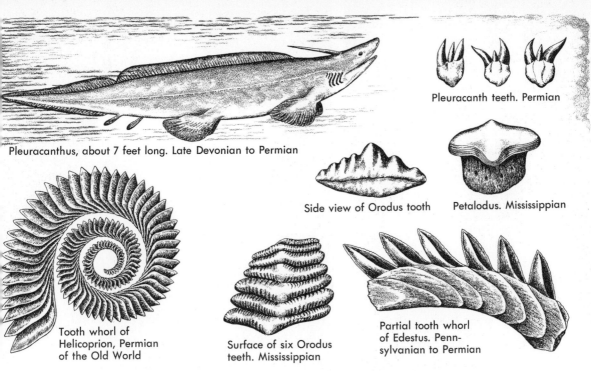

Pleuracanthus, about 7 feet long. Late Devonian to Permian

Pleuracanth teeth. Permian

Side view of Orodus tooth

Petalodus. Mississippian

Tooth whorl of Helicoprion, Permian of the Old World

Surface of six Orodus teeth. Mississippian

Partial tooth whorl of Edestus. Pennsylvanian to Permian

A pleuracanth "shark," and teeth of several primitive sharklike fish

were broad, but pelvic fins were absent, the large eyes were near the front of the head, and the skull was merely a braincase to which the jaws were attached. A few specimens show a broad, thin spine at the front of each dorsal fin. Though *Cladoselache* was a neighbor of *Dinichthys,* it apparently cruised actively instead of lying in wait for food.

Pleuracanths. These descendants of cladoselachian sharks were characterized by a slender body, a dorsal fin that ran almost the length of the back, a homocercal tail that tapered to a point with fins both above and below, and paired fins with central axis and rays that branched off to either side. There also was a long spine behind the head. Most surprising of all is the fact that pleuracanths left the sea and took up life in fresh water, where their remains were covered by deposits of late Devonian to Triassic age.

Hybodonts. The pleuracanths left no descendants, but cladoselachians apparently gave rise to hybodonts, which appeared in the late Devonian and lived on to the end of the Mesozoic era. They resembled modern sharks in shape and reached lengths of 7 to 8 feet. Many species had sharp teeth at the front of the mouth, but low-crowned plates at the back. The former could catch active prey; the latter crushed clams, snails, and other armored invertebrates.

Several late Paleozoic hybodonts developed remarkable series of teeth in the mid-line of both upper and lower jaws. In *Edestus,* of the Mississippian, for example, these teeth formed a serrate curve, with their bases set so firmly together that they looked almost like bone. *Helicoprion,* of the Permian, had medial teeth which grew up to the front of the jaws in a spiral and then curved

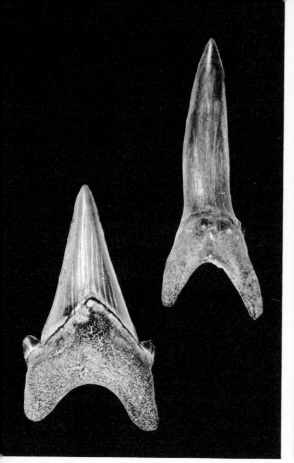 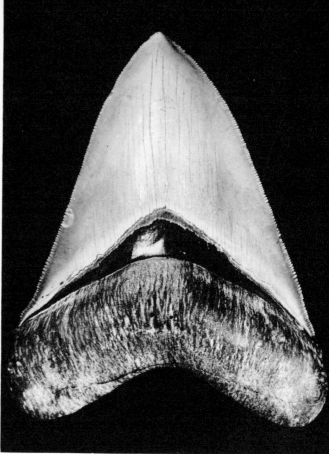

(Left) *Two slender shark teeth from the Pliocene (Red Crag) of England.* (Right) *Tooth of a giant shark, Carcharodon polygurus (Morton). Miocene deposits near Chesapeake Bay*

downward and inward, increasing the spiral's size. No one has explained how this structure could be used.

Modern sharks. True sharks appeared in Jurassic seas and rapidly spread round the world. Some fossils show traces of skin and flesh, but the majority are teeth that range from small affairs with several points to broadly triangular blades. Each shark had dozens or hundreds of teeth in its jaws at one time and grew new ones as old fell out.

Most Jurassic sharks were of moderate size; many resembled modern dogfish, to which they were closely related. When marine reptiles died out, however, sharks became the dominant vertebrates of Tertiary seas. Some were small, slender predators whose pronglike teeth suggest that their owners seized small agile fishes and swallowed them whole. Larger forms were slower and took more substantial food; many species had serrate, triangular teeth that could cut meat from large victims. The giant of them all, *Carcharodon*, was a genus that still survives in the white shark, or man-eater. A big white shark is 30 to 40 feet long and has 3-inch teeth; several Tertiary species had teeth 6 to 8 inches long, set in thick, gristly jaws that were 6 feet or more in width. Though these creatures were more massive than the white sharks and had larger heads, they must have reached lengths of 45 to 50 feeet.

Skates and rays are cartilaginous relatives of sharks that became flattened bottom-dwellers. They appeared in Jurassic seas of Europe; late Cretaceous and Tertiary fossils include sting rays with large poisonous spines, each developed from a fin ray on the tail. There also were eagle rays with blunt heads, whiplike tails, and platelike teeth. These teeth, which cracked the shells of mollusks, are sometimes mistaken for the belly armor of crocodilians or snakes.

CHAPTER XXI

The Bony Fishes

NEAR THE CROSSROADS called Fossil, Wyoming, rise cliffs of white marly limestone and pink shale. Their age is middle Eocene, and they settled in one of three lakes that spread across southwestern Wyoming and nearby parts of Utah and Colorado. The limestone, which is part of the Green River formation, is famous for its abundant and well-preserved fish.

Many placoderms, as we have seen, developed bony plates in the skin but built their internal frameworks out of cartilage. The class to which most Green River fish belonged continued the former trend but reversed the latter. As a result, they built up complex internal skeletons while adding dermal bones to skull, jaws, and shoulder girdle. Except for a few degenerate types, they fully deserve their name of Osteichthyes, which means "bony fish."

THE LOBE-FINS, OR CHOANICHTHYES

Bony fish seem to have come from placoderms, but no one knows which ones. The new class appears full-fledged in middle Devonian rocks as two groups that differ widely. One group, the Choanichthyes, is well described by the popular name of lobe-fins. It tells us that these fish are characterized by fins with fleshy bases, or lobes, containing jointed series of bones distinct from those in the fringelike fin membranes. The notochord is not reduced, and the vertebrae consist of plates and arches built around it. These may be either cartilaginous or bony, and the ribs may be ossified. Early lobe-fins had thick scales in which a layer of bone was covered by pulpy cosmine, which was capped by a shiny crust. Cosmine resembled the dentine of teeth, and the crust was virtually enamel.

Fish and Agnaths of the "Old Red." Lobe-fins are found in lower Devonian

Cliffs of the Eocene Green River formation west of Green River, Wyoming. The finely bedded shale settled in a lake, but sandstone at the top of the cliff was deposited by a river. The shale contains fossil fish.

strata, but the fossils are only fragments. Our first satisfying view of these fishes is provided by well-preserved remains in the Old Red Sandstone.

The "Old Red" is a series of conglomerates, sandstones, and shales, with some coal. Reaching thicknesses of 30,000 to 37,000 feet, it is found in England, Scotland, and Wales, as well as in Spitzbergen, Greenland, and the Baltic region of Europe. The rocks accumulated during middle to late Devonian times, in basins and valleys separated by rising mountain ranges. Lava often erupted from fissures and volcanoes, spreading out in sheets which then were covered by layers of sediment. As in Downtonian times, the climate combined dry seasons with torrential rains whose water rushed down barren slopes, produced muddy streams, and filled shallow lakes in mountain-rimmed valleys. Fish prospered while those lakes were full but died by millions as they shrank during dry seasons.

A roster of Old Red vertebrates reads like a *Who's Who* of Devonian ag-

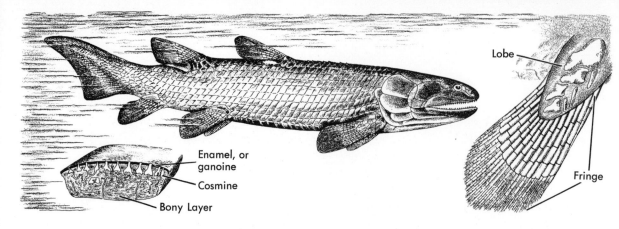

Osteolepis, a lobe-finned fish from the Old Red Sandstone of Europe. At the left is an enlarged section through a lobe-fin scale; at the right is a fin with skin and scales removed, showing bones in the lobe.

naths and fishes. *Cephalaspis* and *Pteraspis* were there; *Bothriolepis* and *Pterichthyodes* crept or swam in pools, and small arthrodires called *Coccosteus*, whose backbones had partly ossified, lay in wait for prey. Acanthodians were numerous, and so were lobe-fins belonging to two divergent groups.

Crossopterygians, or Fringe-fins. The more primitive of these two groups is the crossopterygians ("fringe-fins"). In Old Red days the order was typified by *Osteolepis*, a slender fish 7 to 10 inches long with a blunt head, heterocercal tail, and small rhomboidal scales. Though its vertebrae were still incomplete, its skull and jaws were well ossified, chiefly by dermal bones. The four paired fins were short and had stubby lobes, and the nostrils opened above the upper jaw.

Holoptychius was a late Devonian genus that apparently ranged round the world. Some species reached lengths of 30 inches; they had deep bodies, large

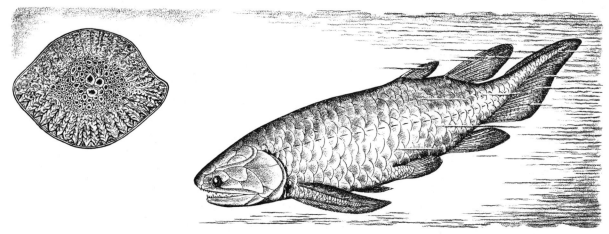

Holoptychius, a late Devonian lobe-fin about 30 inches long. The cross section through one of this fish's teeth shows how the enamel is folded into a "labyrinthine" pattern.

rounded scales, and long, narrow pectoral fins. *Rhizodus,* of Mississippian age, apparently reached lengths of 15 to 18 feet. *Megalichthys* was smaller, in spite of its name; its chief claim to distinction is the fact that (with a few other genera) it survived into Permian times. Most of its relatives died out in late Devonian and Mississippian epochs.

The Persistent Coelacanths. This subgroup of fringe-fins evolved by losing bones from the skull, shortening their bodies, and developing deep, blunt heads. Lobes of the paired fins also shortened, and the diphycercal tail had a three-part fin, like that of some late Devonian crossopterygians. One lung apparently had been lost; the other had moved upward and was used as an

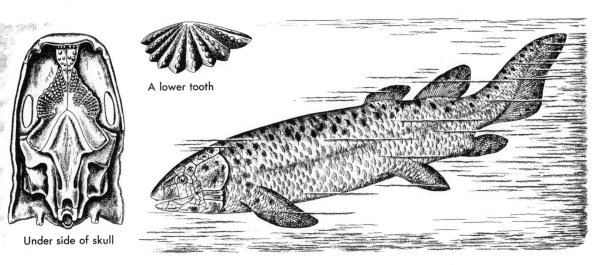

A lower tooth

Under side of skull

Dipterus, a primitive lungfish of middle Devonian age

air bladder that helped keep the body right side up. The bladder also was partly calcified and may be seen in fossils.

Primitive coelacanths lived in Carboniferous and Permian streams, and the Triassic *Diplurus* also inhabited fresh water. One member of this genus achieved fame in 1946, when thousands of specimens were found by men digging the basement for a library building at Princeton University in New Jersey. Specimens were 4 to 5 inches long and inconspicuous, but X-ray photographs reveal their skulls and skeletons in great detail.

Most Jurassic and Cretaceous coelacanths were marine; before 1938 the group was thought to have died out at the end of the Mesozoic era. Then a commercial fisherman off the South African coast brought up a deep-bodied fish about 4 feet 6 inches long, with an odd tail and large blue scales. It was given to the local museum, whose curator had the skin and skull mounted, but when the oily "insides" began to decay they were given to the garbage collector and hauled out to sea. A chemist who was also a self-made expert

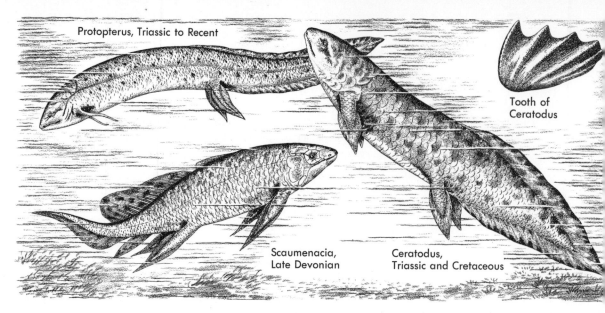

Three specialized lungfish. Two of them are now extinct.

Protopterus, Triassic to Recent

Tooth of Ceratodus

Scaumenacia, Late Devonian

Ceratodus, Triassic and Cretaceous

on fishes found the specimen to be a coelacanth and named it *Latimeria*. Further search has brought other specimens to light, from depths of 45 to perhaps 850 feet. Living specimens swim with an oddly rotating movement of the pelvic fins, which can assume almost any position. The creatures weigh 125 to 150 pounds, are strong and active, and have jaws armed with sharp teeth.

Dipterus, a Lungfish. *Dipterus* looked like a fringe-fin until it opened its mouth. Then it revealed greatly reduced jaws, nostrils at the edge of the jaws, and broad, ridged teeth which suggest that their owner crushed mussels, snails, and other shelled invertebrates. The skull contained many small bones, though some of those surrounding the brain had degenerated into cartilage.

The most significant feature of *Dipterus* is inferred from the fact that teeth and skull bones link it to the living lungfish. Although these creatures have gills, they breathe air and get oxygen from it in saclike lungs that branch off from the throat. We infer that *Dipterus* did likewise, though its lungs probably were more primitive than those of its modern relatives.

But why did a fish with gills need lungs? Here we recall the violent Old Red climate, with its floods and seasons of drought. In the former, fish and agnaths prospered; during the latter, they died on sun-baked flats or were crowded into putrid pools. There many species smothered because decaying vegetation robbed the water of oxygen.

When a lungfish was stranded on barren flats it fared no better than ostracoderms, but in ponds the story was different. While gill-breathing neighbors died, *Dipterus* thrust its head above water and gulped air into its lungs. There oxygen passed through membranes and entered red cells in the blood. This process kept countless lungfish alive during Devonian droughts.

Air-breathing was vitally important, but it was not restricted to *Dipterus*. We have seen that the armored antiarchs also had lungs that branched off from the pharynx, and so did crossopterygians. We decide that the ability to breath air was a very ancient trait, possessed by a wide variety of fishes. Some of those that now breathe only with gills use organs that once were lungs for other purposes.

Later Lungfish. Lungfish must have evolved in fresh water, for no other environment would have made their method of breathing worth while. Yet they soon spread into seas, for their fossils are found in many marine formations. Both marine and fresh-water forms also changed greatly; braincases became cartilaginous, teeth assumed complex shapes, and bodies and fins were modified. *Scaumenacia,* of late Devonian Quebec, had a tapering body, bladelike paired fins, and a very slender tail. *Ceratodus* and its kin developed bodies as much as 6 feet long, with large scales and median fins that merged with those of the tail. *Lepidosiren* and *Protopterus* have become almost as slender as eels, and their paired fins are mere ribbonlike remnants of the lobes seen in *Dipterus*.

Diplurus, a fresh-water coelacanth of New Jersey, was 4 to 5 inches long. Undina, from Jurassic strata of Europe, was marine and reached a length of 2 feet.

THE BONY AND PROLIFIC RAY-FINS

Lobe-fins reached their zenith in Paleozoic times and then ceased to be leaders among the bony fishes. That place was taken and is held by the actinopterygians.

Actinopterygian means "ray-fin," a much more wieldy term. Virtually all these fish have fins stretched over bones which extend directly from the body, not as fringes on both sides of a bony and muscular lobe. As in coelacanths, one lung has been lost; the other has become an air bladder that lies above the midline of the fish, reduces its weight, and helps it remain upright. Heavy organs below the bladder serve as ballast, like the ballast in a boat.

Primitive Ray-fins (Chondrosteans). Primitive ray-fins are typified by *Cheirolepis*, which appeared in middle Devonian Europe and reached North America some millions of years later. *Cheirolepis* was a slender, blunt-nosed fish about 9 inches long, with a V-shaped heterocercal tail, an unconstricted notochord, and incomplete vertebrae that were mostly cartilaginous. The skull was bony and the eyes were large; the paired fins were broad at the base and could not move freely, though their rays were jointed. The body was covered with small, rhombic scales of the type called ganoid. Microscopic sections show a basal layer of bone, a little cosmine, and a thick, brilliant coat of ganoine, closely related to enamel. Similar scales covered acanthodian "sharks."

From this simple beginning the early ray-fins evolved in divergent ways. Some enlarged their eyes, thickened their bodies, and reduced the paired fins until they were almost useless. Others became deeper-bodied and thinner than any sunfish, which they resembled in size. Still others lost most of the bone in their heads and vertebral columns and reduced the scales to a few rows of large, bony plates. One result of this trend was the sturgeons, a group of bottom-scavengers that live in bays, lakes, and a few large streams. Paddlefish, which appeared in the Eocene, are even more degenerate. They have only a few small scales left at the base of the tail.

Intermediate Ray-fins (Holosteans). Though some specialized forms, such as sturgeons, survived, most primitive ray-fins died out at the end of the Triassic period. Their places were taken by a group whose scales had lost all trace of cosmine, and whose homocercal tails had only a few upcurved vertebrae as

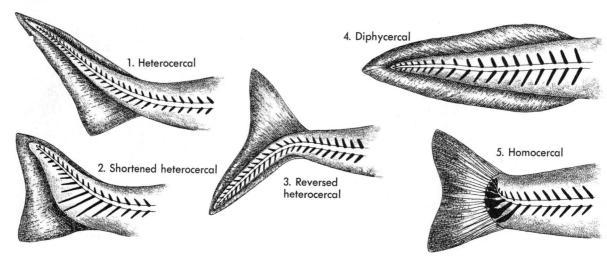

The five principal types of fish tails; 3 and 4 are also found in reptiles and 4 in amphibians.

(Right) *Dapedius, a deep-bodied Jurassic holostean 14 inches long.* (Left) *Semionotus, a fresh-water holostean of Triassic age. This species, 7 inches long, inhabited Arizona.*

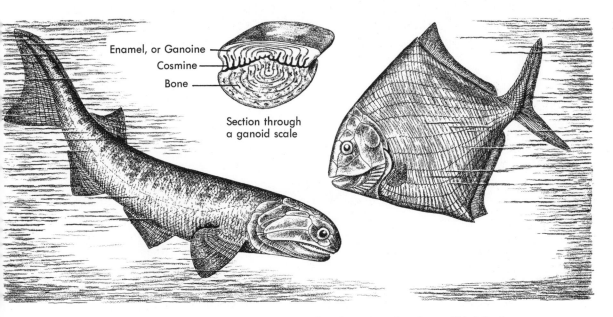

(Left) *Cheirolepis, a primitive Devonian ray-fin about 9 inches long.* (Right) *Amphicentrum, a deep-bodied Carboniferous ray-fin about 6 inches long. It may have been a reef-dweller.*

relics of the heterocercal lobe. Vertebrae still were composed chiefly of carti-lage, and the fin-rays were no longer jointed.

A pioneer in this group was *Semionotus,* which lived in late Triassic waters. Later came fish with deep, narrow bodies, stubby tails, and many bones in the skull. They reached 12 to 15 inches in length and developed blunt, peg-shaped teeth with which they crushed mollusks and other invertebrates.

Most holosteans were Mesozoic, but two families—both North American—have survived into modern times. The gars include savage, long-jawed fish which may be descended from semionotids. Their skulls are thick, their skele-tons are bony, and the large ganoid scales are heavy. When the quiet waters

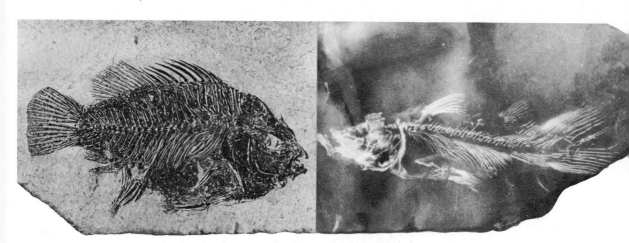

(Left) *A bony fish, Priscacara, from the Green River formation of Uinta County, Wyoming.* (Right) *An X-ray photograph of Diplurus in red Triassic shale from Princeton, New Jersey*

in which they live become foul, gars gulp air and take oxygen from it with the swim bladder, which thus reverts to the role of lung. One fossil gar is found, though rarely, in the Green River beds.

Bowfins are the other living holosteans. They appeared in streams and lakes of the Jurassic period and evolved into their surviving genus, *Amia,* as the Cenozoic era began. They were and still are powerful predators 24 to 30 inches in length, with a long dorsal fin and a blunt tail which still has a few upturned vertebrae. Bowfins feed largely on small fish but also consume cray-fish, worms, insects, and other odds and ends. The males dig nests and guard the eggs, and both sexes are able to use the air bladder as a lung.

Modern Ray-fins (Teleosts). These are the most up-to-date of all bony fishes, the latest products of evolutionary changes made during 140,000,000 years. Teleosts appeared in early Jurassic seas and varied widely during Cretaceous times, when they outnumbered marine holosteans. In the Eocene epoch they became the dominant fishes of both fresh waters and seas.

We are tempted to define teleosts as the boniest of bony fishes and let it go at that. Unlike holosteans, chondrosteans, and lobe-fins, they have fully ossified internal skeletons in which long-established structures are often supplemented by a variety of new spines and bones. The tail is homocercal, which means that the backbone stops short, letting fin-rays grow out from its end. Scales are thin, with no trace of the ganoid layer, and they normally overlap like shingles. They also may be reduced in size or may disappear.

Since fossil teleosts belong to all principal subgroups, we examine them for relatives of familiar modern fish. Among primitive forms are the tarpons, *Tarpon* itself in the late Cretaceous of Europe and the bulldog tarpon, *Portheus*, in both Europe and North America. The American species had a blunt head and jaws set with sharp teeth, reached a length of 12 feet, and weighed 500 to 600 pounds. It fed upon smaller fish and the young of marine reptiles described in Chapter XXV. One huge *Portheus* even gulped down a 6-foot neighbor but died before digesting its meal.

The salmon-trout family also appeared in late Cretaceous seas of North America; some species moved into fresh water during Tertiary epochs. Suckers lived in Eocene Asia, where they probably became the ancestors of carps. Pike, perch, bass, sunfish, snapper, mackerel, marlin—these and many others were common in Tertiary fresh waters and seas.

Along with these "normal fish" were aberrant, highly specialized forms. Catfish, for example, lost their scales, though several species developed bony skin plates. Eels became long and slender, changed the structure of their jaws, and developed continuous fins on the back, tail, and under side. Some species also lost their scales, though others kept tiny ones deep down in the skin. The gurnards and sea robins developed large, spiny heads and fins in which two or three rays form separate, fingerlike organs. The fish use them to walk about on the sea bottom and to pry into shells or overturn stones as they search for food.

CHAPTER XXII

New Plants on Old Lands

W<small>E HAVE REVIEWED</small> monerans, protists, animals, and lowly plants whose story runs through more than 1,600,000,000 years. Most of these organisms were aquatic, and the vast majority were marine. Exceptions, such as fresh-water snails and fish or terrestrial insects, were late-comers. They appeared ages or even eras after their relatives had become plentiful in the sea.

This fact shows that we did not begin our survey with marine fossils for convenience and are just getting round to the others. If that were true we could now turn back to Precambrian deposits and begin a new series of chapters on inhabitants of the land. For lands existed in those ancient times, forming shores of the constantly shifting seas and providing most of the sediment that filled burrows, covered trails, and enclosed dead shells or corals. Yet from those lands have come few fossils; none at all that antedate the Silurian period. Insects, which now outnumber all other terrestrial creatures, did not appear until Devonian times.

Still, we must not infer that all pre-Silurian lands were barren. Some of the Precambrian formations that are richest in stromatolites also include sediments that seem to have come from lands with protective coats of plant life. These otherwise unknown plants probably were small, soft forms that may have re-sembled modern lichens such as reindeer moss, but apparently were descended from seaweeds that lived in shallow water. Since the earliest seas were not very salty, the transition from shallow bays to low, moist shores should not have been difficult. To go from swamps to uplands was a much greater step, but one for which scores of millions of years were available before mid-Pro-terozoic or Eozoic time. Modern plants such as eel grass have left dry land and returned to salt water in a much shorter period.

THE EARLIEST LAND PLANTS

All this, of course, is speculation based on indirect evidence. It tells what may have happened and reminds us that plants have probably lived on land for more than 1,000,000,000 years. Yet when land plants did become fossils, they had not progressed very far beyond their aquatic predecessors. Some of the oldest and simplest are found in late Silurian rocks of Australia. They are rootless, leafless affairs with underground stems and upright shoots whose tips bore small cases containing *spores,* or nonsexual reproductive cells. Other fossils, quite as ancient but not so simple, were related to modern ground pines and looked like them. Both types probably grew beside streams, near low coasts, from which their remains were washed into stagnant seas. There the plants were buried in black mud containing graptolites and other marine animals.

Prototaxites is as old as these Australian fossils, for it has been found in late Silurian rocks of Wales and western New York, as well as in Devonian formations of Scotland and Quebec. Though described as a very primitive yew tree, it now seems to be an aberrant descendant of brown algae that was able to live in swamps as well as in shallow brackish bays. Its stalks reached lengths of 60 feet and were 2 or 3 feet thick at the base.

DEVONIAN BOGS AND FORESTS

Tourists who use the Silver Gate entrance to Yellowstone National Park pass the site of another early land flora. To reach it they climb some thousands of feet by automobile and travel across an ancient and now uncovered sea floor dotted by glacial lakes. Beside one of these rises Beartooth Butte, a cliff of marine strata that range from Cambrian to Devonian in age. Near the top

Some very early land plants

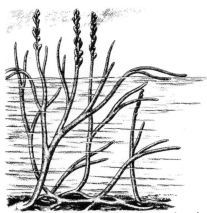 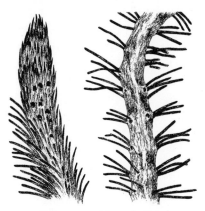 

Zosterophyllum. Late Silurian and early Devonian, Australia and Europe

Baragwanathia, a lycopod. Early Silurian, Australia.

Yaravia. Early Silurian, Australia

Beartooth Butte, Wyoming. Fossil plants and vertebrates are found in dark-colored river deposits above the letter R.

is an early Devonian river channel, worn in older beds while northwestern Wyoming was a lowland crossed by meandering streams.

Photographers pause to "shoot" the lake, but fossil hunters park their cars and climb the southern face of the butte. Near its base they find green to brown shales and sandstones, some showing filled burrows of middle Cambrian annelids. Then come dolomites and limestones containing stromatolites, followed by red, buff, and gray river deposits whose thickness reaches 150 feet. Laid down near the mouth of a sluggish stream, these sediments contain eurypterids, ostracoderms, fish, and a variety of land plants. The commonest of these is *Psilophyton,* a prickly, leafless shrub allied to one of Silurian Australia. Another plant had spore-bearing stems resembling those of certain primitive ferns.

Plants much like those of Beartooth Butte lived in eastern Canada during early to middle Devonian times; their remains, generally poorly preserved, may be found in the Gaspé sandstones of southeastern Quebec. Our best record of middle Devonian vegetation comes from western Europe. There, in what once were sheltered valleys between mountain ranges, grew fungi, rush-like plants, and others that resembled ground pines in shape though not in structure. There also were woody shrubs that reached heights of 8 to 12 feet. The best-known types were found in a one-time peat bog near the village of Rhynie in Aberdeenshire, Scotland. Fed by silica-bearing water from nearby hot springs, this bog produced fossils whose cells appear in thin sections cut from layers of chert.

LATE DEVONIAN FORESTS

Returning to North America, we find that mountainous areas, probably islands, extended from Georgia to Newfoundland during late Devonian times. Those mountains were moist, with many streams that flowed westward to the retreating sea. Where the streams reached salt water they built up deltas which spread until they formed an almost continuous lowland covered by some of the earth's first forests.

The existence of those forests had been suspected since 1869, when a freshet raged down Scoharie Creek, wrecking bridges, washing out culverts, and exposing a few fossil tree stumps near the village of Gilboa, New York. Additional fragments were found in 1897, and in 1920 collectors discovered a forest stratum higher than the one reached by the freshet. At last, in 1921, the city of New York opened two quarries to get stone for dams. The dams were built

Some primitive Devonian land plants

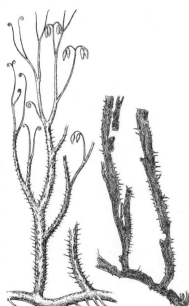

Psilophyton, restoration and fossil. Early Devonian of North America and Europe

Rhynia. Middle Devonian of Europe

Protolepidodendron. Middle Devonian of Europe

Asteroxylon. Early and middle Devonian of Europe

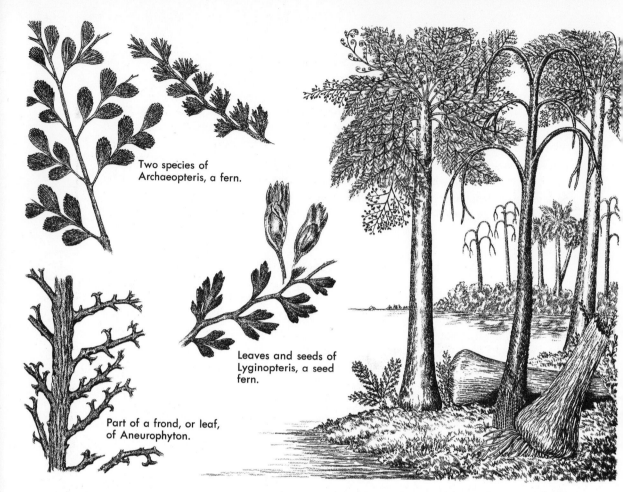

Two species of
Archaeopteris, a fern.

Leaves and seeds of
Lyginopteris, a seed
fern.

Part of a frond, or leaf,
of Aneurophyton.

A scene in the late Devonian forest of Gilboa, New York, and fossils of some late Devonian plants. The trees with fernlike leaves are Aneurophyton; the others are Archaeosigillaria, a genus of lycopods.

to hold back water, but the quarries completed the story of Gilboa's ancient woods.

"Eospermatopteris." The most plentiful trees in the Gilboa forests had straight trunks 20 to 40 feet high, with swollen, onion-shaped bases 3 to 4 feet in thickness. The roots were slender, straplike affairs that ran out in all directions, like the roots of present-day palms. The leaves were fernlike and 6 to 8 feet long, and their tips bore pointed structures resembling seeds. Because of them the trees were assigned to a group called the seed ferns and were named *Eospermatopteris.* Later studies have shown that some of the "seeds" still contain spores, while the trunks and leaves are identical with others long known as *Aneurophyton.* Though their exact place in the plant world is uncertain, they may be descendants of the spiny *Psilophyton* found on Beartooth Butte.

Early Lycopods. Much less common in Gilboa's swampy woods were two species of lycopods, plants that still survive in the form of club mosses and ground pines. Those of Gilboa were slender trees with drooping branches.

One species had narrow leaves about 12 inches long, but those of the other species were wider and shorter and overlapped like scales. They grew upon both trunk and branches and must have made the trees look as if they were covered with moss. Cones at the tips of some branches were filled with spores, not seeds.

This matter of spores versus seeds is important in plant classification and progress. At its simplest, a spore is a single cell that can grow into a new plant. Such spores are found among molds, fungi, mosses, and ferns. In many other plants, however, two cells must join and form a single new one before development can begin. These "marrying cells" may be identical, as they are in lycopods and some algae. They also may differ in size and shape, as they do

Lepidodendron   Sigillaria   Cordaites   Calamites

Tree Fern

Plants of a swampy Pennsylvanian forest, in almost any part of the world

in horsetails and rockweeds, to choose only two examples. As with simple spores, the product is always a new plant that must make its way unassisted through the early stages of its life.

A seed, on the other hand, is a new plant enclosed in parental stores of food and in armor. The seed begins when two cells—always different—unite and grow into a partly developed plant known as an embryo. The parent plant provides this embryo with food and covers it with a husk or shell that furnishes protection. When this structure, the seed, is fully developed, the embryo in it may begin to grow. It also may lie for months or even years before it germinates.

Callixylon. There must have been seed-ferns in late Devonian times, but they left no remains in the Gilboa forest. That forest also contained no trace of *Callixylon,* a tree that grew upon near-shore lowlands from Russia to Oklahoma, Indiana, and New York. It had a tall, straight trunk 2 to 5 feet thick, with a crown of slender branches that bore pointed, fleshy leaves. The best-known species is found in a late Devonian formation (the New Albany shale) of southern Indiana and Ohio. The wood generally is well preserved; when microscopic sections are made, it can be recognized by thick-rimmed pits that penetrate the cell walls. The chances are, however, that any petrified wood from the late Devonian of southern Indiana or Ohio belongs to *Callixylon Newberryi.* The species found in western and central New York (*C. Zalisskyi*) has narrow rays and is generally represented by twigs an inch or less in diameter.

Modern forests shelter small plants, and woodlands of the late Devonian also had a prolific undergrowth. It included several true ferns, one of which had fronds 3 feet long, bearing many toothed leaflets. There also were plants resembling horsetails and others that were creeping vines with leaves arranged in rosettes. Their closest relatives became common during Carboniferous times.

COAL AGE AND COAL FORESTS

The Devonian period came to an end as rocks crumpled into mountain ranges that stretched from Newfoundland to what is now North Carolina. Then came the early Carboniferous, or Mississippian, a period or subperiod that lasted 30,000,000 years. During most of those years, shallow seas spread widely across the interior of North America, but much of the eastern region was lowland. Fossils show that the bulbous-trunked *Aneurophyton* had vanished, along with the drooping trees of Gilboa. In their stead grew other lycopods, as well as ferns, seed-ferns, and trees related to *Callixylon.* Unfortunately most fossils are so poorly preserved that only the expert can learn much from them. To get a really satisfying picture of Carboniferous plant life we must go to the next division of earth history.

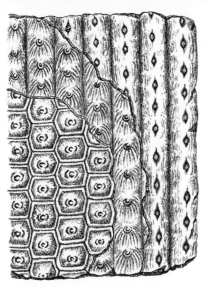 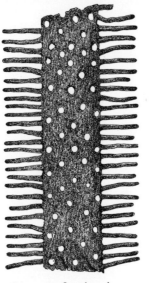 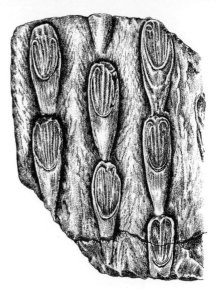

Sigillaria, showing three different layers of bark. The outermost
is at the left.

Stigmaria ficoides, the
rootlike organ of a tree
such as Lepidodendron

Psaronius, the stem of a seed-
fern. The scars show where leaves
were attached.

Bark, roots, and a stem from typical Pennsylvanian plants

That division bears various names: Pennsylvanian, late Carboniferous, and Coal Age. It was a time when seas repeatedly advanced, only to disappear as streams filled them with sediment. Other streams flowed to inland basins, which sank about as rapidly as they were filled by detritus. The result was a vast series of swamps whose waters sometimes were clear, sometimes were muddy, and sometimes were almost filled by deposits of mud, gravel, and sand.

Those swamps were a paradise for plant life, offering rich soil, an equable and humid climate, and a generous supply of moisture. As a result, vegetation grew in such abundance that its decaying remains built up beds of peat which then hardened into coal. Late Carboniferous formations of western Pennsylvania, for example, contain thirteen important coal beds, one of which—the Pittsburgh "seam"—is 6 to 14 feet in thickness. The number of leaves, stems, and trunks in such deposits defies imagination.

Besides forming beds of coal, land plants of Pennsylvanian times left an abundance of fossils. Some of them are films of carbon left in fine sand and mud as leaves, stems, and roots decayed. Others are mere impressions in sandstone, but many are perfect petrifications found in lumps of calcite, or "coal balls." Trees range from carbonized layers to casts made of sediment that filled holes left by trunks or stumps after their pulpy wood had decayed. In many places these fossil stumps and trunks have been found standing erect in rock. Those at Joggins and Sidney, Nova Scotia, are among the finest and most famous in North America.

Anyone who identifies Pennsylvanian plants soon finds that they are widely distributed. Many species that are plentiful in Nova Scotia, West Virginia, and Illinois or Kansas were discovered and named in Europe; other European species are common in Africa, China, and Australia. These wide-ranging fossils are a great help in correlating formations. And, since each species generally fits a definite set of surroundings, wide distribution also indicates uniformity of climate and other conditions in places thousands of miles apart.

SOME TYPICAL PENNSYLVANIAN PLANTS

No one book, and assuredly no single chapter, can describe the vast array of Pennsylvanian plants. We can, however, mention the genera one is most likely to find, which also are the ones that establish the general character of the flora in Coal Age forests and swamps.

Lycopods. Modern lycopods, as we already know, include the club mosses and ground pines: small plants that creep on the ground, send up stalks and branches, and reproduce by means of spores borne in conelike organs. Most Pennsylvanian lycopods were trees, and *Lepidodendron* was one of the tallest, for some species reached heights of 100 to 125 feet. The trunk was straight and simple at its base, but higher up it formed two branches that bifurcated again and again. Young parts of the tree were covered with dagger-shaped leaves that grew close to the thick bark. When leaves dropped from the trunk and older branches they left scars that look like diamond-shaped scales and gave the plant its name, which means "scale-tree." The spore-bearing cones were long and grew either at the tips of branches or along their sides. The species of *Lepidodendron*—they number more than a hundred—are distinguished largely by the shape and other details of these scars.

The base of each *Lepidodendron* trunk divided into two underground parts that bifurcated again and so formed a network of woody organs that bear the

Four typical Pennsylvanian plants

Annularia and Asterophyllites. Both are branches and leaves of scouring rushes, or calamites.

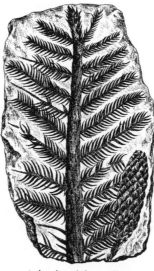

Lebachia (also called Walchia), a conifer

Sphenophyllum, a small creeping plant

deceptive name of rootstocks. Each rootstock gave off what botanists often call "lateral absorptive appendages," since they may or may not be true roots. They left small round scars on the rootstock—scars that are more widely spaced than those on the bark of branches and trunk.

Stigmaria. Before the nature of the rootstocks was known they were named *Stigmaria.* There is little doubt that most so-called stigmarians belong to *Lepidodendron,* though some may be the underground stems of other lycopods. The commonest type bears the specific name *ficoides* (figlike) because it slightly resembles the branchlets of fig trees. *Stigmaria ficoides* tapers gradually to a blunt tip about one inch in diameter. The "rootlets" seldom measure more than a quarter inch in width and look like narrow black ribbons on layers of gray shale that once were soil.

Sigillaria ranked next to *Lepidodendron* in Pennsylvanian forests. It was sturdier but not so tall; one species became 6 feet in diameter at the base, tapered to 12 inches at a height of 18 feet, and measured less than 40 feet over all. The leaves were slender, pointed, and longer than those of *Lepidodendron;* some suggest very large blades of grass. When the leaves fell they left scars which seldom were closely crowded. In some species the bark between scars was smooth; in others it bore ridges that ran up and down the trunk. Most species did not branch, or branched only once or twice. The cones, 4 to 8 inches in length, hung from long stems on trunks or branches, just below the leaves.

Cordaites and Conifers. These fossil plants remind us that trees are not a natural group but merely are large, woody plants which may or may not be related. Most Coal Age trees were lycopods, but *Cordaites* was distantly related to pines and stands close to *Callixylon* of the late Devonian forests. *Cordaites* itself was a tall, slender tree with a trunk that bore a crown of branches. The leaves were wider, thinner, and less pointed than those of lycopods; as fossils they suggest broad, blunt cattail leaves 9 to 40 inches long. Flattened, heart-shaped seeds were borne on stalks among the leaves.

Cordaites is another example of plants whose separate parts were discovered and named before anyone suspected that they belonged together. As a result, the seed-bearing stalks became *Cordaianthus,* casts of pith in the trunks were named *Artesia,* and roots were called *Amyelon.* None of these names is necessary, yet they must be used when we label specimens.

Walchia and *Lebachia* are true conifers and so are related to redwoods, spruces, and pines. The Pennsylvanian plants were straight, slender trees whose branches bore small twigs arranged like the barbs of a feather. Leaves were short, narrow, and pointed, like the leaves of modern araucarians, or monkey-puzzle pines.

Horsetails and Their Kin. Modern horsetails, also called scouring rushes, live in both wet and very dry places. Their straight, slender stems are jointed and are made gritty by large amounts of silica. *Calamites,* the chief Pennsylvanian genus, grew 2 or 3 to as much as 40 feet high, with stems that were smooth or

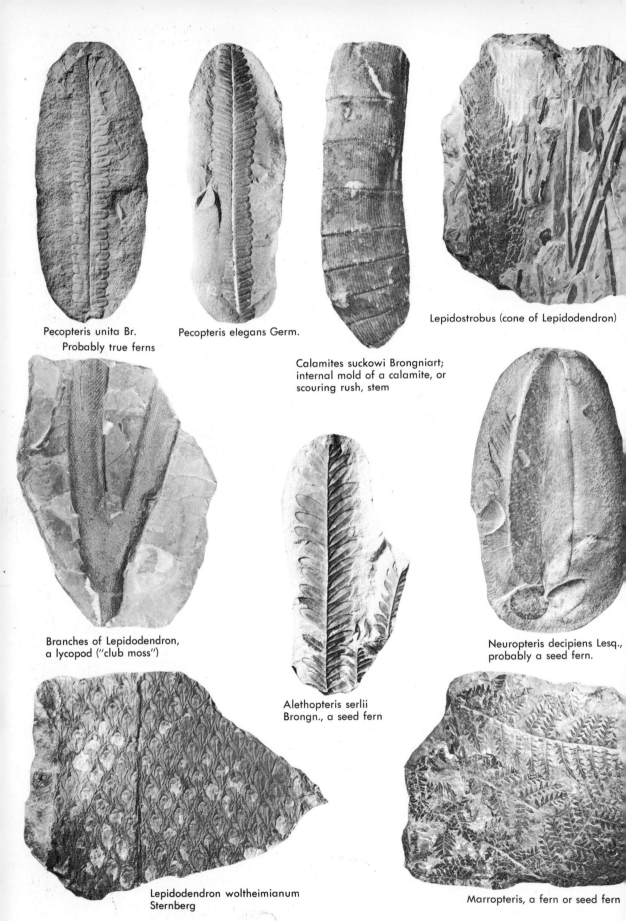

Pecopteris unita Br.
Probably true ferns

Pecopteris elegans Germ.

Lepidostrobus (cone of Lepidodendron)

Calamites suckowi Brongniart;
internal mold of a calamite, or
scouring rush, stem

Branches of Lepidodendron,
a lycopod ("club moss")

Alethopteris serlii
Brongn., a seed fern

Neuropteris decipiens Lesq.,
probably a seed fern.

Lepidodendron woltheimianum
Sternberg

Marropteris, a fern or seed fern

Fernlike leaves, lycopods, and a scouring rush, all Pennsylvanian

(*Left*) Snails, clams, and uncoiled ammonoids (Baculites) in a Cretaceous sea. (*Right*) Placenticeras, a coiled ammonoid. Above it swim two belemnoids, whose shells are covered by their fleshy mantles.

SOME MARINE FOSSILS AS THEY LOOKED DURING LIFE

(*Below*) Part of a Devonian (Onondagan) coral bank in New York or Ontario. It shows corals, brachiopods, trilobites, and a straight-shelled cephalopod. Dioramas in the Exhibit Museum of the University of Michigan.

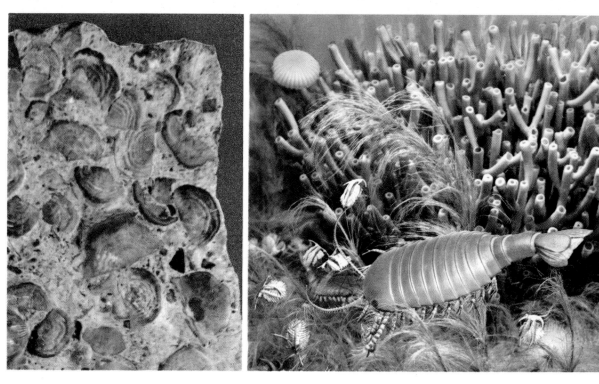

(*Left*) Leptaena and other late Ordovician brachiopods, Oxford, Ohio. (*Right*) Arthropods, sponges, and jellyfish of the middle Cambrian Burgess shale. The large animal is Sidneyia; the small ones are Marrella.

BRACHIOPODS AND RESTORATIONS OF FOSSIL INVERTEBRATES

A Mississippian crinoid bank in what is now Indiana. One starfish lies on the bottom; another clings to the yellow crinoid at the right. This and the Burgess diorama are in the Exhibit Museum, University of Michigan.

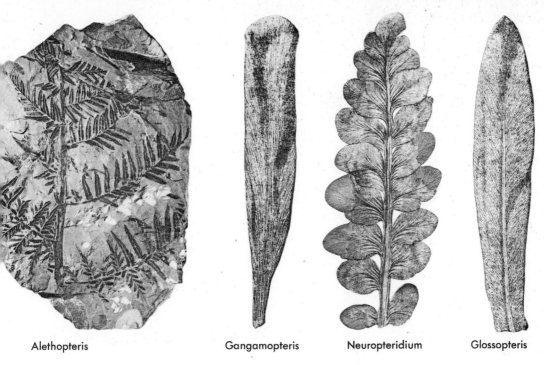

Alethopteris   Gangamopteris   Neuropteridium   Glossopteris

Alethopteris is a Pennsylvanian seed-fern. The three other genera belong to the Permian Glossopteris flora of the Old World.

had lengthwise ridges. Specimens 3 inches in diameter are common, and some plants must have been 10 to 12 inches thick. The upright, woody stems grew from rootstocks and were supported by roots that came from the lowermost joints, like the prop roots of corn. Some species were unbranched, but others had branches that grew from the joints, or nodes. Clusters of slender leaves also grew from nodes, especially on young branches, though they often remained on good-sized stems.

Calamites formed extensive jungles beside rivers and lakes, as well as in shallow swamps. Petrified stems are found on some shales, and carbonized leaves are common. Still more familiar are sandstone casts replacing the pith which once filled upright stems. These casts generally show ridges as well as nodes and pits to which branches were attached, but the ridges do not correspond to those that once appeared on the surface.

Annulaira is one of the names applied to leaves of *Calamites*. The leaves are bladelike, with a single vein, and form clusters around branches or stems. Still other names are applied to roots.

Sphenophyllum was a small vinelike plant that probably grew in mats like the modern *Vinca,* or periwinkle. The small leaves, which were triangular or divided into lobes, grew in whorls; roots grew from joints on the slender stem.

Seed-ferns. Coal Age deposits contain great numbers of fossil leaves that once were thought to be true ferns. But ferns reproduce by means of spores, and these ancient plants bore seeds. The fossils therefore represent a special

group called seed-ferns, or pteridosperms. They are distantly related to conifers but show closer kinship to cycads, which now include the sago "palms."

Some seed-ferns, such as *Lyginodendron,* bore their seeds upon otherwise
naked fronds that looked like small, branched stalks. Others carried seeds at
the ends of some leafy fronds, though other fronds were sterile. In certain
species the fronds branched by dividing into two and bore toothed or divided
leaflets or pinnules; others had leaflets that were broadly attached at the base.
Since most fossil seed-ferns are separate leaflets or bits of fronds, it is not easy
to tell what the living plants were like or even to make sure they were seed-
ferns. Thus some of the leaves called *Pecopteris* bore seeds, but others that
look like them may have belonged to the true ferns. There is a growing tendency, however, to assume that any leaf corresponding to a known seed-fern
really belongs to that group.

True Ferns. True ferns of the Pennsylvanian range from plants resembling
the modern royal fern to others that were trees. One of the latter, called
Psaronius, had a tall slender trunk and a crown of leaves much like those of
the seed-fern, *Pecopteris*. Roots grew from the lower part of the trunk, forming
a matted sheath as much as 15 inches in thickness. Silicified trunks with these
root-sheaths are found near Athens, in southeastern Ohio. Polished slices
make attractive display specimens, while sections of individual roots can be
cut into showy gems.

PARADISE PAST; THE PERMIAN FLORA

Coal Age swamps were a paradise for plant life, but a paradise that disappeared as soon as conditions changed. This happened at the end of the Pennsylvanian and during the Permian period, when continents rose, mountain
systems were built, and glacial ice spread into the tropics, even crossing the
equator. Between glaciations came epochs of moisture and warmth, as well
as others in which deserts appeared in the rain shadows cast by mountains.

These changes affected the Southern Hemisphere more than the Northern,
where broad and often swampy lowlands persisted for some millions of years.
We find, therefore, that early Permian plants of the Northern Hemisphere are
much like their Pennsylvanian ancestors. In the Southern Hemisphere, however, the great lycopod forests vanished, along with calamite jungles and seed-
ferns. In their place appeared smaller, hardier plants that were able to live between glaciations. Indeed, some of their remains have been found in deposits
left by bergs that broke loose from the moving ice.

Glossopteris and Its Kin. This hardy flora contained a variety of plants—true
ferns, conifers, small calamites, and so on. Its foremost member, however, was
Glossopteris, a seed-fern with thick bladelike leaves. Each leaf contained a network of veins and a sturdy midrib, but the latter was lacking from the leaves

of another seed-fern, *Gangamopteris.* A third genus, *Neuropteridium,* had a coarse central stalk with lobed leaflets that were broadly attached at the base.

As time passed, the *Glossopteris* flora spread northward to Russia and Siberia, though it seemingly did not reach Western Europe or North America. Conditions meanwhile became somewhat more mild in the Southern Hemisphere, allowing lycopods to cross the equator again, though not in very great numbers. A *Psaronius* 60 feet tall reached Brazil, where its fossil stumps resemble those found in older rocks of Ohio.

The Hermit Flora. A surprising array of Permian plants has been found along trails that descend into Arizona's Grand Canyon. On the way they cross the Hermit formation, a deposit of shale that filled shallow basins and arroyos eroded in sand. The strata range from brick red to blood red, contain casts of salt crystals, and are deeply marked by mud cracks. They plainly formed in a semi-arid region whose torrential rains were followed by droughts during which streams ran dry and ponds became sun-baked flats. Except for color, they resembled mud flats at the north end of Pyramid Lake in present-day Nevada.

Swamp-dwelling plants could not have survived in such a habitat. Instead, the red rocks contain mats of algae that spread over muddy slime, and leathery seed-ferns that grew beside both ponds and intermittent streams. There also are a thick-stemmed species of *Sphenophyllum,* a *Walchia* with little leaves, and several other conifers.

THE END OF AN ERA

The Permian period was a time of upheavals so intense and widespread that they rank as a geologic revolution. Seas and swamps became land and then turned into mountains—a magnificent chain that stretched 2,000 miles from Newfoundland to southern Alabama, as the first and greatest Appalachians. In the Far West, volcanoes erupted from Mexico northward to Alaska, and in Europe the Ural and Variscan Mountains reached their greatest heights. Climates became rigorous over a large part of the globe.

As lush, mild lowlands disappeared, primitive land plants also vanished. First to go were the great lycopod trees, few of which survived into late Permian epochs. *Sphenophyllum* also vanished, as did most of the seed-ferns and such tree ferns as *Psaronius.* Some other ferns survived, it is true, as did cycads, conifers, and true horsetails. These, however, were not primitive plants, but descendants that were able to develop and prosper in the new and more rigorous era that began as the Paleozoic closed.

CHAPTER XXIII

Lungs, Legs, and Land-Dwellers

Since lungfish breathe air, early theorists tried to make them the ancestors of terrestrial vertebrates. That effort foundered upon specialized teeth, degenerate bones, and elongate fins—all characters that separate lungfish from the main course of vertebrate progress. Lungfish were evolutionary great-aunts and -uncles, not the parents, of terrestrial vertebrates.

FROM FISH TO AMPHIBIANS

For the actual ancestors of four-legged air-breathers, we return to the Old Red Sandstone and *Osteolepis*. It is qualified as an ancestor by a full set of bones in skull and jaws, by teeth whose enamel was crumpled in a complex, or labyrinthine, pattern, and by short fins with broad, stubby lobes. They were much sturdier than the slender fins of *Dipterus* and its kin.

This may seem like a trifling difference, but its significance appeared during seasons of drought. Both lobe-fin and lungfish took refuge in pools; both breathed air into their lungs; both fared equally well until the pools evaporated. Then *Dipterus* lay on the mud and died, for its slender fins could not drag its body overland to other pools. *Osteolepis* fared better, for its stubby fins enabled it to half crawl and half wriggle once it was out of water. Often, of course, these struggles were useless, but sometimes the fish reached water before its strength gave out.

Water—permanent water—meant survival, but that was not the end of the process. As millions of years went by, some of the survivors produced offspring with fin lobes in which bones assumed the skeletal pattern of legs, feet, and toes while the marginal fringes dwindled away. The result of these changes was a race of four-legged breathers of air that could travel on land even though they might do so only while seeking water.

Ichthyostega, a late Devonian amphibian of Greenland. It had four legs but fins on its tail. Length about 4 feet

Eusthenopteron, a Devonian lobe-finned fish that breathed air. Length 40 inches

We call these four-legged creatures amphibians in recognition of the fact that they could lead two kinds of lives. Though no one saw them evolve, their descent from fringe-finned fish is convincingly documented by fossils. Besides *Osteolepis,* we have the more progressive *Eusthenopteron,* whose tail had become diphycercal and whose enlarged fin lobes contained bones recognizably like those of the foreleg and foot. A partial skull from Quebec has gone still further, presenting a mixture of fishlike and amphibian characters in which the latter barely predominate.

Other links have been found in fresh-water deposits of Greenland; their age is late Devonian or earliest Mississippian. Fossils called *Ichthyostega* have skulls about 8 inches long, with bones like those of *Eusthenopteron* but with

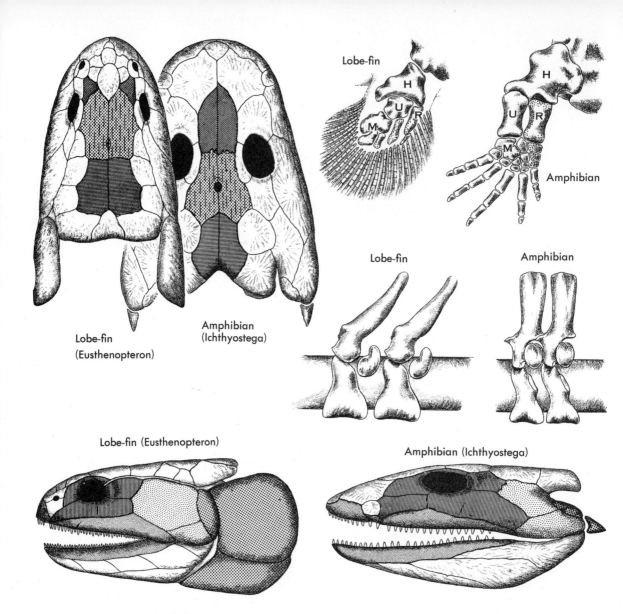

How skulls, leg bones, and vertebrae changed as lobe-fins evolved into amphibians. Identical bones in the skull are marked by similar shading; those in front fin and foreleg are indicated by letters. Bones in the vertebrae changed too little to need special markings.

nostrils at the edge of the upper jaw. Orbits for the eyes are large, and the teeth have deeply crumpled enamel. Though the young *Ichthyostega* doubtless breathed with gills, the creature had lost the broad bony plates (opercula) that covered the gills of fringe-fins. The loss was a recent one, however, for the skull still had two bones which once anchored opercula to the cheeks.

All in all, we may picture *Ichthyostega* as a sluggish yet probably savage creature 4 to 5 feet in length whose skin was still covered with scales. The body was beginning to spread, but fins on the tail were supported by small bony rays. The four legs were short and thick, and the toes were stubby. When the creature ventured on land, which may not have been often, it probably crept with a wriggling motion that put little strain on its legs.

Labyrinthodonts. These early amphibians are called labyrinthodonts, because the enamel of their teeth showed the same crumpled pattern found in such fish as *Osteolepis*. Their descendants left few fossils in Mississippian strata, yet they must have evolved and adapted themselves to a variety of conditions. When the Pennsylvanian period dawned, labyrinthodonts ranged from creeping forms allied to *Ichthyostega* to small animals that climbed trees and others

Eogyrinus, a Pennsylvanian embolomere about 15 feet long.

as big as alligators. The latter, called embolomeres, were swamp-dwellers with heavy heads, long bodies and tails, and diminutive, useless legs. Embolomeres must have spent their lives in streams and pools, where they swam and dined on fish or other amphibians.

The Nonexistent Branchiosaurs. Many Coal Age amphibians were small creatures once called branchiosaurs. They had short skulls, long tails, and bones that were mostly cartilage; the fossils of some show external gills like those of modern mud-puppies and tadpoles. Critical study finally proved that these supposed adults actually were partly developed, or larval, stages of other amphibians. Many doubtless became long embolomeres, though others grew up into massive forms with broad heads, short legs, and long tails. We shall encounter one of these animals later, under the name of *Eryops*.

AMPHIBIANS INTO REPTILES

Pennsylvanian amphibians prospered; their variety is proof of that. Yet they had to compete with more progressive creatures, the reptiles, which first conquered the land and then invaded both fresh and salt water.

To understand the rise of reptiles we must review the conditions under

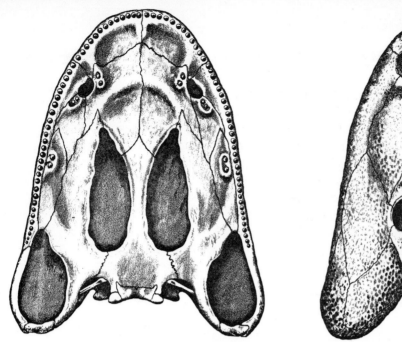

Skull of Eryops from the Permian of Baylor County, Texas. Length about 18 inches

which Devonian fish evolved legs from short-lobed fins. They did not do this while escaping from enemies in the water, for fringe-fins themselves were the most active, most savage, and best-armed creatures in middle Devonian rivers and ponds. Those fish also did not go ashore to find food or in response to some mystic lure of atmospheric oxygen. As flesh eaters, the fringe-fins ate other fish, and they could get all the oxygen they needed simply by gulping air into their lungs. This ability often saved their lives when dwindling waters became fouled by decaying vegetation.

The real reason why *Osteolepis* and his kin went ashore was their need to remain in water. Unlike the lungfish of modern Africa, they could not curl up in cocoons of mud and hibernate during the dry season. They had to swim about in search of food, and they needed moisture around their bodies. To fill that need, they left pools and streams that had dried up, wriggling overland to others that still contained moisture. The winners in this struggle generally were the fish that had the sturdiest fin lobes and their descendants whose lobes turned into legs. Yet those legs were incidental by-products, undreamed of and unsought by stranded and desperate *fish*.

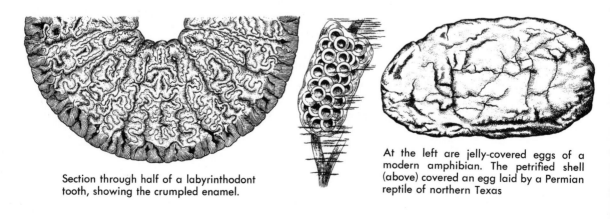

Section through half of a labyrinthodont tooth, showing the crumpled enamel.

At the left are jelly-covered eggs of a modern amphibian. The petrified shell (above) covered an egg laid by a Permian reptile of northern Texas

This explains an otherwise paradoxical fact: that animals which first developed legs remained in water when they could do so, swimming by means of tails while their new limbs dangled unused. One group even evolved into embolomeres with legs so short they could not have walked had they wanted to do so.

An even more critical factor tied early amphibians to the water. Like modern members of their class, they laid eggs that contained small reserves of food and were not protected by shells or membranes filled with liquid. Such eggs had to be laid in water, where they would not dry out, and their embryos soon hatched into young ones that could find their own food for further development. To amphibians, this meant tadpoles whose gills and fins allowed them to live like fish while legs and lungs developed. It also meant that mature animals had to return to the water in the breeding season and there lay their unprotected eggs.

The changing world, however, placed a premium on vertebrates that did not depend on streams and ponds that frequently dried up. It also offered forests and bogs uninhabited except by insects and some other invertebrates. Why shouldn't four-legged vertebrates overcome the threat of recurrent droughts and in doing so exploit a hospitable environment?

Thus the challenge now appears to us; to amphibians it was merely the problem of finding water, combined with food, shelter, and plenty of space for creatures that could stay on land. These factors presumably worked through natural selection, blindly killing aquatic animals that were caught on constantly rising lands, but preserving chance variants equipped for terrestrial life. The first result probably was amphibians with superior legs. Later came variants that gave their eggs reserves of food, wrapped them in liquid-filled membranes, and covered them with porous shells that served as armor yet allowed oxygen to reach developing embryos. Liquid-filled membranes prevented drying and reduced changes in temperature, while abundant food—we call it yolk—enabled the embryos to develop into four-legged animals with lungs before leaving their shells. Thus they skipped the water-bound tadpole stage and hatched as quadrupeds able to live on land.

ANOTHER NON-MISSING LINK

Those early quadrupeds were reptiles; they probably appeared in latest Devonian times, only a few million years after the first amphibians. Unfortunately this and the succeeding Mississippian period were times of geologic change during which few rocks were deposited on land or in estuaries. Our knowledge of the steps from amphibian to reptile therefore comes from primitive types that lingered on and became fossils during later times.

Seymouria was one of those survivors; though its ancestors had lived in

Seymouria (left), *20 inches long, was a link between amphibians and reptiles. Tri-merorhachis* (right) *was a specialized labyrinthodont. Both are from the Permian of Texas.*

Europe, it reached North America during earliest Permian times. Fossils show a massive skull with large orbits for the eyes and an opening for a pineal body which apparently could tell light from shade and is often miscalled an eye. The teeth possessed labyrinthine enamel, but the skeleton combined such a mixture of amphibian and reptilian structures that the creature is sometimes placed in one group and sometimes in the other. There is little doubt that one of *Seymouria's* relatives—an evolutionary great-aunt, so to speak—laid some of the first eggs that developed and hatched out of water, thus establishing the class of reptiles.

Pennsylvanian Reptiles. The oldest reptile so far discovered is a little, headless skeleton of early Pennsylvanian age. It is simple and seems to be primitive, but bones found near Pittsburgh and Danville, Illinois, are not. Dating from the late Pennsylvanian, they show that reptiles had evolved into several distinct and highly specialized types. The most bizarre of these, *Edaphosaurus,* bore a skin-covered "fin" on its back, supported by bony spines equipped with short crossbars. The skull was small and had blunt teeth on the hard palate as well as on the jaws. *Edaphosaurus* probably fed upon plants, though it may also have crushed mussels which it found in pools.

VERTEBRATES OF THE REDBEDS

To view life on land as the Coal Age closed and the Permian dawned, we go to Baylor and nearby counties in north-central Texas. Today the region is rolling upland devoted to cattle ranches and farms. Mesquite is the principal tree; rattlesnakes are the largest reptiles; rains are the fossil hunter's best friends. Their waters, rushing through "breaks," or broad gullies, expose the variegated clays, red shales, and sandstones of the Redbeds, in which vertebrate fossils are found.

When those strata were accumulating, northern Texas was a series of deltas at the edge of a shifting sea. Inland climates may have been arid, but the deltas themselves were well watered and supported lush vegetation much like that of the earlier coal swamps. Calamites grew as tall as small trees; conifers and lycopods formed forests; true ferns were plentiful. *Gigantopteris,* with ribbon-like leaves, was prominent among the seed-ferns.

These forested deltas were the home of both amphibians and reptiles. Some of the former resembled large salamanders; others, such as *Eryops,* were thick-bodied creatures 5 to 7 feet long. *Eryops* himself had a broad, flattened head, a barrel-shaped body, and a tail about twice as long as his skull. His ribs were wide but very short, his forefeet had only four complete toes, and

The fin-backed Edaphosaurus and its skull, showing the teeth used to crush mollusks. At the lower right is Ophiacodon, a fish-eater. Both from the Permian (Clear Fork) of Texas

his legs, though heavy and powerful, were too short to lift his body from the ground. He probably crawled out to sun himself on mud banks but spent his active life in water, where he swam or lay in wait for prey in the manner of modern alligators. His food probably was a mixture of fish and lesser amphibians, supplemented by occasional reptiles.

Two reptiles were common on the deltas—*Dimetrodon* and *Diadectes*. The former was a carnivorous relative of *Edaphosaurus,* with a back fin supported by spines that were not equipped with crossbars. The head was narrow and high; some teeth were daggerlike, but others were better fitted to shear flesh from bones. The chief victim probably was *Diadectes,* an awkward, defenseless reptile with broad body, thick tail, and massive skull. Late Pennsylvanian species weighed as much as 200 pounds and fed upon plants as well as mollusks. Thus the reptiles spent part of their time within reach of *Dimetrodon* and part at the edge of the region where *Eryops* was supreme.

Throughout much of the world the Pennsylvanian period came to an end amid upheavals that turned shallow seas into land, drained the great coal swamps, and built mountain ranges. In Texas, however, the sea advanced briefly and then receded, while the climate became less humid but underwent no radical change. Then came a transitional epoch in which sand and mud built brick-red formations some 800 feet thick which bridge the gap that elsewhere divides Pennsylvanian from Permian strata. The sole trace of greater changes appears in fossils, which show that hordes of amphibians and reptiles returned to the deltas or invaded Texas from other parts of the world. Appearing during the transitional (Permo-Carboniferous, or Wichita) epoch, they reached their full development during true Permian times.

Foremost among the amphibians that returned was *Eryops,* which remained the largest member of his class, with the greatest appetite for meat. *Seymouria,* however, was an immigrant; a leftover from earlier times that wandered from the Old World and finally reached Texas. The Redbed species was a stocky creature some 20 inches long, with a stout body, a rather short tail, and sturdy but sprawling limbs. Its sharp teeth suggest active prey, which probably ranged from young amphibians and reptiles to roaches 3 or 4 inches long.

Seymouria could hardly cope with *Cacops,* a land-dwelling version of *Eryops* only 16 inches in length. *Cacops* had a large head, a stubby tail, and well-developed legs. Its backbone was capped by a series of bony plates which apparently served as armor, though in doing so they kept their owner from bending his short, plump body.

Trimerorhachis, which was smaller than *Cacops,* also had a large head and broad body but stayed in water except when it crept from one pool to another. Still more fully aquatic was *Diplocaulus,* an animal which also ranks as the most grotesque of amphibians. Although it still possessed legs, they were tiny organs that hung beside its long but flattened body. *Diplocaulus'* head was a massive crescent or triangle of bone which varied in shape from species to

Cacops, a labyrinthodont 16 inches long, from the Permian Red Beds of Texas. At the right is a larval "branchiosaur" from Europe.

species but invariably ended in points. Eyes and nostrils were directed upward, but the small mouth lay underneath. *Diplocaulus* must have spent its whole life in the water, where it sometimes lay in one spot for hours or even days at a time. Waking, it ate such small fry as it could find on the bottom. It breathed with gills, probably internal, whose openings lay in folds of skin behind the massive head.

Reptiles—both old inhabitants and immigrants—ranged from pools to the highest parts of the Permian delta. *Ophiacodon,* 10 to 11 feet long, had a lizardlike body and tail, strong legs, and clawless toes that indicate aquatic habits. The skull was large and high but narrow, and the slender teeth were sharp. Though *Ophiacodon* could and did walk on land, its leg bones ossified so slowly that it generally relied upon water to help support its weight. Its diet consisted largely of fish, though it may also have eaten aquatic amphibians. A few specimens from marine deposits suggest that *Ophiacodon* sometimes left fresh water and ventured out to sea.

Edaphosaurus returned to forests and horsetail brakes in species much larger than those of Pennsylvanian times. One of the first to arrive was 8 feet 5 inches long, but a later one reached 11 feet and weighed about 600 pounds.

Dimetrodon became even larger, for one species 11 feet long weighed at least 670 pounds. The legs of this giant were short but sturdy, the teeth pro-

Diplocaulus, a thick-skulled amphibian 2 to 3 feet long

Dimetrodon, a fin-backed reptile of late Pennsylvanian and Permian times. This species, from the Permian of Texas, was 10 to 11 feet long.

jected as much as 2 inches from the jaws, and the skull was 18 inches in length. Though he was carnivorous, we cannot picture him as an active hunter, for his muscles were not equal to an extended chase. *Dimetrodon* probably hid where the spines of his fin could blend with the stalks of calamites. When prey approached he rushed upon it, killing it with swift slashes of his bladelike teeth. Shorter teeth at the back of his jaws then sheared off chunks of meat, to be swallowed without chewing.

The back fins of *Dimetrodon* and *Edaphosaurus* have been a long-standing puzzle. Some scientists have seen them as overdeveloped nuisances, others thought them devices for concealment, and at least one called them sails with which the reptiles could tack upstream in a brisk breeze. It seems probable, however, that the "fin" was a combination of heat receptor and radiator. In cool weather *Dimetrodon* and *Edaphosaurus* stood broadside to the sun, soaking up rays that warmed their blood and activated their sluggish bodies. On hot days the animals rested facing the sun or in shade, where warmed blood carried to the fins lost its excess heat. Modern reptiles regulate their temperatures by moving into sunshine or shade, though none of them has any special heat-gathering and heat-losing device.

Pelycosaurs and Cotylosaurs. Though *Opiacodon, Edaphosaurus,* and *Dime-*

trodon varied, their skulls show that all three belonged to a group called the pelycosaurs. So did *Varanosaurus* and *Casea,* the former a long-tailed, long-nosed creature that had no means of defense against his savage relative. *Casea* was blunt-nosed and slender and probably found safety in running. One of its relatives, in Oklahoma, became larger than *Dimetrodon.* Though little more than 12 feet in length, its massive body reached a weight of 730 pounds.

A less advanced group, the cotylosaurs, was represented by *Diadectes* and several newcomers. One, *Labidosaurus,* was a primitive creature some 5 feet long that had found a sheltering niche in the Old World before it wandered into Texas. Two other forms, like *Diadectes,* were more advanced and had several rows of teeth in the cheeks. These may have been used to crush the shells of mussels and snails.

PERMIAN REPTILES OF THE OLD WORLD

The Texas Redbeds provide our most comprehensive record of early Permian reptiles and amphibians. The story is continued in Africa and Europe, where middle and late Permian deposits contain bones of reptiles very different from any in North America.

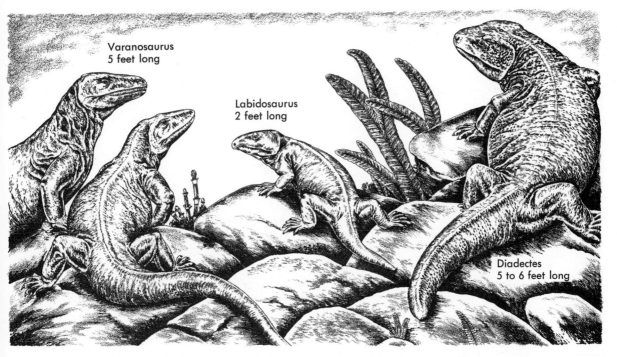

Some lesser reptiles from Permian Red Beds of Texas. The plants are horsetails and ferns.

Kannemeyeria, a Triassic dinocephalian of southern Africa. Length about 6 feet. At right is the skull of Dicynodon, a dinocephalian with tusks and beaks. Permian and Triassic.

Pareiasaurs. During the middle Permian, a group of South African reptiles evolved into bulky, grotesque creatures known as pareiasaurs. The largest species were 10 feet long, with thick legs, barrel-shaped bodies, and weights exceeding a ton. The skull had become massive and knobby, the skin was studded with bony plates, and teeth on the jaws were serrate. Skeletons have been found in a standing position, just as the animals sank into mud while they were feeding on swamp plants. Pareiasaurs became rare in Africa during the late Permian, but before that happened they wandered northward to Scotland and Russia. There the last survivors died out in the Triassic period.

Skull of Elginia, a late Permian pareiasaur of Scotland; length 10 inches. Brady-saurus (right) measured about 8 feet. This pareiasaur lived in South Africa during middle Permian times.

Mud that filled these footprints of an amphibian has hardened into red shale. Mississippian (Mauch Chunk formation), near Pottsville, Pennsylvania. Museum of Comparative Zoology, Harvard University. Photograph by Dr. Don Baird.

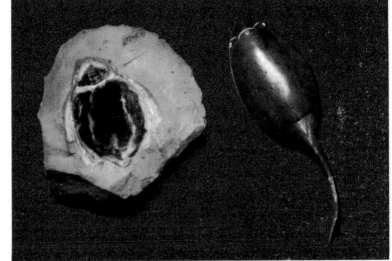

Two jawless vertebrates, or agnaths. (*Left*) Armor from the back and head of Cyrtaspis. (*Right*) Restoration of Protaspis as it looked when alive. Early Devonian river bed, Beartooth Butte, Wyoming. (*Princeton University*)

AMPHIBIANS AND TWO ARMORED
AGNATHS

Impression of a frog's skeleton (Palaeobatrachus) in shale. Remains or impressions of frogs are very rare fossils, and this specimen from the Oligocene of Germany is unusually good. It is in the Museum of Comparative Zoology, Harvard University. Photograph by Dr. Don Baird.

Skull of Stegoceras, a relatively primitive "boneheaded" dinosaur. Late Cretaceous, Alberta, Canada.

TWO REPTILES AND A PERMIAN AMPHIBIAN

(*Right*) The skull and part of the lower jaw of Alligator prenasalis (Loomis) from the Oligocene of the White River Badlands near Scenic, South Dakota.

(*Below*) A skeleton of Dissorophus, a labyrinthodont amphibian of early Permian age from Baylor County, Texas. The skull is thick, and bony armor plates cover the back. The scale is 20 centimeters, or almost 8 inches long.

Specimens are in the Museum of Comparative Zoology, Harvard University. Photographs by Dr. Don Baird.

Dinocephalians. These "giant-heads" looked like pareiasaurs but really were more closely related to *Dimetrodon.* Found in middle Permian deposits of South Africa and Russia, they were large animals of two general types. Primitive forms were carnivores with sharp teeth and bladelike canine tusks; others became vegetarians with weak jaws and blunt teeth. Both groups had massive skulls and remarkably large pineal bodies. The largest species were 14 to 16 feet long.

Dicynodonts were even more aberrant. Some were small, with skulls an inch or two in length; others evolved into giants whose heads measured 3 feet from base to snout. Teeth had all but disappeared, though the males—and females of some species—kept their canine tusks. Both sexes developed bevel-edged beaks with which the reptiles nipped leaves from plants, a mode of feeding now practiced by box turtles and desert tortoises. Like the pareiasaurs, dicynodonts made their way from southern Africa to Scotland and Russia. They entered eastern Asia early in the Triassic period, and before it closed they had reached both North and South America.

CHAPTER XXIV

Amphibian and Reptile Groups

O UR VIEW of Permo-Carboniferous Texas showed amphibians and reptiles living together but gave scant attention to groups and relationships. We must now undertake an orderly survey to complete the tale of amphibian progress and furnish a framework for further discussion of reptiles.

MAIN GROUPS OF AMPHIBIANS

Some old books call amphibians Batrachia and group them with reptiles in a single class, the Reptilia. This was done before biologists realized the importance of egg membranes, stored food, and lungs that were ready to use as soon as their owners hatched. The result was a group so diverse and complex that neither savants nor fossil hunters could make head or tail of it.

We therefore begin this survey by accepting amphibians as a class on a par with agnaths, bony fish, or reptiles. We next recognize two subclasses, which apparently separated soon after the first amphibians appeared. One subclass, the apsidospondyls, has stayed close to the ancient fringe-fin plan of vertebrae that began as arches of cartilage around the notochord and later turned into bone. Lepospondyls, on the other hand, developed vertebrate that form as bony spools around the notochord, with no cartilaginous stage. Since we often think that change means progress and success, we take note that apsidospondyls include the bulk of ancient amphibians as well as frogs and toads, which are the most successful members of their class in our modern world. Lepospondyls were never so varied or abundant, and survive only in salamanders, newts, and the legless "worm-snakes." Though these creatures are common in some places, they are much less important than frogs.

Early Labyrinthodonts. The story of apsidospondyls began with the fishlike *Ichthyostega* and its relatives of Greenland. All were labyrinthodonts, having teeth with deeply crumpled enamel and thick skulls completely covered by bone. Most Mississippian amphibians were labyrinthodonts, too, as were the specialized embolomeres and all except a few amphibians of the Texas deltas. The pictures in Chapter XXIII, therefore, suggest the great variety achieved by members of this superorder, some of which retained small, fishlike scales.

The Degenerate Stereospondyls. Most primitive labyrinthodonts died out long before the Permian period ended. In the Triassic their places were taken by a "derived" group, the stereospondyls, of skeletal degenerates. They lost a portion of each vertebra, let the braincase revert to cartilage, developed great gaps in the palate, and got along with legs too small to support the broad, depressed bodies. The heads were flat, with eyes that looked directly upward; three expanded bones formed a chest plate on which the creatures rested. We picture them as bottom-dwellers that crept on the mud and lay almost motionless for long periods.

Buettneria, of late Triassic age, had a broad, flattened body and head, and weak legs. This labyrinthodont almost never left the water.

Eryops was a big, powerful, and active amphibian of early Permian times.

Diplovertebron, a Pennsylvanian labyrinthodont, had a slender body and rather weak legs. The head was not very large, nor was it much flattened.

Some sterospondyls were small and had short skulls; others, aptly called mastodonsaurs, had skulls as much as 3 feet long and reached over-all lengths of 12 to 15 feet. They were so abundant in Triassic Germany that their remains often collected in "cemeteries." *Buettneria,* of Triassic New Mexico and Texas, looked like a flattened version of *Eryops* with eyes far forward on its skull. *Trematosaurus* and its relatives were long-snouted swimmers that ate fish; some species apparently were marine, though they probably returned to

Bones and six skulls of Buettneria found in what once was a pool. Triassic near Santa Fe, New Mexico. (Photograph from U. S. National Museum)

streams to lay their eggs, as shad and salmon do today. This assumption is based on the fact that both eggs and larvae of modern amphibians are killed by salt water.

FROGS, TOADS, AND THEIR ANCESTORS

Frogs and toads (the Salientia) are the most abundant of living amphibians as well as the most successful. They live in fresh water, on land, and in trees;

those that lay eggs in pockets of skin have even freed themselves from dependence on water during the breeding season. But this seems to be a recent development, of which we find no trace in fossil frogs and toads.

"Dawn-frogs" and "Pro-frogs." The "dawn-frogs," or Eoanura, were creatures about 4 inches long which lived in swampy Coal Age forests of central Illinois. They had broad, blunt heads, large eyes, and well-developed tails, but the skull had already lost some bones, the hind legs were longer than the forelegs, and the vertebrae were degenerate. "Pro-frogs," the Proanura, had lost still more bones in the skull but kept the primitive salamanderlike body. Pro-frogs probably crept through moist, shady Triassic forests, eating insects and wriggling into the water when danger threatened on land.

Anurans, the "Tailless Ones." Many changes and 30,000,000 years separate Triassic proanurans from late Jurassic anurans. During that time the skull developed large openings while the tail disappeared, ribs were lost, the hind legs became jumping organs, and bones of the lower legs were fused. Vertebrae both degenerated and vanished, reducing their total number to six or eight plus a long bone that seems to represent a dozen or more vertebrae

How vertebrae and openings in the palate changed

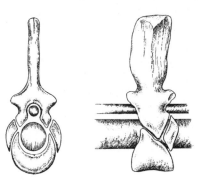

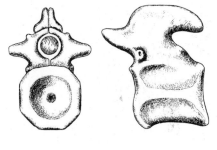

End and side of a primitive
labyrinthodont vertebra

Vertebra of a
stereospondyl

End and side of a lepospondyl
vertebra

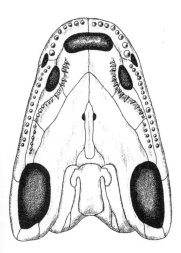
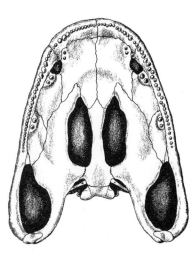
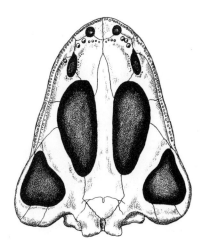

Ichthyostega, Devonian

Eryops, Permian

Buettneria, Triassic

fused into one. The habits of Mesozoic species are uncertain, but toads appeared during the Eocene epoch and ranged round the world in the Miocene, when tree toads were well established and frogs finally appeared. These facts suggest that Mesozoic anurans were land-dwellers except in the breeding season, and that full-scale invasion of water was delayed until mid-Tertiary times. The success of that venture is proved by the hordes of frogs now found in streams, ponds, and swamps.

THE ABERRANT LEPOSPONDYLS

Some animal groups are inborn conservatives; they live for ages and produce new forms that adhere closely to ancestral patterns. Other groups, perhaps at the same time and in identical surroundings, indulge in orgies of variation. They change shapes, structures, and habits, producing descendants that seem unrelated to their progenitors.

This is true of the lepospondyls, which combine relative unimportance with great variety in form. Some Mississippian members of the group lost their legs and became snakelike crawlers with 100 or more vertebrae and lengths of 20 to 30 inches. During the Pennsylvanian, another group evolved into *Diplocaulus,* with its strange, thick skull, useless legs, and elongate body. Microsaurs, which were common in swamps of the Coal Age, ranged from quadrupeds with bony skulls to legless types that looked like plump earthworms. Their shape and habits are repeated by the "worm-snakes," one of the two lepospondyl groups that survive today. The other group (urodeles) consists of salamanders and newts: four-legged creepers and swimmers whose skulls and skeletons are mostly cartilage. Though most species are small, some Miocene genera reached lengths of 35 to 45 inches and so equaled the giant salamander of modern China and Japan.

SKULL OPENINGS AND GROUPS OF REPTILES

Limnoscelis, of Permian Texas, had a skull much like that of *Seymouria,* with an unbroken expanse of bone behind each eye opening, or orbit. Other

A primitive Pennsylvanian salamander

Miobatrachus, a Pennsylvanian "dawn-frog," about 3 inches in length

(Left) *Andrias, a late Miocene salamander from Europe. Length 2 to 4 feet.* (Right) *Palaeobatrachus, a Miocene frog 3 inches long*

reptiles had one or more gaps, the temporal openings, occupying various positions and enclosed by various bones. Though these patterns vary in details, the gaps themselves—and solid skulls—divide the whole class of reptiles into five principal groups:

Anapsids. Most primitive of these groups are the anapsids; creatures such as *Limnoscelis,* which had no temporal openings. Behind each eye five bones fit tightly, as we see in cotylosaurs, turtles, and tortoises. The first of those groups died out as the Jurassic period dawned, but turtles and tortoises still prosper.

Synapsids. This old group, extinct since the Triassic, was not truly primitive. Its members had one temporal opening on each side of the skull, *below* two bones called the postorbital and squamosal. *Dimetrodon, Edaphosaurus* and their relatives are placed in this group, along with dicynodonts, dinocephalians, and the beastlike reptiles described in Chapter XXIX.

Parapsids. In these reptiles, two bones that had been high on the skull moved down to the side, and the temporal opening lay *above* them. These bones are called supratemporal and postfrontal. The parapsids (also called ichthyopterygia) include fish-shaped Mesozoic reptiles and their late Paleozoic ancestors. Both are described in Chapter XXV, and neither has living relatives.

Euryapsids. The skulls of these creatures show openings that once were mistakenly called parapsid; they lie above the squamosal and postorbital bones. This group contains the aquatic plesiosaurs and their ancestors, which ranged from early Permian to late Cretaceous times.

Diapsids. As their name suggests, the skull of these reptiles contains two temporal openings on each side—one above and one below the squamosal and postorbital bones. Since their appearance late in the Permian period, diapsids have evolved into two principal divisions: scaly reptiles (lepidosaurs) and

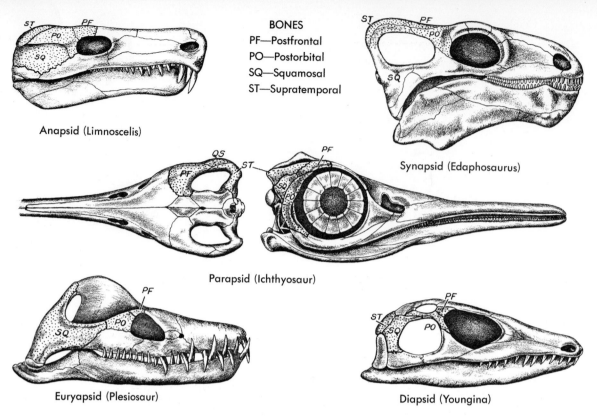

BONES
PF—Postfrontal
PO—Postorbital
SQ—Squamosal
ST—Supratemporal

Anapsid (Limnoscelis)

Synapsid (Edaphosaurus)

Parapsid (Ichthyosaur)

Euryapsid (Plesiosaur)

Diapsid (Youngina)

Skulls in the five main groups, or subclasses, of reptiles. The anapsids have no temporal opening; diapsids have two openings. In other groups the one opening varies in position above or below the dotted bones.

"ruling reptiles" (archosaurs). The former group includes lizards, snakes, and mosasaurs (Chapter XXV); the latter comprises dinosaurs, crocodiles, flying reptiles, and their varied relatives. For more than 150,000,000 years they have outranked most other reptiles in abundance, variety, and size.

No neat formula will summarize the story of these five subclasses. Mentally, reptiles have remained dull-witted animals whose conduct is governed by instinct and reflexes, with ganglia doing many jobs which higher creatures do with their brains. Structurally, however, reptiles have been arrant and frequently rugged individualists. Some have grown large while others have become dwarfs; a few groups started out on one course and abruptly switched to the other. In many families the number of bones was reduced in both skull and skeleton. Others added many new ones, and some—notably the serpents —lost the bones of such organs as legs but multiplied their primitive allotment of vertebrae and ribs. Lizards and their kin have taken up life in swamps, deserts, seas, and even in trees; parapsids became more fishlike in outline than several specialized fish. Sphenodonts, however, made no such changes and have lived 155,000,000 years without a major innovation in habits, structure, or shape.

Divergence, then, is the one factor we can count on in the history of reptiles. Let us trace its principal patterns and examine the goals to which it has led.

CHAPTER XXV

Farewells to Land

Reptiles evolved when the changing earth gave four-footed vertebrates a chance to succeed on land. No sooner was this accomplished, however, than some of the newly developed creatures took up aquatic life.

We already know *Ophiacodon*, a fish-eating Permian synapsid which must have been an active swimmer, though it could also walk on dry ground. More truly aquatic was *Mesosaurus*, a rare and short-lived genus from the late Pennsylvanian of southern Africa and South America. A slender creature about 3 feet long, *Mesosaurus* had jaws full of needle-shaped teeth. It apparently used its forelegs as balancing organs, driving its body through the water with its broad hind feet as it swam in pursuit of fish.

(Left) *Eunotosaurus, a Permian ancestor of the turtles.* (Right) *Mesosaurus, an aquatic reptile of late Pennsylvanian or Permian age. Length 16 inches.*

315

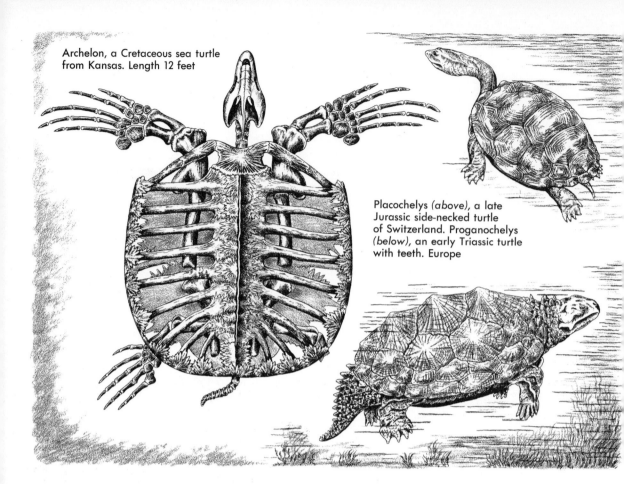

Archelon, a Cretaceous sea turtle from Kansas. Length 12 feet

Placochelys (*above*), a late Jurassic side-necked turtle of Switzerland. Proganochelys (*below*), an early Triassic turtle with teeth. Europe

THE STURDY AND CONSERVATIVE TURTLES

When we speak of aquatic reptiles today we think of turtles, or chelonians, which appeared in mid-Triassic times and have been common during all subsequent ages. They invaded swamps, lakes, rivers, and seas, and developed the finest armor to be found among four-footed vertebrates. Most of them also clung to their early anatomical virtues, which explain why they have been successful for 170,000,000 years.

In spite of this record, few fossils trace the steps by which turtles came into existence. *Eunotosaurus,* of mid-Permian South Africa, may be one of their ancestors, for its 3-inch body was wide and depressed, with leaf-shaped ribs that touched each other on the back. Beyond this we can only say that unknown Permian anapsids settled down to life in quiet and probably swampy waters, where their bodies widened while their feet became paddles with webs between the toes. A shell, or carapace, appeared on the back and fused with the ribs; it consisted of bony plates that formed in the skin and were covered by scales that expanded into horny scutes. Scutes also covered the ventral armor, or plastron, which was joined to the carapace at both sides. Teeth became small and finally vanished, while horny beaks grew on the jaws.

Three Groups of Turtles. With this beginning, turtles evolved into three principal groups. One, the amphichelids, is typified by *Proganochelys,* found in late Triassic strata of Europe. Its jaws were already toothless, but tiny teeth remained on the palate. Neither head nor tail could be tucked into the shell but both were protected by spines. The legs, which also may have remained outside the shell, were protected by long, sharp-edged scutes. Amphichelids ranged the world during Mesozoic and early Tertiary times and found refuge in Australia when competition became too keen elsewhere. One of the last

(Left) *Shell of Toxochelys, a Cretaceous sea turtle that resembled the modern loggerhead.* (Right) *Testudo ammon, a land tortoise from the early Tertiary of Egypt. Shell 40 inches in length.*

Australian survivors, of Pleistocene age, was a giant whose horned skull grew to be 24 inches wide.

Pleurodires possess some primitive features, but they swing their long necks sidewise and so tuck their heads under shelter. Fossils, which date back to the Cretaceous, are surprisingly like forms that still live in the Southern Hemisphere. All surviving turtles of Australia belong to this "side-necked" group.

Cryptodires ("hidden-necks") include all other turtles. They tuck both head and neck away by bending the latter into an S between the shoulder blades. Fossil cryptodires began as marsh-dwellers that swam well, often sunned themselves on logs or sandbanks, and frequently walked on land. Some of their descendants became aquatic but remained in rivers and swamps, though others took to the sea. Foremost among these was *Archelon,* a giant more than

12 feet long with a narrow head, hooked beak, huge flippers, and a weight of about 6,000 pounds. *Archelon* lived in late Cretaceous seas of South Dakota, Kansas, and adjacent regions, which swarmed with large fish and savage reptiles closely related to lizards. The finest skeleton of *Archelon* has one hind paddle bitten off, probably by one of these predators.

At this point we encounter more of those contrasts and contradictions that mark the evolution of reptiles. Turtles began by developing shells and taking to water; some forms, such as the modern snapping turtle, almost never leave it. Others gave up armor or went back to the land, though none of them did both.

Archelon was one of the turtles that lost most of their armor, covering the bones that remained with tough skin. Two other groups of marine turtles repeated the process, and so did the stream-dwelling softshells. Early Tertiary members of the last group had shells made up of thin, pitted plates; later types lost all their armor and appeared in leathery carapaces. Broken bones of Tertiary softshell turtles are so common on bare hills near the Continental Divide, in south-central Wyoming, that they make up a large part of the pebbles. Apparently both shells and skeletons fell to pieces soon after death, for complete specimens are rare.

Pond turtles often venture upon land today and have done so for ages. Perhaps the best-known fossil pond turtle is *Stylemys,* which lived on the moist plains of South Dakota, Nebraska, and eastern Wyoming during the Oligocene epoch but was less common in Miocene times. Typical specimens are 5 to 8 inches long, but shells 20 to 36 inches long have been reported.

Tortoises are terrestrial turtles with club-shaped feet that have lost the webs between their toes. Large shells called *Stylemys* may actually belong to *Testudo,* a fully terrestrial genus that includes our modern gopher and desert tortoises as well as the giant species of the Galápagos and Aldabra Islands. Appearing in the Eocene epoch, tortoises became so varied during the Oligocene that eight species are found in lower strata of the South Dakota Badlands, where *Stylemys* also is common. The largest are about 3 feet long, and *Testudo ammon* of early Tertiary Egypt reached a length of 39 inches. *Colossochelys,* from the Pleistocene of India, had a shell 5 feet wide and 5 feet 6 inches long and weighed more than 2,000 pounds. No mean record for a terrestrial reptile whose undersized ancestors had abandoned the land!

ICHTHYOSAURS, OR FISH-LIZARDS

Jurassic strata of northern Europe contain many fossil reptiles whose vertebrae are convex fore and aft, like those of fishes. Indeed, they were described as fishes in 1699 by Edward Llwd, curator of the museum at Oxford. He also explained that they came from eggs of marine fishes that had been lifted up

Cymbospondylus

Ophthalmosaurus

Tail of Mixosaurus, of Triassic age.
Vertebrae were bent downward, and
the upper lobe of the tail fin had
begun to expand.

*Cymbospondylus was a primitive ichthyosaur of Triassic Nevada. The backbone did
not bend downward in the tail, and there may have been no fin on the back. Ophthalmosaurus, from the Jurassic of Wyoming, was highly specialized. Its tail was
sharklike and its teeth were very small.*

to the clouds by vapors and then had fallen with rain. It carried the eggs into
the ground, where they grew into imperfect versions of the creatures they
would have been had they hatched in salt water. More than a century later
the fossils were christened ichthyosaurs ("fish-lizards") on the assumption that
they linked those two groups.

One theory holds that ichthyosaurs were descended from relatives of *Mesosaurus.* Another merely says that ichthyosaurs evolved from undetermined
aquatic reptiles during the Permian, appearing in Triassic seas as a well-estab-
lished group with few traces of kinship to mesosaurs or other known predecessors.

This does not mean that these reptiles failed to progress during the 100,000,-
000 years of their known history. Their most primitive members, which appeared

in mid-Triassic seas of California, Spitzbergen, Europe, and the East Indies, were slender creatures whose tails were compressed but almost straight, with narrow fin folds above and below. In time the backbone began to bend downward while its upper lobe enlarged. At last the tail became reversed heterocercal, a swimming organ equal to that possessed by the swiftest shark. The slender jaws were set with many teeth; the front flippers were larger than the hind, though in both the leg bones were shortened while new ones were added to what had been toes. Vertebrae also were short and numerous, and the enormous goggle eyes were strengthened by sclerotic rings of bone. Ichthyosaurs plainly hunted by sight, and their eyes were equipped to catch a maximum of light.

In picturing fossil vertebrates, we usually have to restore their soft parts from evidence supplied by their bones. Not so with ichthyosaurs. Dark Jurassic rocks of Germany contain skeletons surrounded by carbonized films which show the streamlined body, the broad flippers, the tail, and the shark-like dorsal fin, which was boneless. These films also prove that the skin was smooth, with only a few small scales on the forward edge of the flippers. Tiny pigment grains show that fish-lizards were dark above but whitish beneath, coloration which increased their resemblance to sharks and helped conceal the reptiles from their prey.

Though ichthyosaurs still breathed air, they led purely aquatic lives. They fed upon fish, squids, and belemnites, whose remains sometimes lie between their ribs. They probably never went ashore and, instead of laying their eggs, allowed them to hatch internally. Specimens show skeletons of very small ichthyosaurs inside large ones, with no hint that the former were eaten instead of belemnites or fish. On other slabs, young animals appear to be coming from the region in which eggs were kept. Either the mother ichthyosaur died during "childbirth" or the young ones emerged soon after her death. The latter sometimes happens in lizards and snakes whose eggs hatch inside the body, after which the young wriggle out.

FROM CLIMBERS TO PLESIOSAURS

Among the reptiles of early Permian deltas was a slender creature with whiplash tail, called *Araeoscelis*. Its form suggests that it often climbed trees, though it was protected by ventral ribs that slightly resemble chain mail. The temporal openings in its skull place it among the euryapsids.

Nothosaurs. Neither firmly fixed in its ways nor specialized, *Araeoscelis* was just the sort of creature to make a promising ancestor. As the Triassic period began, some of its descendents took to the sea and became nothosaurs. They had slender necks, triangular heads, and slightly widened bodies. Like modern seagoing crocodiles, they probably went ashore whenever they wished to do

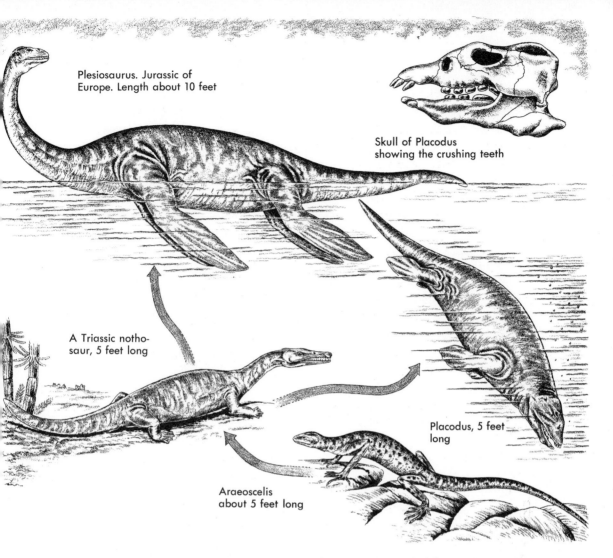

Plesiosaurus. Jurassic of
Europe. Length about 10 feet

Skull of Placodus
showing the crushing teeth

A Triassic notho-
saur, 5 feet long

Placodus, 5 feet
long

Araeoscelis
about 5 feet long

*The aquatic nothosaurs, plesiosaurs, and placodonts are descended from a Permian
land-dwelling reptile, Araeoscelis, 30 inches in length.*

so. Their bones have been found in marine deposits of Europe, Australia, and
North America.

Though nothosaurs were unspecialized, their offspring quickly lost that virtue. The placodonts, which appeared in Europe, became streamlined creatures
with blunt heads, plump bodies, and paddle-shaped legs; they resembled the
modern manatee, or sea cow. They paddled through shallow waters, eating
mollusks and crushing their shells with broad, low teeth on the jaws and bony
palate. In *Placodus* the ribs of the back were very thick, while a "basket" of
abdominal ribs protected the under side. *Placochelys,* of the late Triassic,
covered its back with armor.

Plesiosaurs. The name of these descendants of nothosaurs means "like lizards" or "almost lizards," but few creatures were less lizardlike in appearance

and habits. Plesiosaurs were marine reptiles adapted to life on the open sea, though they sometimes invaded swamps and estuaries. One group of these reptiles had short, flattened heads, long necks, and plump oval bodies strengthened by mats of abdominal ribs. Their tails, though fairly long, were finless; they swam by means of legs and feet that had grown into oarlike paddles. Bones of the hips and shoulder were broad, providing attachment for the powerful muscles which brought the paddles down and backward. Lengths ranged from 8 or 10 to 50 feet, and the number of neck vertebrae from 30 or 40 to almost 80.

A second group of plesiosaurs were similar in body, paddles, and tail, but their skulls were extended by long, slender jaws. Their necks also were short, those of some species containing only thirteen vertebrae.

Both long- and short-necked plesiosaurs appeared in early Jurassic seas of Europe; for millions of years they were plentiful there but scarce or absent elsewhere. Then, during Cretaceous times, they both spread widely and grew to very large size. *Kronosaurus,* of Australia, had a skull almost 9 feet long;

Contrasts in late Cretaceous plesiosaurs, both from western Kansas. Elasmosaurus was 40 to 50 feet in length, but the short-necked Trimacromerum was barely 10 feet long.

Trimacromerum and bones of
its right hind paddle

Elasmosaurus and
its skull

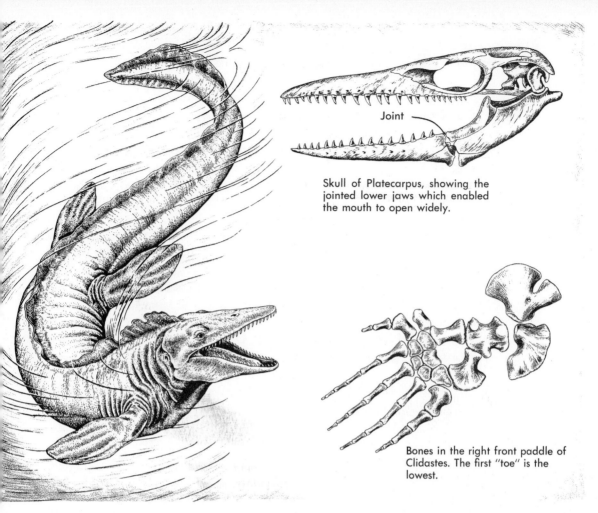

Joint

Skull of Platecarpus, showing the jointed lower jaws which enabled the mouth to open widely.

Bones in the right front paddle of Clidastes. The first "toe" is the lowest.

Mosasaurs, or marine lizards, of late Cretaceous age. Tylosaurus, from Kansas (left) was about 22 feet long.

elasmosaurs in seas of the Great Plains region possessed slender tails and necks as much as 23 feet long. They explain why plesiosaurs are sometimes compared to snakes threaded through the bodies of turtles. No known plesiosaur was armored, however, nor could even the longest species coil and twist its neck like a serpent. Plesiosaurs apparently rowed at the surface or just below it, diving infrequently. Prey consisted largely of fish, belemnites, and squids, seized with a forward rush or a quick sidewise thrust of the head. Victims too large to be swallowed whole were torn to pieces by jerks, a method now used by crocodiles and alligators.

MOSASAURS, TRUE AQUATIC LIZARDS

Early accounts occasionally described plesiosaurs as "savage monsters of horrid mein." Actually they seem to have been sluggish, dull-witted creatures that threatened only the animals on which they customarily fed. Lurid adjectives apply more aptly to the great aquatic lizards known as mosasaurs.

Mosasaurs were bizarre reptiles, and their introduction to science was equally spectacular. In 1780, workmen discovered a petrified skull in a subterranean sandstone quarry under the Pietersberg (Peter's Mount) near the city of Maastricht, Holland. The men sent for an army surgeon and naturalist who had collected fossils from the quarry. He directed work so skillfully that the entire skeleton was removed.

Dr. Hofmann recognized the specimen's value, paid for removing it, and prepared it for exhibition. But land above the quarry was owned by one Canon Goddin, who went to court, won his case, and seized the fossil. Then, in 1795, a French army besieged Maastricht, and so famous had the fossil become that the general in command told his gunners to spare the part of the city containing Canon Goddin's house. Suspecting the reason for this favor, Canon Goddin hid his specimen, trying to keep its location secret after the city surrendered. The French thereupon offered a reward—said to have been six hundred bottles of wine—for the specimen, and a band of thirsty grenadiers soon found it. Taken to Paris, it was described as a "primordial" whale, or "breathing fish," and then as "the Great Lizard of the Meuse," the river that flows past the Pietersberg. A British author translated this cumbersome term into the Latin *Mosasaurus*.

Mosasaurs ranged round the world during late Cretaceous epochs, reaching their zenith in seas that spread inland from the Atlantic Ocean and the Gulf of Mexico. The finest specimens come from chalk deposits of western Kansas, but the largest known species was a giant some 45 feet long whose jaws and teeth are found in greensand beds of New Jersey. Strangest member of the group was *Globidens,* of the southern United States and Europe. It apparently fed upon the sea bottom, where it grubbed for clams, snails, and other sluggish mollusks whose shells it crushed between bulbous teeth that had all but lost their once-sharp points.

The typical mosasaur, such as *Tylosaurus* of Kansas, was an active swimmer with a long body, flattened tail, and feet that had become broad, webbed paddles with well-developed toes. Bony plates covered the top of the head; neck, body, and tail were covered by lizardlike scales still preserved in a few carbonized fossils. Sclerotic rings strengthened the eyes, and the eardrum consisted of thick cartilage. The lower jaws, each armed with sixteen to eighteen sharp teeth, were connected by ligaments at the front and had double hinges behind. Like serpents, mosasaurs were able to drop their jaws and spread them widely in order to swallow oversized food.

Petrified stomach contents show that fish formed the chief food of mosasaurs. With lengths of 20 to 30 feet, they were the only vertebrates that could capture such forms as the "bulldog tarpon" (*Portheus molossus*), which weighed 600 to 800 pounds and was as dangerous as most reptiles. Since old, dull teeth

Machaeroprosopus, a Triassic phytosaur from the Painted Desert of northern Arizona; skull 42 inches long. The plants include cycads, calamites, ferns, and araucarians. The tree at the right is Araucarioxylon; to its left is Woodworthia.

dropped from the jaws and were replaced by new ones, mosasaurs never lacked weapons with which to attack rivals or prey.

THE WRONGLY NAMED PHYTOSAURS

If mosasaurs did go into streams, they sometimes saw crocodiles as much as 50 feet in length. Yet they were much too late to encounter the creatures whose habits, form, and bony structure mark them as false crocodiles.

Technically, we must call these creatures phytosaurs ("plant lizards"), not because the name fits them, but because an almost forgotten professor thought they were herbivores. Actually phytosaurs were carnivorous reptiles that ranged from 6 to 20 feet in length and were covered with bony armor overlain by horny scutes. The skull resembled that of the modern gavial, a true crocodile with bulging "forehead" and slender jaws. The gavial's nostrils, however, are on his snout; those of the phytosaurs lay close to the eyes, generally on mounds of bone rising above the rest of the skull.

The oldest known phytosaurs are found in the early Triassic of Europe. They spread round the world during late Triassic epochs; their bones have been found in Europe and South America, across the Hudson River from New York City, in North Carolina, and at many places in the Southwest. The reptiles lived in sluggish streams and in swamps, swam with their compressed tails, and often lay with only their nostrils above the water. Though they doubtless ate amphibians and other reptiles, their principal prey must have been fish.

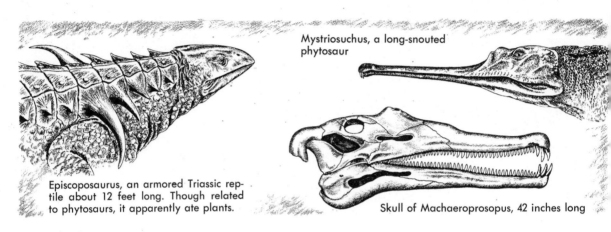

Mystriosuchus, a long-snouted phytosaur

Episcoposaurus, an armored Triassic reptile about 12 feet long. Though related to phytosaurs, it apparently ate plants.

Skull of Machaeroprosopus, 42 inches long

CROCODILIANS

Crocodilians form a long-lived order that includes true crocodiles, gavials, alligators, caimans, and their fossil relatives. The first of these appeared in late Triassic swamps which now are the bright-hued semideserts that include the famous Petrified Forest of northeastern Arizona. One ancestral genus, *Protosuchus*, was a reptile about 30 inches long, with a relatively short head, large eyes, and a tail of moderate length. Its back, belly, and tail were encased in rectangular plates which probably gave protection from the teeth of hungry phytosaurs. Limbs were typically crocodilian and could be used for either walking or swimming. The hind legs were longer than the forelegs, a condition that still prevails. It also is one of several features which show that crocodilians are related to the ancestors of dinosaurs.

Mesosuchians. Crocodilians enjoyed two bursts of racial prosperity. One came during the Jurassic period, when a group called the mesosuchians ranged both the New World and the Old. The smallest were less than 12 inches long and had almost no armor; the largest were slender-snouted creatures that resembled modern gavials and reached lengths of 15 to 20 feet. All had large

Protosuchus, an ancestral crocodile from Arizona, about 30 inches long

upper temporal openings and vertebrae that were flattened or slightly convex at both ends. Those vertebrae and isolated teeth are the commonest mesosuchian fossils.

Most mesosuchians were active hunters that prowled along coasts and in swampy shallows, seeking fish or reptilian prey. The group misnamed geosaurs, or "earth-lizards," went to sea and there competed with ichthyosaurs and mosasaurs. Geosaurs were smooth-skinned, armorless reptiles with slender bodies, long snouts, and very long tails in which the backbone bent downward, indicating a terminal fin. Most of their swimming was done with the tail; the limbs, which had become flippers, served as balancing organs. Most geosaurs lived in Jurassic seas of Europe, but other mesosuchians ranged seas of Europe, Africa, and the Americas, surviving through the Cretaceous and into the Eocene epoch.

Modern Crocodilians. The next great wave of crocodilian progress began at the dawn of the Cretaceous, or Chalk Age. Within that long period it produced

Geosaurus, a marine crocodile of late Jurassic age, with paddles and sharklike tail. At the right, skull of Alligator thomsoni, a fresh-water reptile from the late Miocene of western Nebraska

the three groups that still exist: snouted gavials, sharp-nosed crocodiles, and broad-nosed alligators. Except for a few alligators, all these modern crocodilians, or eusuchians, lack armor on their sides and bellies. Their temporal openings are small, and their vertebrae are concave in front but convex behind. They also have found a final solution for the problem presented by external nostrils on a long nose or snout. The phytosaurs had avoided it, since their nostrils remained near the eyes. In mesosuchians, bones of the upper jaws and palate produced a tube that lay under the true roof of the mouth and took air to openings below and back of the eyes. In eusuchians, nostrils remained on the snout while the air tube stretched to the hinder part of the skull near the opening of the windpipe. With this improvement, plus a membrane that closes the throat, these reptiles are able to breathe without getting water into their lungs, even when their mouths are open.

Phobosuchus, a crocodile found in Cretaceous strata of Europe and the Big Bend region of Texas, had a skull more than 6 feet long and reached lengths of 45 to 50 feet. It was rivaled by *Deinosuchus,* a 35- to 40-foot giant from late Cretaceous rocks of Fergus County, Montana. Though these were vastly larger than living species, the modern Indian gavial reaches 23 feet in length, while the seagoing crocodile, which ranges from India to the Solomon Islands and northern Australia, becomes 20 feet long. In both bulk and length it dwarfs the geosaurs, though it is not so highly specialized for aquatic life. Thus its limbs still are legs and feet, and its tail, though a first-rate swimming organ, shows no trace of a fin.

Two factors impress us most deeply as we trace crocodilian history. One is the apparent ease with which the reptiles developed the body form of phytosaurs—not once but twice, at separate times, and long after the former group died out. The second fact is the ability of unspecialized animals to survive while others became extinct. With a few exceptions, such as the geosaurs, crocodilians are less specialized than ichthyosaurs, plesiosaurs, and mosasaurs. Yet these "superior" forms became extinct, while crocodiles kept plodding along their conservative way. Like the turtles, they still survive—not as relicts on the verge of extinction, but as a large and vigorous group. Unless man wilfully destroys them, they seem fated to live and prosper through millions of years to come.

CHAPTER XXVI

Scale-bearers and Lizard-hipped Dinosaurs

W<small>E HAVE FOUND</small>, again and again, that important ancestral organisms seldom are imposing. Most of them are small, ordinary in appearance, and relatively inefficient. Few of them became abundant; fewer still managed to live through more than one or two epochs. As one expert has said, organisms can seldom spend long ages as generalized ancestors. They either die out or produce descendants which in habits as well as anatomy become specialists at the job of living. As these specialists become established their primitive forebears disappear.

There are exceptions to this rule of simplicity and short life, but not among ancestral diapsids. They appeared in southern Africa during late Permian times but were replaced by more progressive descendants as the Triassic dawned. One of the best-known types was of lizardlike build, with a long tail, slender legs and a skull about 2.5 inches long. The jaws were set with pointed teeth; other teeth, shorter and not so sharp, were scattered over the roof of the mouth. Both temporal openings were well developed, and the pineal "eye" was relatively large.

SCALES, SKULLS, AND SNAKES

From this beginning came a varied array of more progressive reptiles. One group, the lepidosaurians, developed scales and other modifications. Some genera clung to a crawling upland life; others developed blunt teeth and parrotlike beaks which suggest that they prowled in shallow waters, while others assumed crocodilian forms. A more important group lost one cheekbone and reduced the size of two others, thereby becoming true lizards. Early types were related to the iguanas and monitors, which survive in our modern tropics. They were followed by chameleons and other specialized saurians.

329

Certain late Cretaceous monitors produced descendants whose legs became shorter and shorter, while their backbones added vertebrae and their ribs increased in number. The first result of these changes was a group of long-bodied, short-legged lizards that crept by wriggling. These aberrant lizards then produced snakes: stocky serpents related to modern boas and pythons, which still keep traces of legs. Early snakes also lost the remaining arch of bone lying back of the eye, so that what once were two temporal openings became a single broad gap. The jaws also became loosely attached and double-jointed, able to spread so widely that their owners could swallow creatures thicker than themselves.

Most ancient snakes were nonpoisonous; though fossils which may represent vipers have been found in very late Cretaceous and Paleocene formations, the first convincing specimens came from Miocene rocks. They include both cobras and true vipers. Pit vipers, which include rattlesnakes, appear in Pleistocene formations.

FROM THECODONTS TO DINOSAURS

We now return to the Triassic world. Our first stop is South Africa, where creatures called thecodonts—the name means "socket-teeth"—ran jerkily on

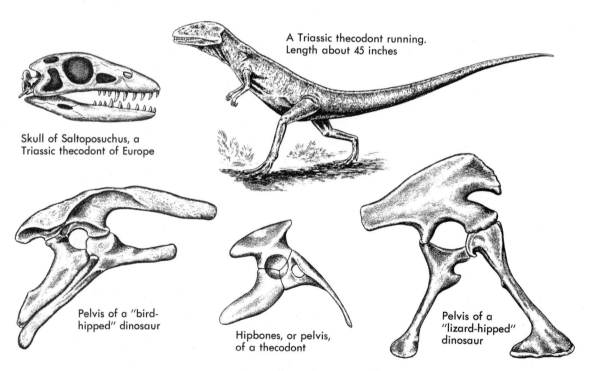

A Triassic thecodont running. Length about 45 inches

Skull of Saltoposuchus, a Triassic thecodont of Europe

Pelvis of a "bird-hipped" dinosaur

Hipbones, or pelvis, of a thecodont

Pelvis of a "lizard-hipped" dinosaur

Thecodonts and contrasting pelvic bones of the two orders of dinosaurs

long hind legs, balancing their half-erect bodies with long, stiffly held tails. Lengths ranged from 3 to 4 feet and heights from 10 to 15 inches.

Besides getting up on their hind legs (a significant change), the evolving thecodonts developed new characters of skull and hip girdle, or pelvis. The former included an opening in front of each eye; the pelvis provided firm linkage with the backbone, had broad surfaces for the attachment of muscles, and contained a deep socket for the head of the upper leg bone. All these were essential to semi-erect, bipedal life.

No sooner did thecodonts evolve than they began to vary. Some remained thecodont in structure but not in appearance and habits, since they either walked on all fours and lived in marshes or became phytosaurs. Others evolved into crocodilians and reptiles with wings, while two groups became the creatures called dinosaurs. The whole varied array is often termed archosaurs, or "ruling reptiles."

Two Dinosaurian Orders. This term *dinosaur,* which means "terrible lizard," is both useful and deceptive. It is useful because it can be applied to a great variety of archosaurs that prospered during Mesozoic times and have no other everyday name. It is deceptive because it implies that all these reptiles were huge and ferocious carnivores that belonged to a single natural group. Actually, the so-called dinosaurs ranged from massive creatures weighing 40 or 50 tons down to delicately proportioned reptiles no larger than a barnyard rooster. Though many species were carnivores, they were outnumbered by contemporaries that ate only plants. Finally, these varied reptiles formed two distinct orders, even though both were descended from early thecodonts.

The chief difference between these orders appears in the hipbones, or pelvis. In the saurischians, or "lizard-hips," this structure retains the three-pronged form developed by early thecodonts and found in the skeletons of crocodiles. Among ornithischians ("bird-hips") the pubic bone normally has two branches, one of which reaches forward while the other extends backward under the ischium. The teeth of saurischians also extend to the very front of the jaw, while those of most ornithischians stop short of it. In all except a few genera the jaws were covered by horny beaks. Both they and the character of the teeth show that ornithischians were herbivores, though the saurischians include both eaters of meat and of plants.

THE MOST ANCIENT DINOSAURS

The change from thecodont to saurischian dinosaur was not great and apparently took place before middle Triassic times. During the latter half of that period, saurischians roamed across Europe and Asia and became abundant in valleys of eastern North America. There they left a few skeletons and countless footprints in beds of dark red, muddy sand that hardened into stone. Now hard to find, these tracks were common in the days when Triassic "brown-

Coelophysis, a primitive dinosaur from the late Triassic of northern Arizona and New Mexico. Length to tip of tail, about 8 feet

stone" was quarried to build churches, mansions, and even railroad culverts or jails.

Triassic Dinosaurs. Both bones and footprints show that most late Triassic dinosaurs were carnivores with slender legs, long necks, small heads, and long tails. Many were 3 to 4 feet long, those that measured 7 or 8 feet were large, and creatures 16 to 20 feet long were giants. All walked on their hind feet, which had three—rarely four—long toes and one more so short that it seldom left an impression. For this reason their fossil footprints were first mistaken for those of birds.

Our best picture of late Triassic life is provided by the Chinle formation of northeastern Arizona and adjacent parts of Utah and New Mexico. It shows us uplands covered with forests of cone-bearing araucarian "pines," whose fallen trunks were washed downstream and deposited on mud banks to form the Petrified Forest of Arizona and other forests of less spectacular beauty. Large ferns grew under the trees, small cycads filled openings, and horsetails formed thickets along streams. The climate was moderate, though clouds of ash from volcanic eruptions sometimes filled the air.

Streams, ponds, and shallow lakes were the home of mussels, lungfish, ganoids, and large amphibians. Armored thecodonts reached lengths of 12 to 15 feet; one had spines along its sides and five pairs of bony spikes protecting its neck and forelegs. Phytosaurs were common in swamps, and at least one dicynodont with tusks and beaked jaws apparently lived in upland forests. There it encountered saurischian dinosaurs that were slender bipeds about 8 feet long, with high, narrow skulls and hollow leg bones. Like their thecodont ancestors, they walked and ran on their hind legs, captured prey with fore-limbs and jaws, and balanced their swaying bodies with stiffly extended tails. Their weight has been estimated at 40 to 50 pounds. Those of the Painted Desert and northwestern New Mexico belong to the genus *Coelophysis.*

THE REIGN OF GREAT SAUROPODS

As the Jurassic period dawned, western swamps gave way to deserts that spread from New Mexico and Colorado to southern Nevada. Winds howled across their barren slopes, piling sand into dunes which today form cross-bed-ded sandstones 3,500 feet thick. Travelers see them in the Vermilion and Echo cliffs, in the red, buff, and white walls of Zion Canyon, and in the arches, towers, and spectacular chasms in the region of Moab, Utah.

Deserts made poor homes for dinosaurs, and few of their bones have been discovered in hardened Jurassic dunes. Other regions were more inviting, and lizard-hipped saurischians thrived in their warm and often swampy lowlands. The reptiles also divided into two groups called theropods ("beast-footed") and sauropods ("lizard-footed"). Neither name is very appropriate, but the groups

(Left) *Plateosaurus, a primitive sauropod of the European Triassic; 16 to 20 feet in length. Yaleosaurus* (right), *of eastern United States, was about 8 feet long.*

themselves are important. With a few exceptions, the theropods were bipeds that walked on three birdlike toes, had short forelegs, and were carnivorous. Sauropods, however, walked on four feet, developed massive legs both fore and aft, and had teeth that were suited only to a diet of soft, juicy plants.

Ancestors of Giants. This twofold division of the lizard-hipped dinosaurs had begun in Triassic times. Among the slender reptiles that ranged through eastern valleys was a heavier creature with stocky hind legs called *Anchisaurus* or *Yaleosaurus.* It had a smallish head, blunt teeth, and five toes on each foot, four being usable. *Yaleosaurus* apparently could walk half erect or on all fours and ate plants as well as animals. While feeding it may have waded into shallow swamps.

This creature still was a theropod, but one that promised to produce something else. That promise became clear in *Plateosaurus,* a late Triassic reptile some 20 feet long, or more than twice the length of a large alligator. The neck was long and so was the tail; the forelegs were thicker and stronger than those of *Yaleosaurus.* The head was small and the blunt teeth were good only for eating plants.

The Triumph of Sauropods. After this comes a gap that extends through most of the Jurassic period. It is bridged only by imperfect remains which are just sufficient to show that true sauropods evolved and wandered into various parts of the world. Then they achieved abundance and variety, as well as enormous size.

This triumph is best recorded in the Morrison formation, a complex series of clays, shales, and sandstones that settled in swamps, shallow lakes, and broad streams that wandered over low-lying plains. Ranging from late Jurassic to early Cretaceous in age, it shows that climates were mild and equable. Cycads, ginkgos, and conifers formed forests, shading an undergrowth made up largely of ferns. Horsetails and succulent plants grew abundantly in swamps.

Both swamps and meandering streams were the homes of sauropods. One of them, *Camarasaurus,* was a relatively unspecialized creature 30 to 40 feet long when fully grown, with slender neck and tail and short forelegs—the last a condition reminiscent of theropod ancestors. Both fore- and hind feet were stubby, and the former had only one complete toe.

Apatosaurus—better though wrongly known as *Brontosaurus,* the "thunder lizard"—was a huge and highly specialized relative of *Camarasaurus. Apatosaurus* was 65 to 77 feet long, with a deep, short body, a flexible neck, and a tail that was massive near the hip but ended in a whiplash tip. The legs formed thick columns ending in broad feet as much as 26 inches wide, padded like those of an elephant. The fully developed toes bore claws—one on each forefoot and three massive claws behind. The total weight of this reptile is estimated at 30 to 35 tons.

As *Apatosaurus* lolled in bayous or swamps, he often encountered a relative known as *Diplodocus.* This creature reached lengths of 80 to 87 feet and

Brachiosaurus (left) *and Apatosaurus, the brontosaur* (right), *were two of the largest "lizard-hipped" dinosaurs. Both lived in Colorado and adjacent regions during Morrison times. Brachiosaurus also inhabited central Africa.*

was 13 feet tall at the curve of his back, forward from the hips. Almost one third of the length was neck, and more than half consisted of tail that ended in a slender lash. Even so, *Diplodocus* was a giant weighing 20 tons or more, or about five times as much as a large elephant.

In front of this enormous bulk was a weak-looking head about 2 feet long. The nostrils opened through a single hole between and above the eyes; the muzzle sloped down to the jaws; blunt teeth were tipped outward and must have been used to pull plants, not to nip them off. The brain was a small, smooth organ weighing only a few ounces. *Diplodocus* must have been a sluggish creature that used moderate amounts of food, got along without thinking, and let its body take care of itself. The brain was just able to sort out

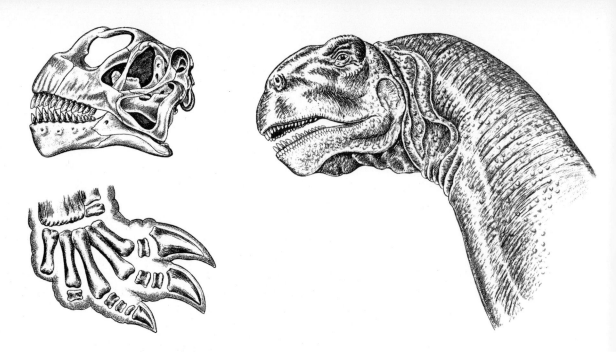

Skull, head, and left foot of Camarasaurus, from the late Jurassic Morrison forma-
tion. The full-grown reptile was 30 to 40 feet long.

messages of sight, hearing, and smell and pass them to ganglia above the
shoulders and hips. These nerve-knots took care of such jobs as walking,
swinging the tail, or reaching out for food. These activities, plus mating, filled
the life of *Diplodocus.* Thinking was a luxury in which he could not indulge.

Larger still was *Brachiosaurus,* whose remains have been found in Colorado,
central Wyoming, and East Africa. Unlike other sauropods, this giant had
forelegs longer than the hind, so that the back of the massive body sloped tail-
ward like that of a giraffe. The upper "arm" bone, or humerus, was 7 feet long;
the height above the shoulder was 19 feet, the neck was almost 28 feet long,
and the head was carried more than 39 feet above the ground. Though the
tail was much shorter than that of *Apatosaurus,* the total length was more
than 74 feet. A massive body—the ribs were 8 feet 7 inches long—brought the
weight to at least 40 tons. The brain, however, weighed only 7 ounces and was
as simple and ineffective as that of *Diplodocus.*

These are measurements made from one skeleton: that of a brachiosaur
whose growth was not complete. Other bones are larger by as much as 13 per
cent. They indicate that full-grown animals were as much as 44 feet high and
84 feet long and weighed 45 to 50 tons.

The Sauropod Skeleton. Sauropods were not only the world's largest reptiles; they also were the largest of terrestrial animals. Size and environment
together posed problems which were solved by a complex of bones, ligaments,
muscles, habits, and reproductive organs.

The first and most obvious problem was that of providing a framework for
the body. Part of that framework was ribs, but its critical portion was the

backbone. Vertebrae had to be large and strong but not solid, for solid vertebrae would have added more weight than legs were able to support. As sauropods became giants, therefore, they developed "excavated" vertebrae which
seem to be made up largely of holes. Actually, evolutionary changes omitted
bone where it did no good but added it in bars and ridges that met every
normal stress. The result was a structure much like that of a modern
steel bridge, held together by ligaments and interlocking joints instead of by
rivets or bolts.

Once framed, the body had to be supported and moved from place to place.
For these tasks the sauropods used long, massive legs that stood upright,
though the forelimbs were somewhat bowed. Their size is indicated by the
humerus of *Brachiosaurus,* which was 7 feet long. The thigh bone (femur) of
Apatosaurus was more massive, with a length of 6 feet 6 inches and a girth,
near the middle, of more than 3 feet.

Sauropod Ways. There is a long-standing argument as to whether even
these massive legs could support the huge sauropod body. Those who say
they did not, point to long bones, which were capped by cartilage that presumably would have been crushed by weights of 20 to 50 tons, leaving the
reptiles unable to move. This disaster would have been avoided, however, if

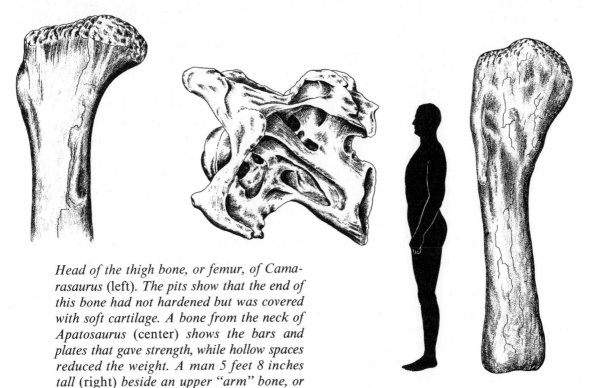

*Head of the thigh bone, or femur, of Cama-
rasaurus* (left). *The pits show that the end of
this bone had not hardened but was covered
with soft cartilage. A bone from the neck of
Apatosaurus* (center) *shows the bars and
plates that gave strength, while hollow spaces
reduced the weight. A man 5 feet 8 inches
tall* (right) *beside an upper "arm" bone, or
humerus, of Brachiosaurus. The bone, found near Fruita, Colorado, is 7 feet in length.*

Apatosaurus wading with his forelegs but swimming with his hind legs. Below Apatosaurus is Diplodocus wading in shallow water; his tail is half afloat.

the sauropods waded in water deep enough to partly float their bodies and ponderous tails. Wading would also explain the "water line" that runs from shoulders to hips. Above this line the bones are "excavated," as if to reduce their weight and thereby increase buoyancy. Bones below the line are massive, concentrating weight in parts that normally were submerged. They would help wading dinosaurs keep their balance, just as lead weights on the feet of a diver help him remain upright as he walks.

All this is inference, but it seems to be supported by sauropod trails found in early Cretaceous rocks along the Paluxy River (or Creek) near Glen Rose, Texas. The trail-makers probably were closely related to *Apatosaurus* and *Diplodocus,* though the hind feet bore four claws instead of three and the forefeet had none. The creatures evidently waded in coastal marshes of a very early Cretaceous sea, leaving footprints in beds of limy sand that also contained oyster shells and other marine remains. Prints of the hind feet were as much as 38 inches long and 26 wide and were separated by 12-foot strides.

Most of the footprints were made by animals that walked on all fours, with their tails half floating at the surface. One dinosaur, however, dragged its tail for some distance; another walked on its forefeet while its hindquarters floated.

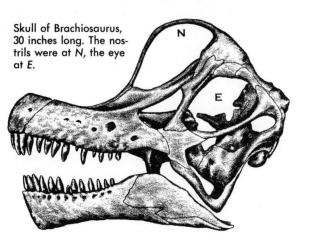

Skull of Brachiosaurus, 30 inches long. The nostrils were at *N*, the eye at *E*.

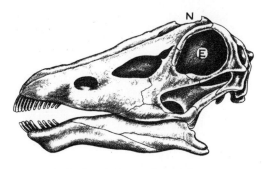

Skull of Diplodocus, about 2 feet long. The orbit of the eye is marked *E*; the nares are shown by *N*.

In order to turn, this reptile struck outward and upward with only one hind foot. Its claws dug deep gashes that remained when the sediment became stone.

Critics do not question these facts, but give them another interpretation. The leg bones, these critics say, prove only that sauropods grew as long as they lived. Cartilaginous ends, therefore, were not replaced by bone, but the cartilage might have been strong enough to bear the weight of the body. More important, the Glen Rose trails combine proof that big dinosaurs often waded with strong hints that they did not always do so. Tracks of the former type are deep but indistinct, as if sediment slumped into them as soon as the reptiles passed on. Other tracks are clear-cut but relatively shallow, as if the sediment was firm. Lack of tail marks suggests that water was deep enough to float the tail but not to buoy up the body. This inference is supported by footprints of a carnivorous dinosaur following and even pressed into those of an herbivore. Though the carnivore might have been able to wade, it apparently could not half walk and half float, as the sauropods did.

Thus stands the argument; a solution awaits the finding of sauropod tracks in sediments laid down on land or in shoals whose depth can be determined

Both Diplodocus and Brachiosaurus could breathe while their heads were submerged.

within a foot or two. Meanwhile we can only say that sauropods often waded in water that did buoy up their bodies, and that they sometimes went into water that covered all but the tops of their heads. Evidence of this is found in their nostrils, which opened high upon their skulls. Like the raised nostrils of crocodiles, they enabled the reptiles to breathe while even their eyes were submerged.

One problem still remained to be solved: that of producing young ones. Some small sauropods probably went ashore to lay eggs in sand or decaying vegetation, for remains of one European species have been found near fragments of shell. Giants probably did the same if they could walk on dry land after becoming mature. If not, eggs were kept in the body until they hatched. They were not laid in water, for there they would have died.

How Long Did Sauropods Live? Sauropods reached their zenith in late Jurassic and early Cretaceous times. We once thought they then went into a rapid decline, with only a few stragglers of moderate size lingering into the late Cretaceous. Recent discoveries, however, suggest that large sauropods persisted throughout most of that period. A late Cretaceous vertebra from Texas, for example, is as large as that of *Apatosaurus.* A Cretaceous dinosaur from South America may have been even larger than *Brachiosaurus.*

Three carnivorous dinosaurs of late Jurassic age. They lived in what now is the Rocky Mountain region.

Allosaurus
34 feet long

Ceratosaurus
17.5 feet long

Ornitholestes
6 feet long

THE PREDATORY CARNOSAURS

The sauropods provided vast amounts of meat in timid, defenseless packages weighing from a few hundred to 90,000 pounds. Thanks to these riches, carnivorous dinosaurs also were able to evolve into giants.

We have met early meat-eaters among the little three-toed, bipedal theropods of the middle Triassic. Before that period closed, some of their descendants became 8 to 12 feet long, weighed upward of 150 pounds, and were much stronger than the largest modern lizards. They doubtless preyed on such creatures as *Plateosaurus* while those awkward reptiles were turning into sauropods.

Perhaps meat-eaters even got ahead of their prey. The oldest known sauropods are found in early Jurassic rocks, but full-fledged carnosaurs appear in late Triassic deposits of Europe, South Africa, Asia, and North America. In early Jurassic times one family, appropriately called the megalosaurs, or "large saurians," included members 12 to 20 feet long, with 12-inch skulls and serrate teeth that became recurved when fully developed. The forelegs were shorter than those of *Plateosaurus,* the hind legs were long and powerful, and the feet bore long curved claws. Megalosaurs probably lay in wait for their prey, rushed upon it, and killed it by biting through the backbone. The claws held food while it was being eaten, as vultures use their claws today.

Few middle Jurassic carnosaurs are known, but the group became large and varied during the Morrison epoch. One of its best-known members is *Ceratosaurus,* found in steeply tilted rocks near Canyon City, Colorado. When walking, this reptile measured 17 feet 6 inches from nose to tail tip and was 7 feet high. The head was 20 inches long and 13 high, with saber-shaped teeth that extended 2 inches beyond the jaws. The nose bore a blunt, narrow horn, and a bony knob rose in front of each eye. Like the megalosaurs, *Ceratosaurus* walked and ran on its hind legs, with its body balanced by its long tail.

Though a powerful and savage hunter, *Ceratosaurus* seems small when placed beside *Allosaurus,* also called *Antrodemus.* This reptile was 34 feet long, stood more than 8 feet high as it stooped to eat, and when aroused could raise its head 14 or 15 feet. The head was 36 inches in length, and the 6-inch teeth had serrate edges. The lower jaw was hinged far back on the skull, giving a tremendous gape to the savage mouth. Thus the creature could deliver powerful, slashing bites and could also gulp down food in massive, unchewed lumps.

We must guess what many ancient reptiles ate, but not so with *Allosaurus.* At Dinosaur National Monument, Utah, remains of *Allosaurus* have been found among those of *Diplodocus* and other sauropods. At the famous Bone Cabin dinosaur quarry, near Como Bluff, Wyoming, bones of *Apatosaurus* and other sauropods are scratched by the teeth of *Allosaurus,* which also lie

(Right) *Struthiomimus, the "ostrich mimic" of Cretaceous Alberta. Height 8 to 9 feet.*
(Left) *An early species of Gorgosaurus, 7 feet high at the hips. Cretaceous of Alberta*

among the remains. Evidently the huge carnivore bit so hard that it broke off some of its 6-inch teeth and left them with the refuse of its meal.

Only one question remains. Did *Allosaurus* kill the great, defenseless sauropods, or were they carrion found on banks and sand bars? Some experts say one and some the other, and both may be correct. It seems probable that allosaurs captured young giants and forms such as *Camarasaurus,* which often waded in shallow water or even ventured on land. Moreover, we have found that at least one carnosaur as large as *Allosaurus* stalked a sauropod in the coastal swamp whose deposits are found near Glen Rose, Texas. On the other hand, sauropods could escape into greater depths. When they did so, meat-eaters doubtless were glad to devour carcasses stranded on bars or shores. Since such remains predominate among Morrison fossils, the wonder is that more do not show the marks of carnosaur teeth.

Deinodonts, the "Terrible-teeth." *Allosaurus* died out at the end of the Morrison epoch, but other carnosaurs survived. During the first half of the Cretaceous period some of them evolved into the deinodonts ("terrible teeth"), which then became the largest of all terrestrial carnivores.

Among the earlier deinodonts was a relatively slender species of *Gorgosaurus* that ranged through moist, thickly forested lowlands in what is now the province of Alberta. Standing about 7 feet high at the hips, it had a low skull armed with surprisingly long teeth. There were two toes on the forefoot and

Tyrannosaurus, a carnivorous dinosaur 47 feet long and 18 feet high, and its skull, about 50 inches long. Cretaceous of Montana

four on the hind, with a remnant of a fifth. Ventral ribs protected the belly, a primitive character.

This, however, was only the beginning; a later species of *Gorgosaurus* reached a length of 29 feet, stood 9 feet high at the hips, and had a low skull some 22 inches long, armed with recurved teeth. Ventral ribs still were well developed, but the vestigial fifth hind toe had been lost. The reptile probably walked with a stoop, as did *Ceratosaurus* and the *Allosaurus,* but could run swiftly for short distances. Its forelegs, however, were small and virtually useless. So were the diminutive feet, which had only two toes.

Last of all came *Deinodon* and its better-known cousin, *Tyrannosaurus.* Both were massive, erect dinosaurs with the largest heads known among saurischians. *Tyrannosaurus* was 47 feet long, 18 feet tall, and weighed 8 to 10 tons. Its knee joint was 6 feet aboveground; the claws on its hind feet were 6 to 8 inches long; its skull measured 51 inches from front to back; its teeth were serrate blades 3 to 6 inches long and an inch in width. The forefeet are unknown but, like those of earlier deinodonts, they probably had only two toes and were too small to be of much use, even in handling food.

We are tempted to picture the food of *Tyrannosaurus* in massive proportions to match his size. Actually, the great carnivore lived during latest Cretaceous times, when *Diplodocus* and *Brachiosaurus* had been extinct for 50,000,000 years and lesser sauropods were rare. The tyrant saurian's prey consisted of herbivorous reptiles 20 to 30 feet long that waded, swam, and walked on lowlands of western North America. What they lacked in bulk they made up in numbers. The tyrant seldom went hungry; he merely took more meals than his predecessor, *Allosaurus.*

Spiny Carnivores. The strangest of all carnosaurs lived in Europe and northern Africa, also in late Cretaceous times. Though the fossils are far from perfect, they show large creatures whose backs bore neural spines resembling those of *Dimetrodon* and as much as 6 feet long. One wonders how such reptiles walked on two legs and killed active prey. Did they merely lie in wait for victims, or did they eat carrion?

Bird Catchers and Bird Mimics. While the carnosaurs evolved into giants, other theropods became slender and agile. Some even developed legs, bodies, and necks much like those of the modern ostrich.

This trend began with such Triassic forms as *Coelophysis* or with the slender, bipedal *Compsognathus,* which lived on forested seashores of late Jurassic Germany. Since two thirds of its 30 inches were neck and tail, this dinosaur probably weighed less than a good-sized rooster. The toes were long and bore claws, and the small jaws were set with sharp teeth. *Compsognathus* probably ranged through underbrush and preyed upon still smaller reptiles. In fact, the remains of such a meal still lie in the abdominal region of one specimen.

Ornitholestes, of the Morrison formation, was 6 feet long, with a stout body and a long, rather inflexible tail. Forefeet had become three-toed grasping organs; hind legs and feet were long, slender, and well adapted to running. Often pictured in the act of catching a bird, *Ornitholestes* (the name means "bird robber") probably dined chiefly on small, agile reptiles such as the early lizards.

Struthiomimus, of the late Cretaceous Northwest, stood 8 to 9 feet high when erect and combined the proportions of an ostrich with such typically reptilian features as a saurischian pelvis, four legs, and long tail. The small head was ostrichlike, too, and its toothless jaws were covered by a horny beak.

Struthiomimus apparently lived on humid lowlands and sandy plains, where it walked or ran swiftly on its long hind legs. It also found safety in flight, not in self-defense. Its slim, three-toed hind feet could not be used to kick, like the heavy feet of ostriches.

Ornithomimids (the family name) probably were omnivores. They could easily pull fruit from low trees; their beaks could snap up small reptiles; their handlike forefeet could dig eggs from nests on the ground and hold them while their beaks broke the shells. Generally the thieves escaped, but one Mongolian form, called *Oviraptor,* was killed while robbing the nest of an armored dinosaur. The crushed skull was preserved among the petrified shells.

GIANTS VERSUS DWARFS

We have traced the history of saurischian, or lizard-hipped, dinosaurs during the late Triassic, Jurassic, and Cretaceous periods, which totaled about 110,000,000 years. During those ages several families and larger groups

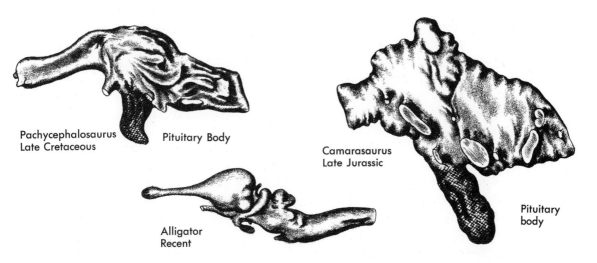

Pachycephalosaurus
Late Cretaceous

Pituitary Body

Camarasaurus
Late Jurassic

Alligator
Recent

Pituitary
body

Large size and thick bones may be produced by enlarged pituitary bodies, located under the brain. Here we see the pituitaries of an ordinary alligator, a 40-foot Camarasaurus, and a bone-headed Pachycephalosaurus described in Chapter XXVII.

evolved into giants while others remained modest in size or even became dwarfs. What advantages did good-sized reptiles gain by growing larger, and what penalties did they incur? How did their little relatives profit, and what did they lose as their size decreased?

The penalties of giantism have been stressed in articles, books, and even animated cartoons. One of these is size itself; the big animal must constantly struggle against its own bulk and the downward pull of gravity. We have seen how these factors forced the great sauropods to develop complex vertebrae and massive limbs and to take up life in a medium—water—which partly supported their weight. Even there they were at some disadvantage; witness those heavily weighted bones, which helped the giants remain right side up. On dry land, such monsters as *Deinodon* and *Tyrannosaurus* approached the limits to which ligaments could keep the body together and muscles could propel tons of blood, flesh, and bone fast enough to capture food.

Food—enough food—posed another problem. A big animal eats more than a small one, be it herbivore or carnivore, fish, mammal, or reptile. Today such large creatures as elephants and tigers cannot dwell on small islands; the latter contain too little food to support a breeding population. Similarly, great sauropods could not inhabit small swamps, nor could hordes of them exist in large ones. Carnosaurs always were fewer than their prey, and each one probably had a home range which it defended against invaders. Instinct prompted it to do so, but the basis of that instinct was the need for nourishment.

Such were the penalties for size, but it also brought advantages, especially to herbivores. The really big animal is always relatively free from attack, no matter how dull he is or how poor his defenses. The big sauropods were so witless that most of their acts had to be governed by glands and by ganglia located yards or rods away from the feeble brain. Still, no ceratosaur would have been so stupidly overconfident as to attack a full-grown *Apatosaurus* or *Diplodocus,* and even an allosaur probably looked twice—he could hardly think —before attacking one of those creatures. The allosaur himself had no known enemies once he reached his growth, and the deinodonts were equally secure.

Even the need for food had its favorable side. True, a 30-ton dinosaur needed more food than one weighing 60 pounds, but not a thousand times as much. The cost of living for a great sauropod, therefore, was much less than that for an equal weight of Triassic dinosaurs. At the same time, the sauropod gained the advantages of size and a long life span, which probably exceeded that of any modern reptile.

Finally comes the matter of heat. As reptiles, dinosaurs were cold-blooded inhabitants of warm lowlands and swamps. Even there, nights were less hot than days, deep water was cooler than shallows, and relatively chill winds sometimes blew. Under such conditions small reptiles were chilled and became sluggish, but the giants lost heat so slowly that their temperatures hardly changed. For them there probably was no slowing down at night, no stiffening in cool water, no retirement during chilly periods. However sluggish their ways may have been, they could live at an almost uniform rate.

This advantage also worked in reverse. Accustomed to stress the effects of cold, we forget that modern reptiles are equally sensitive to heat. They estivate in summer months, hide from the hot midday sun, and may die after surprisingly short exposure to it. But the great dinosaurs, with small surface area in proportion to their bulk, absorbed a minimum of sunshine and thus reduced its effects.

The gains and losses of dwarfism are those of large size reversed. The dwarf is not burdened by weight; it lives actively with a modest framework and prospers in places out of bounds for big animals. It also thrives on very little food, which means that it does not need an extensive home range and is seldom beyond reach of a mate. On the other hand, it can be killed by all except mature giants, whose very size makes them indifferent to small fry. Its consumption of food is relatively high, which forces it to compete with creatures of similar needs. Its life span is almost sure to be short; a few years against decades or even centuries. Finally, no dwarf can keep a uniform temperature or live at a uniform rate. It may live rapidly—for a reptile—when conditions are right, but it must slow down when the weather grows cool and take shelter from too much heat and sunshine.

We need not and cannot weigh these advantages and penalties. All we can say with assurance is that one set let certain saurischians prosper as giants while the other allowed some of their kin to remain small or evolve into dwarfs. It means nothing that giants are common and small forms scarce, for the former stood a much better chance of becoming fossils. It also is not significant that the giants died out and were replaced by smaller reptiles, for some of those forthwith became large. The process did not stop until the Cretaceous period ended—and then dinosaurs vanished without descendants. If survival is our criterion of evolutionary success, giants, dwarfs, and intermediates all failed.

CHAPTER XXVII

Bird-hipped Dinosaurs

In 1822 the wife of Gideon Mantell, a British country doctor, found some petrified teeth in rocks of late Jurassic or early Cretaceous age. Her husband later secured additional teeth and a few bones which experts in England and France assigned to a rhinoceros, a hippopotamus, and a fish. Dr. Mantell himself thought the teeth belonged to a reptile resembling the modern lizards called iguanas, and therefore named them *Iguanodon*. Years passed before the teeth and bones were recognized as remains of an ornithischian, or bird-hipped, dinosaur.

ORNITHOPODS, OR "BIRD FEET"

Iguanodon is an advanced member of a suborder called ornithopods, or "bird feet," though their feet really are less birdlike than those of "beast-footed" theropods. A much more primitive type, *Camptosaurus,* appeared in North America during late Jurassic times and survived into the early Cretaceous. It was a rather clumsy biped 7 to 17 feet in length, with a low and rather heavy skull. The forefeet had five toes and the hind feet four, all tipped with hoof-like claws. The femur was curved, suggesting that *Camptosaurus* sometimes stooped over to walk on all fours. Like all ornithischians, it had an extra bone, the predentary, at the front of each lower jaw. Both upper and lower jaws were tipped by beaks which were used to nip off leaves and fruits. Flattened, bladelike teeth were found in the hinder two thirds of the mouth. The jaw hinge was lower than the teeth, not on a level with or even above them, as in the carnosaurs. Their jaws closed with a shearing motion, but those of *Camptosaurus* came together with a "nutcracker" action that crushed pulpy food.

Hypsilophodon, a primitive bird-hipped dinosaur of early Cretaceous

348

(Left) *Hypsilophodon, about 4 feet 6 inches long, may have climbed trees. Triassic of Europe.* (Right) *Camptosaurus, 17 feet long. A Jurassic ornithischian of Europe*

Europe, was 5 to 6 feet long and had a 6-inch skull. Its forelegs were short, its back and sides bore thin armor, and its feet were adapted to grasping. It may have spent much of its life in trees, feeding on leaves and fruit.

Iguanodon also was European, though it may have ranged into other continents. The varied species were 15 to 30 feet in length and reached 15 feet in height. All had narrow bodies and compressed tails, walked on hind feet bearing three large toes and a very small one, and had five-toed forefeet on which the "thumb" had become a bony spike. Before well-preserved skulls were found, some people thought this spike belonged on the animal's nose.

In the coal-mining district near Mons, Belgium, early Cretaceous streams eroded gorges as much as 600 feet deep in Carboniferous strata. Streams filled the gorges with mud, dead plants, and reptile carcasses brought from swampy lands nearby. In 1878, miners tunneled into an ancient gorge and there found the remains of twenty-three large iguanodonts, as well as crocodiles, turtles, and fish. The iguanodonts seem to represent both sexes of one species, and reveal their anatomy in unusual detail.

Another notable discovery was made in a coal mine near Cedaredge, Colorado. There a late Cretaceous iguanodont walked on muck which now is coal, and its footprints were filled by sand that hardened into gray sandstone. These

Iguanodon, about 11 feet high, and the bones of its right forefoot

Head of Pachycephalosaurus (*above*); the skull is 26 inches long and 9 inches thick.

Stegoceras (*right*), primitive "bonehead"; skull 7.5 inches long

Three bird-hipped dinosaurs of Cretaceous age. Iguanodon lived in western Europe, but the thick-skulled genera are American.

footprints measure 34 inches in width and length, indicating that their owner was much larger than any other known iguanodont.

Duckbills, or Hadrosaurs. These reptiles are distinguished by very long skulls that end in broad, toothless expansions. During life these were covered with horny beaks that may have been flexible and probably were used to pull off soft plants, grub in the mud for roots, and shovel loose food into the mouth. Food was crushed by teeth arranged in overlapping banks which pushed new teeth upward as old ones became worn and fell out. Though confined to the hinder part of the mouth, they numbered 200 to 500 per jaw, or 800 to 2,000 in all. About one third of these were in actual use, the remainder being reserves.

Hadrosaurs ranged from 12 to 40 feet in length, the average being about 30 feet. The creatures walked in a stooping position and frequently dropped to all fours. The body was deep but not very wide, the tail was deep and narrow, and the thin wrinkled skin was covered with platelike scales that did not overlap. There were four toes in front and three behind; the claws were blunt and shaped like hoofs; there were webs between toes of the forefeet and probably between those of the hind. The skull was moderately long and deep, sloped gently from back to front, and had very large openings for the nostrils. The bones surrounding these openings were thin, without trace of a crest or horn.

This basic plan was modified in two general ways. One is seen in *Anatosaurus* (once called *Trachodon*), whose skull became long, low, and narrow. The other involved enlargement of bones surrounding the nostrils, especially the pre-maxillaries. At their simplest these enlarged bones formed a prominent Roman nose. In other forms they produced comblike and divided crests, as well as projections that extended upward and backward far beyond the head. Through these went the nasal passages, forming curves and hairpin loops before they returned to the throat. The loops may have stored reserves of air for use while the dinosaurs fed under water.

There is no doubt that duckbills swam as well as waded and walked on dry land. This is shown by their webbed feet and deep, narrow tails which could be used as sculling oars. The backbone also was strengthened by heavily cal-cified tendons which still allowed the muscles to swing both body and tail from side to side. These tendons are preserved in many petrified duckbills.

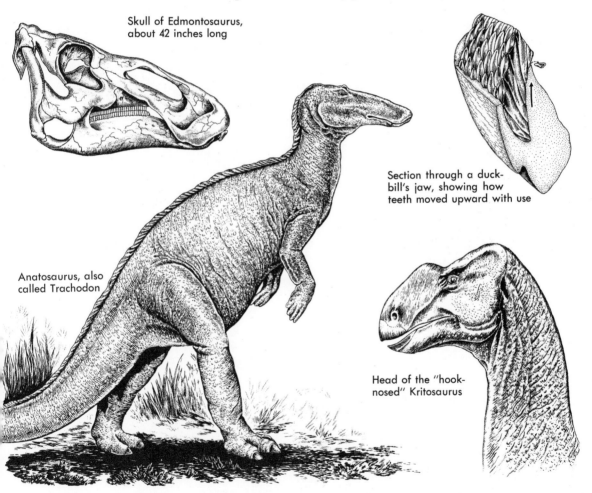

Skull of Edmontosaurus, about 42 inches long

Section through a duck-bill's jaw, showing how teeth moved upward with use

Anatosaurus, also called Trachodon

Head of the "hook-nosed" Kritosaurus

Some Cretaceous duckbilled dinosaurs of North America. Anatosaurus, 15 to 18 feet high, ranged from New Jersey to northwestern Canada.

Hadrosaurs appeared full-fledged in late Cretaceous times, when they ranged into Europe, across Asia, and through North America. They were most abundant in swamps near the Atlantic Ocean and in swampy deltas along the shore of a sea that invaded the West, from Texas to northern Canada. Their fossils are most plentiful in badlands of the Red Deer River, near Drumheller, Alberta, which now are a provincial park. Many almost complete skeletons have been found, some with outlines of the flesh and impressions of the skin. These animals evidently died in the water, floated downstream, and came to rest beyond the reach of carnivores. There also are scattered bones from bodies that were pulled to pieces by deinodonts.

Bone-headed Dinosaurs. These reptiles apparently began with *Stegoceras,* also called *Troödon.* It was a harmless herbivore 5 to 6 feet long, with five short toes on each forefoot and four longer toes behind. It nipped off plants with sharp-edged teeth that came to the front of the mouth, since there was

Three duckbilled dinosaurs with bony crests

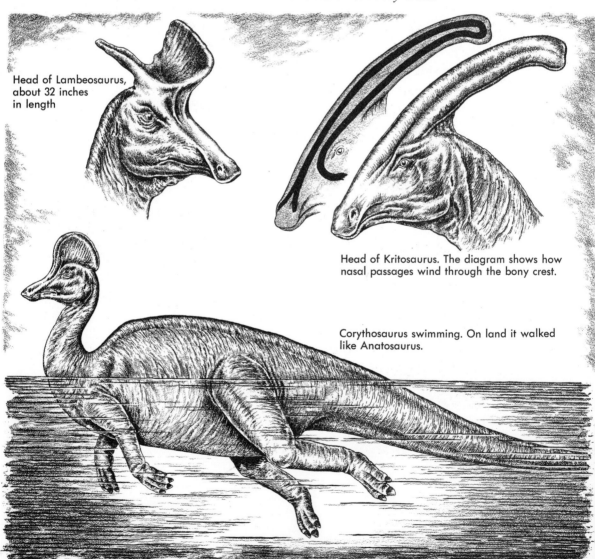

Head of Lambeosaurus, about 32 inches in length

Head of Kritosaurus. The diagram shows how nasal passages wind through the bony crest.

Corythosaurus swimming. On land it walked like Anatosaurus.

Sacral (or hip) ganglion

Brain drawn on same scale as ganglion

Stegosaurus, a Jurassic armored dinosaur of western United States; 18 to 25 feet long. This reptile is famous for its sacral ganglion, or "second brain."

no beak. The premaxillary bones were small, but those forming the roof of the skull were solid and 3 inches thick. Several small spikes appeared at the back of the head.

Pachycephalosaurus, the "thick-headed reptile," lived during the latest Cretaceous epoch, when tyrannosaurs were at their zenith. Its dome-shaped skull was 26 inches long and 9 inches thick over the brain and was trimmed with both knobs and spines. Since the rest of the body was not protected, it is hard to see what *Pachycephalosaurus* gained by evolving this massive skull. One authority thinks it was used as a battering-ram, perhaps against rivals of the same genus. Others doubt that it served any special purpose, though it may have done no harm.

ARMOR-PLATED AND DREADNAUGHT DINOSAURS

Two groups of ornithischians developed armor. The plate-bearers (Stegosauria) appeared in early Jurassic Europe and culminated in *Stegosaurus,* of Morrison age. Full-grown specimens were 18 to 25 feet long, stood 12 to 13 feet high, and weighed 7 to 10 tons. The 16-inch skull was low and flat-roofed, with a well-developed beak and 90 to 100 small teeth. The body was deep but narrow, the hind legs were long while the forelegs were short, and three of the toes on each foot ended in hooflike claws. The broad sides were covered with leathery skin, but two rows of bony plates ran along the neck, back, and tail, which also carried four long spikes.

We picture *Stegosaurus* as a peaceful and very sluggish land-dweller, too low at the shoulders to wade in deep swamps, and too lightly armored to risk encounters with carnivores such as *Allosaurus*. For those plates protected only his back, his tail made only a fair war club, and his sides were wide open to attack. He probably remained among trees, whose trunks stopped the rush and deflected the jaws of big predators.

In doing this he relied upon instinct, for *Stegosaurus* could do no more thinking than other dinosaurs. His brain, which weighed 2.5 ounces, was no larger than that of a kitten and much less competent. Like the great sauropods, *Stegosaurus* left the activities of his forelegs to a ganglion between the shoulders, while hindquarters and tail were regulated by a 50-ounce ganglion above the hips. This arrangement inspired Bert Leston Taylor's humorous poem, *The Dinosaur,* which has become one of the classics of popular paleontology:

> Behold the mighty dinosaur,
>   Famous in prehistoric lore,
> Not only for his power and strength
>   But for his intellectual length.
> You will observe by these remains
>   The creature had two sets of brains—
> One in his head (the usual place),
>   The other at his spinal base.
> Thus he could reason 'A priori'
>   As well as 'A posteriori.'
> No problem bothered him a bit
>   He made both head and tail of it.
> So wise was he, so wise and solemn,
>   Each thought filled just a spinal column.
> If one brain found the pressure strong
>   It passed a few ideas along.
> If something slipped his forward mind
>   'Twas rescued by the one behind.
> And if in error he was caught
>   He had a saving afterthought.
> As he thought twice before he spoke
>   He had no judgment to revoke.
> Thus he could think without congestion
>   Upon both sides of every question.
> Oh, gaze upon this model beast,
>   Defunct ten million years at least.

The Well-protected Ankylosaurs. Technically, "dreadnaught" dinosaurs form the suborder Ankylosauria. Appearing in early Cretaceous Europe, they became broad, low-set herbivores with short, massive legs and stubby, hoof-bearing feet. One of the best-known types, *Ankylosaurus,* was 17 feet long, 6 feet wide, and a little more than 4 feet high. The 27-inch skull was massive, without temporal openings; thick plates of bone overhung both eyes and nostrils and extended outward like ears. Ribs were fused tightly to the vertebrae, and the back and sides were sheathed in thick plates. Other plates covered the tail, which ended in a bony club firmly fastened to the vertebrae. The jaws were heavy, but the teeth were so small as to be almost useless.

Palaeoscincus resembled *Ankylosaurus* but had a less massive head. Its sides were set with plates that extended into spikes which were largest over the legs and curved forward upon the neck. *Scolosaurus* reached a length of 18 feet and a width of 8; its feet were so far apart that it must have taken short, waddling steps. Its body was covered with bone-studded skin that bore bosses and spines ranging from 4 to 6 inches in length. The tail ended in a bony knob and carried two large spines that were sheathed with horn.

Some ankylosaurs have been found in wind-blown sand, which suggests that the animals lived among sand dunes, feeding on plants that grew in hollows. It seems more likely, however, that they spent most of their time in moist

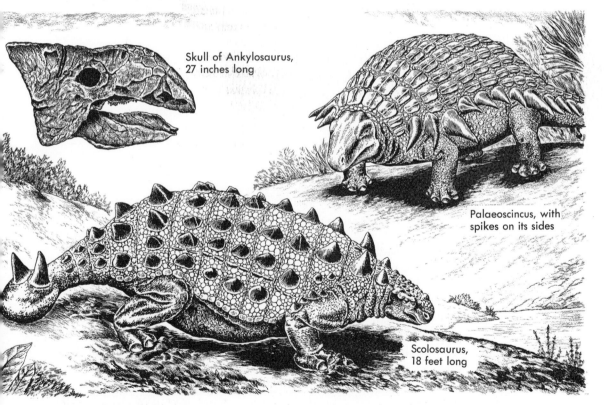

Skull of Ankylosaurus, 27 inches long

Palaeoscincus, with spikes on its sides

Scolosaurus, 18 feet long

Three armored dinosaurs of Cretaceous age, from western United States and Canada

(Left) *Psittacosaurus, 4 feet long, was a very primitive frilled dinosaur.* (Right) *Protoceratops, 5 to 6 feet long, had a frill but almost no horn.*

forests and swamps, where they could crawl about like enormous, rough turtles or slip and scramble over the mud. When enemies found them, they lay flat on the ground with legs tucked close to their sides and tail ready to batter any creature that touched it. Even *Tyrannosaurus* could not pierce their armor or turn them over to expose their defenseless bellies. Like modern porcupines, ankylosaurs found safety merely by keeping still.

EGGS, FRILLS, AND HORNS

In 1887 Professor O. C. Marsh of Yale described petrified horns found near Denver, Colorado, calling them *Bison alticornis.* Two years later, similar horns were found on reptile skulls. Thus the supposed bison became a ceratopsian, or horned dinosaur.

Though these creatures were first found in North America, they probably evolved in Asia. There at least one primitive species lingered on into late Cretaceous times in what now is the Gobi Desert. The fossils have been named *Protoceratops*—literally, "first horn-face," or "first ceratopsian."

This name is inappropriate, since *Protoceratops* had no horn and was not the earliest ceratopsian. Its ancestry goes back to *Psittacosaurus* ("parrot-saurian"), of the early Cretaceous, a biped related to *Hypsilophodon* though it did not climb trees. As millions of years went by, descendants of this

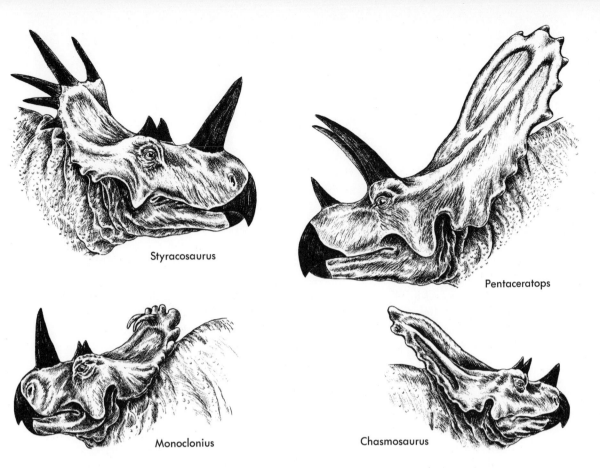

Heads of four large ceratopsians, or dinosaurs with beaks, neck frills, and horns. Late Cretaceous of North America

Styracosaurus

Pentaceratops

Monoclonius

Chasmosaurus

pioneer became quadrupeds with short tail and legs, stocky body, and a bony frill at the back of the head. The teeth were set side by side in a groove, and the upper beak became attached to a new and separate bone at the front of the upper jaw.

These traits survived in *Protoceratops,* a creature 5 to 6 feet in length. Its hind legs still were longer than its forelegs; it had five toes in front and behind, the frill at the back of its skull contained two very large openings, the nose was hornless, and the jaws bore hooked beaks. Two cylindrical teeth remained on each premaxillary bone.

At breeding time the female *Protoceratops* dug a nest in loose sand and laid a dozen or more eggs about 6 inches long. Sand around the eggs sometimes was soaked by heavy rains, smothering the embryos. They then were petrified, as were skeletons ranging from newly hatched youngsters to full-grown dinosaurs. They show, in unequaled detail, the development of animals that lived and died some 80,000,000 years ago.

Ceratopsians reached North America long before *Protoceratops* laid its eggs in Mongolian sand. They also became large animals with thick bodies, droop-

ing tails, and legs that formed upright columns in some groups but bent outward in others. The forefeet had five toes, the hind feet four and a remnant
of the fifth, and all fully developed toes bore hoofs. Horns grew on the nose
and above the eyes, and the skull with its frill became very large. Vertebrae
fused in the neck, and massive muscles attached to the base of the skull supported the heavy head. As in the "dreadnaught" ankylosaurs, the ilium spread
and bent outward, forming a plate above the hip joint, but the skin remained
without armor.

Such was the general plan; we must now consider variations. Early in their
American career the ceratopsians divided into two groups, the long-frilled and
the relatively short-frilled. The former began with types that had short horns
on the nose, long ones above the eyes, and openings in the frills. These characters continued to develop, reaching their zenith in such forms as *Pentacera-*
tops and *Torosaurus,* whose skulls were 7 to 8 feet 6 inches long, with 2-foot
horns above the eyes. The over-all length of these reptiles was about 20 feet.

Changes were less consistent in the short-frilled group. It began with
Monoclonius, a deep-skulled form with a long, straight horn on its nose, shorter
horns above its eyes, two downcurved spikes near the back of the frill, and
knobs along its border. *Styracosaurus* turned the knobs into horn-covered
spikes, but *Triceratops* reversed the trend. Its frill became solid and smooth,
and the horns above its eyes were larger than the narrow one on its nose.

Triceratops marked the high point in ceratopsian progress, as well as its

Triceratops, a late Cretaceous horned dinosaur; 20 to 25 feet long. It was sometimes
attacked by Tyrannosaurus.

end. Varied species were 20 to 25 feet long, 8 to 10 feet high, and weighed 8 to perhaps 12 tons. The skull was about 8 feet in length, carried 40-inch horns above the eyes, and sheltered a brain weighing almost 2 pounds, or a dozen times as much as that of *Stegosaurus.* As dinosaurs went, the creatures were abundant; one collector saw remains of about 500 skulls during seven summers on horseback and foot among the Lance beds of central Montana. These numbers probably are explained by a rare combination of strength, armament, pugnacity, and agility. Scarred frills show that *Triceratops* often fought with its own kind, probably in defense of home territory. With its sturdy legs, strong neck, and dangerous horns, *Triceratops* also could ward off attacks by carnivores or rush under the guard of their jaws and pierce their unprotected bellies. Though deinodonts were dull, they doubtless knew enough to avoid such an enemy unless they could deliver a surprise attack from the rear.

PATTERNS OF ADAPTIVE RADIATION

Dinosaurs present good examples of adaptive radiation, the process by which related animals or plants become fitted to live in various ways and under varied conditions. Thus the saurischians, which began as meat-eating bipeds of modest size, evolved into bipedal dwarfs and gigantic hunters, four-footed waders that ate plants, and ostrichlike animals that lost their teeth and adopted an omnivorous diet. In these various ways they lived and prospered for at least 110,000,000 years.

The ornithischians also sprang from carnivorous bipeds but became confirmed plant-eaters. During the late Jurassic and Cretaceous epochs they developed five different adaptive patterns:

1. Bipedal life among upland forests, sometimes even in trees. The forefeet generally were used to grasp food, though they could be employed in walking. No defense except by flight. (*Camptosaurus,* iguanodonts, troödonts, *Hypsilophodon,* and other primitive types.)

2. Life in forests that provided a firm footing for large, slow quadrupeds. Defense by armor and by swinging the tail, on which spikes developed. (Stegosaurs.)

3. Life in swamps, both fresh and salt water, but with frequent trips on land. Food was pulled or shoveled into the mouth by means of a ducklike beak. Walking was done mostly on the hind legs, but four webbed feet and a tail were used for swimming. Since weapons and armor were lacking, safety was found in escape by swimming. (Duckbills, or hadrosaurs.)

4. Life on uplands and in swamps, where broad-bodied reptiles waddled about or crept over mud. Food was cropped with horny jaws; defense was achieved with bony armor and massive clublike tails, though broad, heavily

armored creatures that merely lay still also were safe from enemies. ("Dreadnaught" ankylosaurs.)

5. Active life on openly wooded uplands amid deltas and swamps; habits much like those of the modern rhinoceros. For defense there was armor (the frill) and horns, behind which was the power of an 8- to 12-ton body. The horns also were used in fights between the dinosaurs themselves. (Large ceratopsians.)

THE PUZZLE OF EXTINCTION

Dinosaurs prospered at various times, in different regions, and in widely divergent ways. In spite of this, they became extinct. Some died out at one time, some at another, and not one survived the end of the Mesozoic era.

Why did they die? To this question most experts and many amateurs have offered conflicting answers.

One theory says that the dinosaurs became too big and remained too stupid to keep on living in a changing world. Unfortunately we have no proof that a dull brain meant unfitness to live, especially when it was supported by ganglia like those of *Stegosaurus,* which provided for very efficient reflexes. Moreover, though some great sauropods died out near the middle of dinosaur history, others lived almost to the end of the Mesozoic era. Similarly, whatever caused the extinction of *Allosaurus* did not keep deinodonts from evolving into *Gorgosaurus* and *Tyrannosaurus,* and ceratopsians grew to be larger than the extinct *Stegosaurus.* Since none of these creatures was brainy, their development seems to do away with this would-be explanation.

But, say other theorists, dinosaurs possessed the power of adaptation only when they were racially young. As millions of years went by they grew old, became set in their ways, lost their vigor, and finally died out from sheer inability to keep on living. This theory may explain the demise of separate groups of dinosaurs, provided they show characteristics found in individual reptiles as they become senescent, or old. But it hardly accounts for the widespread extinctions that followed the Morrison and Lance epochs. Can we believe that all the dinosaurs which vanished then belonged to senile races?

Another theory says that plants eaten by the great herbivores vanished, whereupon those reptiles starved to death and so deprived the meat-eaters of food. Actually, however, there was no radical change in plant life after the Morrison epoch, when huge sauropods and stegosaurs vanished from the Rocky Mountain region. Moreover, Cretaceous plant-eaters provided plenty of food for the deinodonts, which became bigger and seemingly more abundant than Jurassic carnivores.

It has been suggested that the great dinosaurs of Africa vanished because tsetse flies spread germs of sleeping sickness among them. Those flies undoubtedly were common; several species are found in late Jurassic rocks. But we have no evidence that they carried germs or that those germs could live in the blood of Jurassic dinosaurs. Even if they did, we apparently must find some other explanation for the death of sauropods on other continents and at other times.

Equally dubious are suggestions that dinosaurs were destroyed by small mammals that sucked their eggs or fed upon their young ones. No contemporary mammal was large enough to suck the eggs of *Allosaurus* or eat the young of large sauropods. Even less convincing is the theory that Mesozoic reptiles died out because they could not compete with mammals, which had warm blood, active bodies, and superior brains. No Mesozoic mammal was big enough to attack a dinosaur or eat so much of its food that it starved. This is especially true of the small, crude beasts that lived near the huge dinosaurs of late Jurassic times.

A variant of this theory makes dinosaurs compete with each other and awards success to the best. Early sauropods, for example, were small; when bigger, stronger forms evolved they crowded out their predecessors. Similarly, large deinodonts ate food which small ones needed, and pugnacious giants such as *Triceratops* drove weaker, less aggressive types away from choice habitats. This brought slow death to the vanquished—but since it meant survival for victors, the process does not explain why *all* dinosaurs died out.

A more promising theory holds that the great Mesozoic reptiles died out because changes in the earth's surface destroyed their habitats. Thus the great sauropods disappeared from the Rocky Mountain region at the end of Jurassic times, when uplift drained swamps and built great ranges of mountains that extended from Lower California to Alaska. But sauropods lingered on in Texas, South America, and the Old World, where extensive swamps persisted into early Cretaceous epochs.

A still more convincing parallel between changing conditions and extinction is presented by Cretaceous deposits and fossils. This period began with lowering lands and equable climates, which apparently reached their zenith about 100,000,000 years ago. Then climates rapidly became cooler—and a considerable number of dinosaurs died out, including some survivors from the Jurassic and relative newcomers such as *Iguanodon*. After some 6,000,000 years the climate began to grow warmer again—not in one continent or region, but over the entire globe. With this came the great evolution of deinodonts, as well as duckbills, ceratopsians, and other bird-hipped dinosaurs of late Cretaceous times. They prospered for at least 15,000,000 years, though temperatures began to decline about 80,000,000 years ago, with the beginning of the revolution that finally closed the Mesozoic era. It brought temperatures close to those of the mid-Cretaceous decline, at the same time raising mountains and turning swamps into dry uplands. Unless deinodonts and bird-hips were able to find refuges, which seems doubtful, they had no chance to survive.

One final theory builds upon the preceding. It begins by saying that dinosaurs (and countless other organisms now extinct) lost their ability to adapt themselves to constantly changing conditions. The theory then says that new conditions, such as cooling or modified habitats, destroyed the unadapted creatures. Destruction would be greatest, of course, during revolutions that radically modified large portions of the earth.

This theory is not complete, for it does not explain why creatures that once changed greatly should lose their ability to do so. Yet there seems to be good evidence that this happens. If we ever discover the reason, we may understand why strong, successful groups like the deinodonts or duckbills failed and became extinct.

CHAPTER XXVIII

Flying Reptiles and Birds

W HILE Jurassic dinosaurs were becoming giants, two other innovations appeared in the reptilian world. Certain archosaurs developed warm blood, feathers, and wings, thereby becoming birds. Other archosaurs remained reptiles but also took to the air.

THE WINGED PTEROSAURS

The first fossil of a flying reptile was found in the same Jurassic limestones that contain insects, prawns, and well-preserved jellyfish. In 1784 the specimen was described briefly as "one of those vertebrated animals which in olden times inhabited the sea." In 1809 it was restudied by the great French anatomist Cuvier, who probably knew more about bones than any other man then living. He realized that the fossil was a winged reptile and called it *Pterodactylus,* or "wing-finger." The order to which it belonged is now termed the Pterosauria.

We compare pterosaurs with birds, yet they really looked and acted like no other vertebrates. All had short bodies and large, bony heads, with brains swollen in the region devoted to sight, and sclerotic plates in the eyes. Tails were either long or short; the wings were skin on a framework of bone; one species supposedly had hairlike scales on its body. Large wing bones were hollow and filled with air, and a wide breastbone (sternum) furnished attachment for the muscles used in flight.

Like bones in the wings of bats and birds, those of the pterosaurs had once been forelegs and "hands." We trace humerus, radius, and ulna; shoulder, elbow, and wrist. Old books even describe five digits: a greatly elongated "little finger" supporting most of the wing, three short fingers tipped with claws,

Rhamphorhynchus (left) *was a primitive long-tailed pterosaur about 24 inches long. Dimorphodon* (right) *had a deep but very light skull and reached a length of 42 inches. Both lived in Europe during the Jurassic period.*

and a rudimentary thumb. It now seems that this "thumb" was only a hardened tendon, that the "little finger" was the fourth, and that the fifth finger had been lost as pterosaurs evolved.

Long-tailed Pterosaurs. Tails, toes, and teeth divide flying reptiles into two contrasting groups. The older of these was characterized by a long tail, five-toed feet, and teeth that generally were well developed, though they might not be numerous. Fossils have been found only in Jurassic rocks.

Rhamphorhynchus, of the early Jurassic, was a typical long-tail, as well as a primitive one. We see this in the low skull, the five long toes of the hind feet, and the large and fairly numerous teeth. The slender tail ended in an upright flap of skin which probably served as a rudder.

Dimorphodon also lived during the early Jurassic but was more advanced. Its skull was large and deep but very light, with three large openings on each

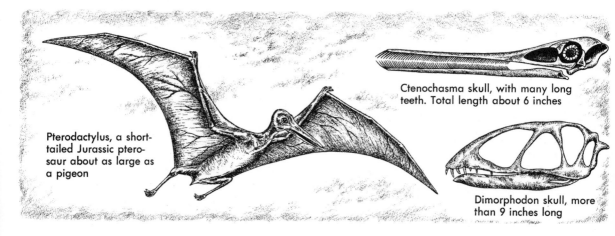

Ctenochasma skull, with many long teeth. Total length about 6 inches

Pterodactylus, a short-tailed Jurassic ptero-saur about as large as a pigeon

Dimorphodon skull, more than 9 inches long

side and a small one in each lower jaw. The hind legs were large for a pterosaur, and the toes bore good-sized claws.

Short-tailed Pterosaurs. These reptiles apparently descended from long-tails, though their exact ancestor is unknown. In their evolution, progress meant reduction of the tail to a stub, shrinking or loss of the fifth hind toe, and teeth that first became slender and numerous but finally gave way to beaks. The group appeared during the late Jurassic and died out before the Cretaceous period closed.

Pteranodon and its skull. This short-tailed, toothless Cretaceous pterosaur from Kansas had a wingspread of 22 to 27 feet.

Ctenochasma, of the German Jurassic, was a primitive and beakless short-tail with a head about 6 inches long. The teeth were almost as slender as bristles, and the hinder part of the skull had lost several bones. In *Pterodactylus* this loss was obscured; though bones that had vanished did not reappear, those that remained expanded over the missing portions. Teeth were lacking from the back of the jaws, and a beak apparently was present.

About two dozen species of *Pterodactylus* ranged from Africa to northern Europe during the late Jurassic and early Cretaceous. Though some species weighed as much as a goose, others were not much larger than an English sparrow.

As short-tailed pterosaurs progressed they increased the spread of their wings. The late Cretaceous *Nyctosaurus,* for example, combined a body about as large as a pigeon's, with wings broader than those of an eagle. Even it was outdone by *Pteranodon,* which ranged from Kansas to Europe and probably around the world. *Pteranodon's* wings, which spread 22 to 27 feet, supported a body 20 inches long (excluding the tail) that weighed 20 to 25 pounds. The neck was longer than the body, and the skull measured 45 to 75 inches, depending on whether or not a bony crest balanced the 3-foot beak. The lower jaw was deeply indented, making room for a large pouch in which food was stored until it could be swallowed and digested.

Habits of Winged Reptiles. Old books show pterosaurs flapping their wings like crows or pigeons, rising into the air from the ground, and walking or sitting on all fours between periods of flight. Modern critics, however, point out that most pterosaur wings were too large and too poorly supported to have beaten up and down rapidly, while the hind feet of many species could not be brought forward into a walking or sitting position. Even those that could walk on all fours would have found it hard to sit up on two legs while flapping their wings for a take-off.

Today's pictures of pterosaurs, therefore, show them resting on cliffs or trees, where those whose feet were directed to the rear hung head downward, like bats. When the time came to fly they released their hold or took weak leaps and then flapped their wings as they started to fall. Once launched, they set their broad wings and soared, relying upon currents to carry them aloft. After that they flapped their wings only to regain altitude lost during long glides or quick swoops to catch food. With greater wingspread in proportion to weight, both soaring and gliding were easier for these ancient reptiles than they are for modern vultures, eagles, and hawks.

Pterosaurs hunted by sight, not by smell, for brain casts show that the centers of sight were greatly enlarged while those of smell had dwindled. Small species may have eaten insects, snapping them up in flight or as they alighted on trees. Large pterosaurs ate both fish and aquatic invertebrates. Remains of food not yet damaged by digestion have been found near the throat of *Pteranodon,* where its capacious pouch once dangled.

Pterosaurs of Jurassic Germany lived on islands and wooded shores, within easy reach of the sea. *Pteranodon* also roosted close to the sea, and strong winds sometimes drove it as much as a hundred miles from shore. Other winged reptiles lived near and hunted over lakes in which fish were plentiful. Even a species that left its tracks in Morrison sandstones of northeastern Arizona probably did not live far from water, though the strata seem to suggest a semiarid climate. This reptile, which took steps 14 inches long, was too large to have fed only on insects.

Three dangers confronted pterosaurs, little as well as big. First came the threat of being eaten by larger winged reptiles as they soared and by mosasaurs or plesiosaurs as they swooped to catch fish or invertebrates. Next came the menace of torn wings, whose thin skin had no support between the body and fourth finger. Last, and perhaps most important, was the threat of forced landings on water or level ground. A pterosaur that came down upon water might float for a while but could not take off; it therefore drowned unless some fish or aquatic reptile swallowed it. Grounded pterosaurs fared almost as badly if we are right in thinking they could not launch themselves into the

Archaeopteryx preparing to flap its wings and glide from a cycad. Length about 18 inches

air except from an elevation. While struggling to reach it they were prey for small dinosaurs, snakes, and other carnivorous reptiles. Unless trees were near —very near—few grounded pterosaurs managed to reach them and escape.

BEGINNINGS OF BIRDS

The late Jurassic limestone in which *Pterodactylus* was discovered also contains very primitive birds. The first specimen, a single feather, was found in August of 1861. A feathered but headless skeleton appeared one month later, and another, complete with skull, was dug up in 1877. Though the first was named *Archaeopteryx* and the second *Archaeornis*, both apparently belong to the former genus.

Archaeopteryx—the name means "ancient wing"—had a slender body and was slightly smaller than our familiar crow. The head was good-sized but rather flat; there were scales instead of beaks on the jaws, which contained forty-six or more teeth firmly set in separate sockets. Both brain and eyes were large; the former suggests the brain of an alligator, and the latter had rings of reptilian sclerotic plates. The tail was reptilian, too, being longer than the body and provided with twenty-one slender vertebrae. Hipbones were not fused (a feature found in most reptiles), but their shape was birdlike. So were the well-developed wishbone and the perching feet.

This mixture of new with ancestral traits persisted in still other parts of the body. The tail and wings, for example, were fully feathered. But the tail feathers were arranged in pairs along the vertebrae, and each wing bore three clawed, lizardlike toes. Most of the feathers on head, neck, and body were lost before fossilization, but impressions indicate that they were not combined with scales.

Archaeopteryx probably flew by flapping its wings and by gliding. It was able to leap from trees; by setting its wings and tail, it could glide more successfully than the modern flying squirrel. To go farther or to rise it flapped its wings, but their muscles probably were too weak for swift, long-continued flight. This suggestion is supported by the fossils, which represent birds that were blown away from land at times of very low tides. After flying as long as they could, they fell and were trapped in banks of sticky lime mud. This mud, as we know, also caught many storm-buffeted insects.

We assume that these early birds were warm-blooded, since warm blood seems essential to flight and is indicated by feathers, which prevent loss of heat. We know that the creatures found food with their large eyes, but cannot tell whether they ate living animals or carrion. Pictures that show them tearing at fruit almost certainly are in error.

TOOTHED CRETACEOUS BIRDS

We know little about early Cretaceous birds, for remains are fragmentary and rare. They must have spread widely and evolved rapidly, however, for highly specialized types ranged from Europe through North America during late Cretaceous times.

One of these was named *Ichthyornis* ("fish-bird") because it apparently caught fish. With its well-feathered body, powerful wings, and keeled breast-

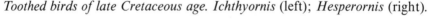

Toothed birds of late Cretaceous age. Ichthyornis (left); Hesperornis (right).

bone, *Ichthyornis* must have looked and acted like a plump tern. The mouth was armed with backwardly curved teeth which did not reach the front of the upper jaws; the lower jaws had extra joints which allowed them to open widely like the jaws of mosasaurs, with which they have sometimes been confused. Though the various species of *Ichthyornis* stood only 6 to 9 inches high, they apparently were able to swallow thick-bodied fish.

Hesperornis is found in the same formations that contain *Ichthyornis* and had similar teeth. It also possessed a sharp beak, but there resemblance came to an end. Instead of being small and ternlike, *Hesperornis* ("western bird") was a torpedo-shaped creature more than 4 feet long that lived on and in sea water. Its ancestors doubtless had wings and legs of use in walking or perching, but as *Hesperornis* took to sea its wings dwindled to hidden remnants, its feet became three-toed paddles, and its legs turned backward so far they could be used only in swimming. The tail also was reduced to a stub whose value was negative; it merely kept out of the way.

Hesperornis had no need for wings or walking legs so long as it stayed in water. There it lived like an oversized, flightless loon, skimming over the surface, diving, and swimming long distances while submerged. It could easily capture small fish while dodging carnivorous reptiles that might have fed upon it. Only on shore did it become awkward, plunging about clumsily with its legs stretched out behind.

But did *Hesperornis* often leave the water? We are tempted to say it did so to nest, but that may be a wrong assumption. Modern grebes, which also swim, dive and feed largely on fish, build floating nests anchored to plants in shallow water. *Hesperornis* may have done likewise, thus avoiding the difficulties and dangers of incubation on land.

FEATHERED, FLIGHTLESS GIANTS

Archaeopteryx, Ichthyornis, and *Hesperornis:* with minor exceptions, they typify known Mesozoic birds. Except for obvious specializations, they also were primitive. All kept reptilian teeth; all had lower jaws that still were separate; all possessed hip girdles in which ischium and ilium were not fused. When these reptilian characters vanished, birds became modernized.

This happened during Cretaceous times, for modern birds were many and varied during early Tertiary epochs. Moreover, a late Cretaceous jaw named *Caenagnathus* seems to belong to a very large bird, not to a beaked dinosaur, as some paleontologists have suggested.

Tertiary Giants. The tendency to produce giants is one we hardly look for in birds. Beginning, we think, with *Caenagnathus,* it appeared in varied groups at various times and is still to be traced in such living forms as the condor, cassowary, and ostrich. One of giantism's early products, *Diatryma,* lived in the West

(Left) *Diatryma, a flightless Eocene bird from Wyoming, about 7 feet in height.* (Right) *Phororhacos, a carnivorous bird from the Miocene of South America. Height about 5 feet.*

during Eocene times but had relatives that ranged to New Jersey and Europe. Suggesting a massive ostrich in form, *Diatryma* stood 7 feet high and had wings that were much too small for flight. Its high, narrow skull was 17 inches long, its curved beak measured 9 inches, and its deep lower jaw was powered by massive muscles. The neck was thick and so was the body; there was almost no tail, and the heavy legs ended in feet with three long toes and a fourth toe that did not reach the ground. *Diatryma* walked and ran through Eocene glades, feeding on a mixed diet of plants and small animals. Its feathers have not been found, but we suspect they were long and thin, like those of the modern cassowary.

Diatryma differs from all living birds, though it may be remotely related to cranes. This also seems true of the phororhacids, which lived in South America during the Oligocene and Miocene epochs. *Phororhacos* itself was 5 feet or more in height, with a skull 13 inches long and 7 deep, with a powerful hooked beak. The neck was long though not cranelike, the wings were too short for use in flight, the long legs were rather slender, and the four toes bore sharp claws. A relative, *Brontornis,* was taller and had much heavier legs. Its drumstick (tibia) was 30 inches long, against 23 for *Diatryma* and 19 for a modern ostrich. A 14-pound turkey's drumstick is 8.5 inches in length.

Claws and the enormous hooked beak suggest that phororhacids were active hunters that walked and ran but could not fly. They probably ranged the

Tertiary prairies of Argentina, preying on mammals, reptiles, and other birds. Perhaps they also ate carrion, as vultures do today.

MOAS AND ELEPHANT-BIRDS

Ostriches, cassowaries, and their kin belong to a varied group of birds sometimes called ratites, though paleognaths is a preferable name. Some of its members were and are small, but others became the largest of all avian giants. They also achieved success, since several are living today.

Aepyornis and Its Kin. *Aepyornis* gives its name to an order, the "elephant-birds" of Africa and adjacent Madagascar. Appearing in the Eocene, they reached their zenith in the Glacial epoch but survived into modern times, when they were killed and eaten by man.

Aepyornis ("lofty-bird") reached a height of 8 feet, which means that the largest species was no taller than a modern ostrich. "Heavy-bird" would have been a better name, for a broad body and massive legs brought the weight to about 1,000 pounds in contrast to 300 pounds for an ostrich. In one species

Two species of Aepyornis, 9 to 10 feet high. At the left are foot bones and eggs of the larger species. The black dot is a hen's egg on the same scale.

the drumstick was 25 inches long, 18 inches around at its broad upper end, and 6 inches near the middle. The thigh bone was shorter but thicker; its girth was made possible, perhaps, by the fact that it was hollow. Eggs were in keeping with the leg bones; 12 to 13 inches in length, their capacity was about two gallons. Long after the last *Aepyornis* died, natives dug egg shells from swamps and used them in place of jugs or bowls. The first ones to be seen by Europeans were brought to a trading post as receptacles for rum.

Moas, the "Terrible Birds." While *Aepyornis* prospered and died in Madagascar, another group of feathered giants went through a similar history in New Zealand.

This second group comprises the moas, whose technical name of Dinornithiformes may be roughly translated as "terrible birds." They actually were peaceful plant-eaters that roamed in small flocks or in pairs and had no means of offense or defense except to kick with their powerful legs. Throughout most of their history they roamed unchallenged over both North and South Islands of New Zealand, from sea level to mountain slopes. Different species developed on each island and one by one became extinct. Only a few lived on until the coming of man, who proceeded to kill them with wooden spears and roast their bones and flesh for his feasts.

The oldest moas lie in clays whose age has been variously estimated at 1,000,000 to 8,000,000 years. The first figure would make them earliest Pleistocene; the second would carry them back to the early Pliocene. In either case, the birds were not giants but ranged from the size of a turkey to 4 or 5 feet in height. Some, at least, still had wings about as well—or as poorly—developed as those of *Phororhacos*.

As thousands or millions of years went by, the moas became larger and more highly adapted land-dwellers. Legs and necks grew long; feet became well adapted to walking; wings commonly disappeared. Remains preserved in dry caves show that the head and most of the neck were naked, like those of the emu, though there was no bony crest. Roots may have been a favorite food, but scythe-edged beaks suggest that the birds were browsers and grazers, and so does partly digested food found with skeletons of moas that were mired in swamps. Heights ranged from 7 to more than 10 feet, weights to 500 pounds, and shapes from graceful, long-legged creatures to barrel-bodied birds whose short legs were thickly encased in flesh. Feathers were thin and silky, like those on the body of an ostrich. Colors ranged from brown or chestnut tipped with white to black and white, like the plumage of a Plymouth Rock hen.

Various theories have been proposed to explain why great members of moas were buried in open fissures and swamps. Early paleontologists thought the bones were washed into these locations; others said that, impelled by glacial cold, the big birds had gone into swamps to warm their unprotected feet. Local "experts" maintained that aborigines had set fires, forcing the moas to

Long-legged and short-legged moas of postglacial New Zealand

take refuge in swamps, where hundreds or thousands were mired. This theory overlooked one fact: most of the mired moas belonged to species that had become extinct before human beings arrived in A.D. 800 to 1000.

Recent excavations seem to have settled the problem. Moas got into broad, deep fissures by falling, just as quadrupeds have done for ages and are doing now. Those that mired did so as they slipped into muck while picking their way in the almost endless search for food. Though only a few might die in a year, their sum became great in the course of thousands of centuries. The great moa deposit in Pyramid Valley, North Canterbury, contains about 800 skeletons per acre.

The Maoris, whose ancestors hunted the last moas, have some significant sayings about them. "As dull as a moa" tells what might be suspected: that the birds were sluggish as well as stupid and probably were easily killed. People fighting "two against two, like moas," indicates that pairs remained together and attacked others that invaded their home territory. But no saying is needed to tell us that the big birds swallowed gizzard stones, used them to grind their food, and disgorged them when they were worn. Piles of rounded stones are found on the ground in moa country and along their still discernible trails. But the stones found in skeletons are relatively fresh and angular, showing that they still were in use when the moas died.

OTHER MODERNIZED BIRDS

We need not review all modern birds of the Tertiary and Pleistocene. They belonged to groups we see every day: ducks, vultures, hawks, owls, plovers, gulls, sparrows, and many others. Many, of course, were small; their bones were preserved only under exceptional conditions, such as those of the California tar pits described in Chapter XXXIII. Those pits contain only one bird that might be called a giant—the vulture *Teratornis*. It stood 30 inches high, weighed about 50 pounds, and had a wingspread of at least 12 feet. This far exceeds the 8- to 9-foot spread of Andean condors, now the largest of all flying birds.

One group that does deserve comment is the penguins, which combine some primitive characters with specialization rivaling that of *Hesperornis*. Penguins, which seem to be descendants of diving birds such as petrels, lost the power to fly, used their wings as flippers, and turned their legs and feet into organs with which they could walk. They even sit on their eggs in an upright position, providing warmth with folds of skin rather than with their breasts. One fossil penguin became as tall as a man, but no species seems to have crossed the equator into the Northern Hemisphere.

CHAPTER XXIX

The Rise of Mammals

W<small>HILE</small> winged saurians flew and wingless birds swam, members of another group awaited a chance to achieve importance. They had done so, indeed, since the early Jurassic, hiding in trees and thickets to escape carnivorous reptiles. Thus they saved their lives yet made so little progress that they still were able to become successful ancestors.

FROM REPTILE TO MAMMAL

We sometimes call these creatures "beasts"; more often we say "animals" in a tone that tries to set them aside from the rest of the animal kingdom. The correct term, however, is *mammals.* It is the only word in English that fits all creatures having hair, warm blood, and glands that secrete milk as food for young ones. With a few exceptions the young also are born instead of emerging from eggs which the mother lays or keeps in her body until they hatch.

Changes in Bones and Teeth. These special characters are found in soft parts and cannot be traced in fossils, but mammalian bones and teeth also differ from those of typical reptiles. The braincase, for example, is much larger, accommodating a brain whose cerebral hemispheres were steadily increasing in size. The old bar or plate behind each opening for the eye (orbit) is lost, though mammals such as monkeys and horses have replaced it with a new one.

The external nostrils occupy a single opening (naris) in the skull, the internal nares move to the back of the mouth, and a new, or secondary, palate is developed. This arrangement, which reminds us of crocodiles but has a different origin, allows mammals to breathe while eating. Each lower jaw contains only one bone, and the teeth are of several types, adapted to such varied tasks as nipping, slashing, cutting, and grinding. The rear, or cheek, teeth also develop two or more roots. The single ball-and-socket joint connecting skull with

375

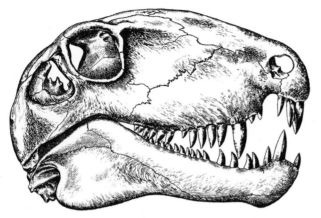

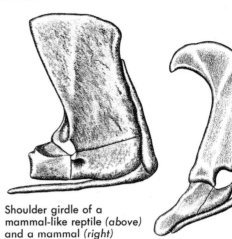

Skull of Dimetrodon, with the varied
teeth that show relationship to mammals

Shoulder girdle of a
mammal-like reptile *(above)*
and a mammal *(right)*

backbone in reptiles has become a structure with two parts, or condyles, one of which lies on each side of the spinal nerve cord.

Other new features appear in the mammalian skeleton. The shoulder girdle has become much narrower than it is in reptiles and commonly loses two bones. The uppermost bone in the hip girdle slants forward, and a large opening develops below the hip joint. Both the hipbone (femur) and upper "arm" bone (humerus) are longer and more slender than those of typical reptiles, and the head of the femur is at one side rather than at the end. This, as well as new attachments for muscles, is associated with changes in movements of the legs. Those of mammals are held close to the body and are pulled backward and forward instead of sprawling sidewise in typical reptilian style.

Links between Reptiles and Mammals. Evolution's first hints of mammalian structure appeared among late Pennsylvanian reptiles. Each time *Dimetrodon* slashed his prey he used jaws in which some teeth were larger and longer than the others, suggesting the canine teeth of dogs and cats. Later, when *Dimetrodon* died, his bleaching bones revealed a shoulder girdle containing the same bones in essentially the same arrangement found in some primitive mammals. Other resemblances appeared in the skull, which was much less highly specialized than that of lizards, snakes, or carnivorous dinosaurs.

The next links between typical reptiles and mammals are found in South Africa. There early Triassic lowlands were inhabited by dinocephalians and dicynodonts, whose thick bodies and specialized skulls are described in Chapter XXIII. Uplands were left to less grotesque relatives that possessed much greater capacity for change.

One of those relatives was *Cynognathus,* whose name is Latinized Greek for "dog-jaw." *Cynognathus* himself was an ugly creature 5 to 7 feet long, with an oversized head, a relatively slender body, and a drooping tail. Fossils show such typically reptilian features as small braincase, widely separate openings for the nostrils, and a complete ring around each eye. This ring, however, is

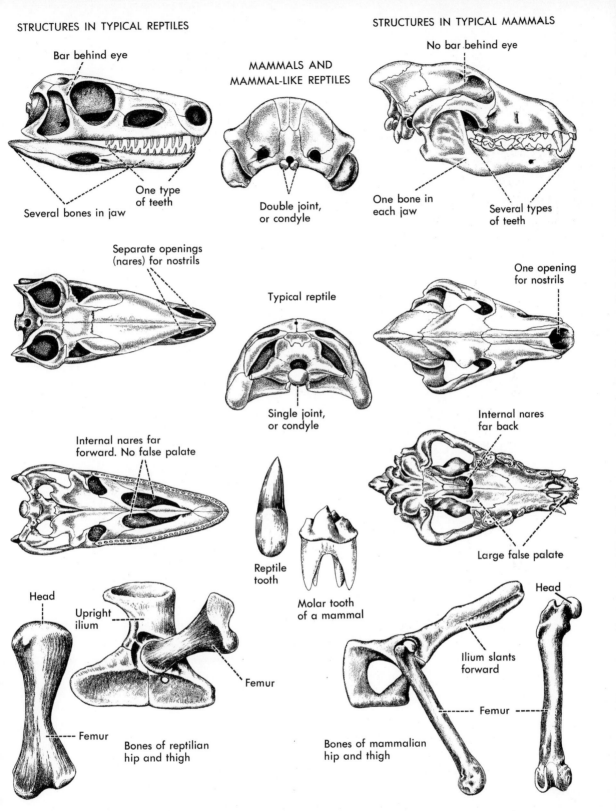

STRUCTURES IN TYPICAL REPTILES

Bar behind eye

One type of teeth

Several bones in jaw

MAMMALS AND MAMMAL-LIKE REPTILES

Double joint, or condyle

STRUCTURES IN TYPICAL MAMMALS

No bar behind eye

One bone in each jaw

Several types of teeth

Separate openings (nares) for nostrils

Typical reptile

One opening for nostrils

Internal nares far forward. No false palate

Single joint, or condyle

Internal nares far back

Reptile tooth

Molar tooth of a mammal

Large false palate

Head

Upright ilium

Femur

Femur

Bones of reptilian hip and thigh

Head

Ilium slants forward

Femur

Bones of mammalian hip and thigh

A comparison of skulls, bones, and teeth in typical reptiles, mammal-like reptiles, and mammals

Cynognathus, a mammal-like reptile from the Triassic of South Africa. Length about 5 feet

composed of four bones instead of six, the number found in typical reptiles. Other new characters include teeth adapted to nipping, slashing, and cutting meat, a partly developed secondary palate, and jaws in which one bone (the dentary) is much larger than the others. There also are double condyles at the base of the skull.

Last Links; the Ictidosaurs. Some beastlike reptiles increased their resemblance to mammals by losing most of the bar behind each orbit. But the next great steps forward were taken by ictidosaurs, which ranged round the world during late Triassic epochs and lived on into Jurassic times. One ictidosaur had a skull with no trace of bars behind the orbits, nostrils whose openings joined, and squarish grinding teeth. Only two small bones behind each dentary prove that this creature should be classed as a reptile.

THE EARLIEST MAMMALS

Mammals may have evolved only once, from a single reptilian ancestor. It seems probable, however, that several offspring of ictidosaurs made the change to warm blood, hair, milk glands, and lower jaws containing only one bone. Evidence for this is found in three primitive orders which differ so much from other mammals that they seem to have had separate beginnings.

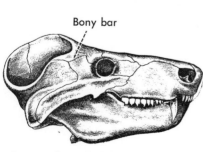

Cynognathus, which had a broad bar of bone behind the eye

Bienotherium, an ictidosaur. No trace of bar behind the eye

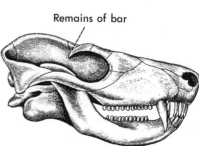

Bauria, mammal-like reptile that had lost part of the bar behind the eye

Three Primitive Groups. One of these groups, the monotremes, contains mammals that lay eggs in reptilian fashion, though they nurse their young. They include the aquatic duckbill and the ant-eating echidna of modern Australia. Since fossil monotremes also are limited to Australia, we suspect that the group evolved on that continent and never reached the rest of the world.

Our second and third orders include fossils found among dinosaur bones in the Morrison formation as well as in late Jurassic rocks of Europe and Asia. The triconodonts include small ratlike creatures whose teeth suggest a diminutive *Cynognathus*. The animals probably lived among underbrush and fallen leaves, coming out at night to feed on insects, eggs, and fruits. Though triconodonts ranged round the world, they died out before the Cretaceous period began.

Multituberculates were more successful, for they lived on through the Cretaceous and Paleocene, and into early Eocene times. Morrison species were small herbivores with rough grinding teeth and long, curved incisors adapted to gnawing. These animals probably lived like woodchucks and other present-day rodents. During the Paleocene one genus became larger than the modern beaver, for its skull is almost 7 inches long.

The Rise of Marsupials. The main trunk of the mammalian family tree begins with two other Jurassic orders, the pantotheres and symmetrodonts. They also were small, ratlike creatures whose chief claim to fame is the fact that some of them—we don't know which—gave rise to marsupials.

We generally think of marsupials as kangaroos and clumsy wombats, both of which inhabit Australia. Actually, the stupid, plodding opossum is more primitive, more typical, and much more common. It also belongs to an old American stock, for small opossums left bones and teeth in western Cretaceous deposits which also contain remains of beaked, frill-bearing dinosaurs. Like most modern marsupials, these pioneers apparently had no effective means of nourishing embryonic offspring. The young therefore were born as tiny, imperfect creatures that crawled into a pouch (the marsupium) on the under side of their mother's body. There they sucked milk from her teats and continued development.

Modern opossums like to wander, and so did their ancient relatives. Marsupials reached Australia in latest Cretaceous times and entered South America before carnivores arrived. On both continents they were isolated as sea water covered isthmuses leading from other lands. One South American group remained opossums, but others developed the forms and habits of rabbits, woodchucks, and wolves. Some of these are described and illustrated in Chapter XXXI.

Even greater changes took place in Australia, which has been separated from Asia for more than 60,000,000 years. During that time opossumlike marsupials produced descendants that assumed the forms and habits of many other animals as well as new ones of their own. Fossils include a marsupial

Skull of Taeniolabis,
about 7 inches long

Jaw of a triconodont from late Jurassic dinosaur beds in Wyoming. Length
about 1.25 inches

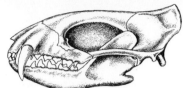

Skull of Deltatherium, an insectivore,
about 1.75 inches long. Cretaceous of
Mongolia

Head of Taeniolabis, a
Paleocene multituberculate

Deltatherium looked and
probably lived like a modern shrew.

Four early mammals of primitive types

anteater complete with digging claws and an animal built like a lion but equipped with huge shearing teeth which it probably used to cut fruit. *Diprotodon* was a plant-eater that looked like a massive, clumsy wombat and weighed about 4,000 pounds. It differed vastly from the herbivorous kangaroos, which became leapers instead of runners. Having done that, some of them took up life in trees!

THE PROGRESSIVE PLACENTALS

Though marsupials did not lay eggs, few of them found an effective way to nourish young ones inside maternal bodies. That change was made in Cretaceous times by a mammal that joined an egg membrane to the lining of its uterus. The result was a new organ, the placenta, through which food and oxygen could reach the young ones, while waste material was removed. Both processes allowed the embryos to develop fully, producing more complex brains and bodies than those of marsupials.

Early Insectivores. All this is inference; inference based on the bodies of existing animals. Late Cretaceous fossils from Mongolia continue the story, for they are remains of placental mammals. Some were specialized beasts related to hedgehogs, but others were very primitive insectivores. Their nearest living relatives are moles and the mouselike shrews.

We may ignore late Cretaceous hedgehogs, but not their primitive neighbors. The latter were inconspicuous creatures which probably fed at night or in twilight on a diet of mature insects mixed with grubs and worms. The head was long in proportion to the body, the legs were short, and the tail was long. Some species, at least, had forty-four teeth, or eleven on each side of both upper and lower jaws. These teeth also were arranged according to a definite order, or formula: three incisors at the front and then one canine, followed by four premolars and three molars. Many later mammals would lose some of these teeth and change the shapes of others, but only a few specialized groups such as whales and edentates would greatly increase their number. In dentition as well as in other features, Cretaceous insectivores were ready to produce more modern orders.

BATS: THE ONLY FLYING MAMMALS

One of these groups is the bats, or Chiroptera, the only mammals specialized for true flight. We often compare them with pterosaurs, since both evolved broad wings covered with very thin skin. But the pterosaur wing ran from body and legs to the fourth "finger," with no support between. Bats avoided this defect by lengthening bones in the "arm" and using four of the five fingers to stretch and strengthen the wing. They also developed strong breast muscles and enlarged the auditory regions of the brain. Ancient bats apparently guided their flight by squeaking and listening to echoes, as their descendants do today.

The oldest known bats were small creatures that had lost a few ancestral teeth and possessed well-developed wings. Some species lived among groves, but others pursued insects over the Green River (Eocene) lakes. Now and then a bat swooped so low that it struck the water. There it soon drowned and sank to the bottom, where its bones and even its skin were preserved in fine-grained sediment.

By Oligocene times the group had divided, one section remaining small insect-eaters while the other began to eat fruit. Its members also increased in size and added length to their skulls, becoming the "flying foxes" that now range from islands near Africa to India, Australia and Japan.

CHAPTER XXX

A Revolution and Its Sequel

T HE ROAD from Bernalillo to Aztec, New Mexico, skirts the Nacimiento Mountains and swings westward into the San Juan Basin. It is a dry region of varicolored shales and sandstones, exposed in canyons, arroyos and badlands. Indians live in isolated hogans, though the ruins of prehistoric towns still stand in several canyons. The largest town, Pueblo Bonito, once sheltered more than a thousand people.

THE LARAMIDE REVOLUTION

Archaeologists detour to these ruins, but fossil hunters seek arroyos in which a long succession of strata tell how the Era of Reptiles ended and the Age of Mammals began. The story opens with coarse yellow sandstones of late Cretaceous age, the Ojo Alamo formation. It contains bones and skulls of frill-bearing dinosaurs, as well as petrified logs and ganoid fish scales. Both rocks and fossils tell of a well-watered lowland where dead reptiles were washed into streams and buried in rapidly growing sand bars. Trees met a similar fate when they toppled from undercut banks.

We do not know how long deposition continued, for the latest Cretaceous deposits were removed by erosion, which also wore pits and channels in the Ojo Alamo formation. These are local evidence of the great Laramide revolution, which closed the Mesozoic era and initiated the Cenozoic. Actually, the revolution was only the culmination of changes that had begun in latest Jurassic or early Cretaceous times and continued intermittently through 65,000,000 to 75,000,000 years. In many places, such as the San Juan Basin, it produced only moderate uplift followed by millions of years of erosion. Elsewhere great belts of rock were forced sidewise until they bent, crumpled, or broke, forming mountain ranges that extended from Cape Horn to the Carib-

382

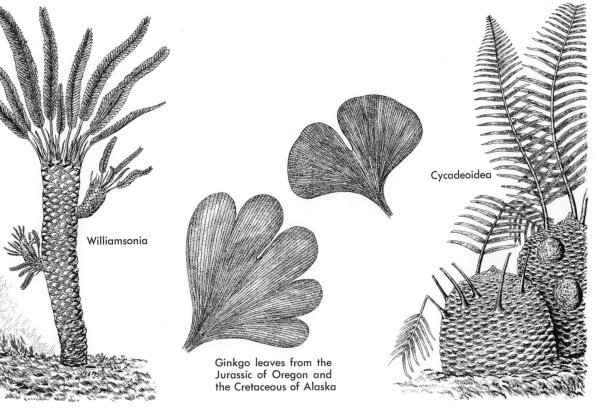

Williamsonia

Ginkgo leaves from the
Jurassic of Oregon and
the Cretaceous of Alaska

Cycadeoidea

Some typical Mesozoic plants

bean Sea, and from Mexico to Alaska. Volcanoes erupted in Colorado, and
huge masses of molten granite were forced upward in western Idaho. Now
deeply eroded by streams and glaciers, those granites form 16,000 square miles
of spectacular scenery.

PLANTS IN A CHANGING WORLD

Land plants responded to these events more rapidly than animals. Late
Jurassic dinosaurs lived among forests of ginkgos, or maidenhair trees, cycads
and Williamsonias—plants that were related to cycads though their trunks resembled those of palms. Flowering plants were rare, but they increased in
numbers during early Cretaceous times. Fossils of the Potomac series in
Maryland, for example, include the poplar and sassafras, as well as leaves
resembling those of oaks, figs, maples, and walnuts. During two late Cretaceous epochs, Greenland became the home of sycamores, magnolias, and
oaks, while a relative of the bigtree (*Sequoiodendron*) grew among conifers.

Late Cretaceous forests of the West included a few cycads and conifers, but 90 per cent of the trees belonged to modern flowering types such as maples, oaks, elms, poplars, tulip trees, magnolias, willows, and sassafras. Screw pines and palms were common on warm, swampy lowlands where duckbilled dinosaurs waded. Eucalyptus trees, now native to Australia, grew near the Atlantic coast. Like palms and magnolias of the West, they indicate much milder and more uniform climates than those that now prevail.

Phlebopteris smithii (Daugherty), a true fern from the Triassic Chinle formation. Petrified Forest National Monument, Arizona

Branching stems of Cycadeoidea, a Jurassic cycad from South Dakota. Entire specimen about 2 feet wide

Two of the most interesting late Cretaceous trees were the redwood (*Sequoia*) and the dawn redwood (*Metasequoia*). The former was essentially like the modern redwood of California's coastal forests. Both are characterized by leaves, or "needles," that grow alternately on twigs and remain—or remained—on the trees all year. The seed cones are borne upon short twigs with stubby leaves, and the scales are arranged in spirals.

Metasequoia is related to a tree discovered in 1946 among rice fields of central China. It looks like a true redwood in summer, but its leaves grow in opposite pairs, its seed cones are borne on rather long, naked stems, and the scales of its cones do not form spirals. When winter comes the tree sheds its leaves, as if it were an elm or maple.

Sequoia grew on late Cretaceous lowlands of Alberta and spread eastward as far as New Jersey. It was common in the region of Yellowstone National Park during the Eocene epoch, reaching diameters of 12 to 14 feet. During the Oligocene, redwoods grew so rapidly in central Colorado that trees only 700 years old were more than 20 feet in diameter at the ground. For millions

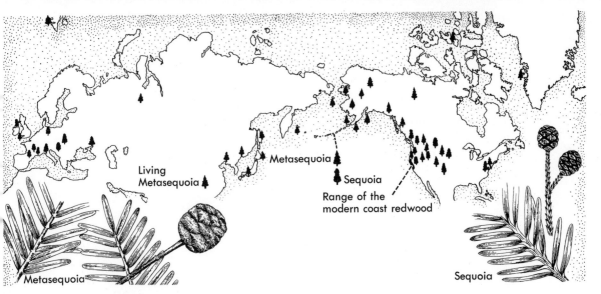

Known distribution of Sequoia and Metasequoia in Recent and ancient times. Neither apparently ranged into the Southern Hemisphere.

of years redwoods continued to thrive in what now is the central Rockies, in valleys and basins whose elevation was then less than 3,000 feet. Later, as climates grew cooler and less uniform, the redwood's habitat was restricted to a strip along the Pacific coast.

Metasequoia was both hardier and less fortunate. Appearing in the late Cretaceous, it soon achieved world-wide range in the Northern Hemisphere. Paleocene fossils are found as far south as North Dakota and northward to Alaska. They show that *Metasequoia* was part of a forest complex that included birches, chestnuts, sweet gums, oaks, and beeches. While climates

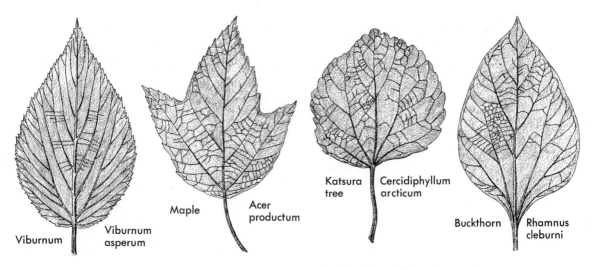

Leaves of some typical Paleocene trees and shrubs. Fort Union formation, near Glendive, Montana

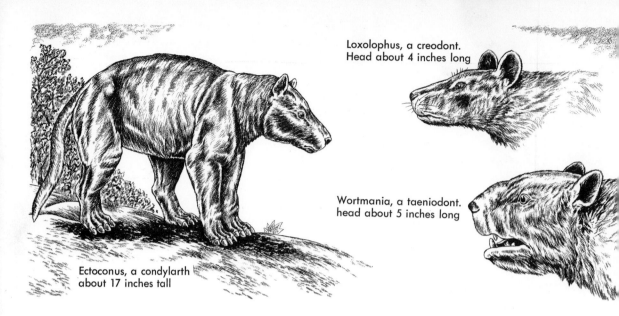

Loxolophus, a creodont.
Head about 4 inches long

Wortmania, a taeniodont.
head about 5 inches long

Ectoconus, a condylarth
about 17 inches tall

Three typical Paleocene mammals

were mild these trees prospered far north of the Arctic Circle, shedding their leaves and remaining dormant during the dark but by no means frigid winters. But as climates cooled, the arctic forest moved southward, probably taking 10,000,000 years to go from Alaska to northern California, and from northern Siberia to Japan. It finally disappeared from the West when summer rains and dry winters were replaced by winter rainfall and arid summers. Though broad-leafed trees found a refuge in southeastern United States, *Metasequoia* failed to do so. It survives as a "living fossil" only in the Szechuan region of China.

BEASTS OF THE EARLY CENOZOIC

We do not know why flowering plants progressed so rapidly during Cretaceous times while contemporary mammals lagged. But, though causes are doubtful, the fact is clear: mammals hardly advanced until the Mesozoic era had ended and great reptiles had disappeared. Then warm-blooded, hairy beasts became so important that we often refer to the new era as the Age of Mammals.

This is a useful characterization, but it does not replace formal names. The era is the Cenozoic, and it is now divided into two periods. The older of these, the Tertiary, lasted some 60,000,000 years and encompassed five different epochs. The first of them, the Paleocene, was the one whose red clays are found on eroded Cretaceous sandstones in the San Juan Basin. The second Cenozoic period, generally called the Quaternary, began roughly a million years ago and still is in progress.

Paleocene Pioneers. Virtually all geologists agree that Paleocene lands were cooler and less humid than they had been before the Laramide Revolution, and some extensive regions were deserts. Yet redwoods ranged round the world in the Northern Hemisphere, and palms grew in North Dakota along with magnolias. They and a host of more familiar trees leave no doubt that climates were both milder and much more equable than they are today.

Into this hospitable world came a variety of mammals. They included new types of opossums, insectivores and multituberculates, as well as mouselike

Barylambda, a late Paleocene mammal about 8 feet long. Near it are the skull and bones of the left forefoot.

rodents, armadillos, and primates that resembled lemurs but were members of an earlier group. These long-nosed ancestors of monkeys climbed trees, from which they looked down on members of two new groups, called creodonts and condylarths. The former were primitive carnivores, while the latter were pioneers among hoof-bearing beasts that ate plants.

Having made this distinction, we admit that it did not amount to much early in the Paleocene epoch. Both carnivores and hoof-bearers consisted of ugly, awkward animals with blunt heads, long stocky bodies, and thick tails. Heavy legs ended in five spreading toes, each of which carried a structure that was neither a well-developed hoof nor a typical claw. Unspecialized teeth imply that most members of both groups ate a mixed diet of fruit, juicy stems, leaves, and half-decayed carrion. Only the largest condylarths were exclusively herbivorous.

That word *largest* does not mean "gigantic," for few early Paleocene mammals were larger than a modern police dog. As millions of years went by, however, broad-footed beasts called amblypods ("blunt-feet") became larger than sheep. *Barylambda* was 8 feet long, with a short, deep body, thick legs, and a heavy tail. A relative, not quite so large, had long canine tusks and claws instead of hoofs.

The Paleocene epoch lasted 10,000,000 years, coming to a gradual close as salt water spread northward to Illinois and covered Central America and the Isthmus of Panama. The climate grew milder, too, for forests of cypresses, sycamores, and elms made western Greenland resemble modern North Carolina. Date palms, figs, and breadfruit grew beside the enlarged Gulf of Mexico.

WHEN MAMMALS MODERNIZED

Though Eocene plants are found in the South, most fossil vertebrates come from New Mexico and Wyoming. Specimens record both the progress of archaic American mammals and their losing struggle against modernized invaders that presumably came from Asia by way of a land bridge between Siberia and Alaska.

Early Eocene Mammals. We first seek out the native types: condylarths, creodonts, and lumbering amblypods. Among the first of these was *Phenacodus,* a genus that had appeared during the Paleocene epoch. Though some species were as small as a fox, others reached the height of a sheep but were not so heavy. All had long heads with eyes that were placed far forward, long tails, and five-toed feet that bore small hoofs.

The creodonts include *Oxyaena,* a short-legged carnivore more than 3 feet long whose general form reminds us of the modern wolverine. Some authorities think *Oxyaena* swam like an otter, catching fish and softshell turtles. Others suggest that he stayed on land and ate carrion or prey that could be killed from ambush. All agree that the beast's brain was incapable of the cunning which is routine to a wolverine.

Amblypods vary greatly in size as well as in general form. *Coryphodon* is the most familiar, for its thick bones resisted destruction and therefore became good and common fossils. Though some species were no larger than tapirs, others weighed as much as an ox (1,600 to 1,800 pounds) and were more heavily built. *Coryphodon* had a long body, short legs, and five-toed feet that resembled the feet of an elephant. The skull was large, broad, and blunt, and the canine teeth had become tusks which the males used in fighting. The general form was that of a pigmy hippopotamus, suggesting that the animal spent much of its time in swamps.

Eocene Giants. Though the Eocene was an epoch, not a period, it lasted some 10,000,000 years. During that time many mammals died out while others developed bizarre forms and even evolved into giants.

Though *Patriofelis* and *Dromocyon* were not giants, both were good-sized

Patriofelis, of middle and late Eocene age, was a creodont some 5 feet long, with a skull as large as a lion's.

Dromocyon, a doglike creodont of middle and late Eocene age. Length about 4 feet.

Phenacodus (below), and early Eocene amblypod about 5 feet 6 inches in length

Oxyaena, of early Eocene age, probably was the ancestor of Patriofelis. Length about 39 inches

Skull of Coryphodon

Coryphodon, an early Eocene amblypod about 8 feet long. It may have been a swamp-dweller.

Some typical mammals of the early Eocene epoch.

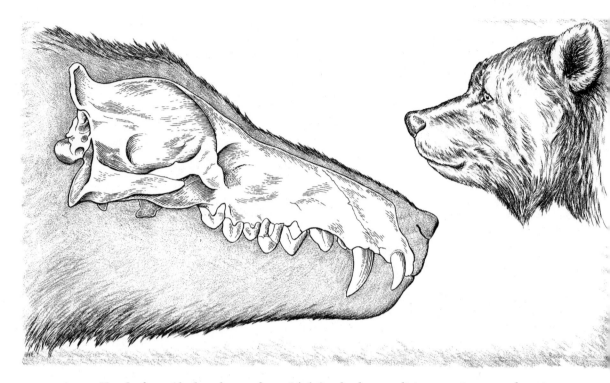

Head of an Alaskan brown bear (right), *the largest living carnivore, and a giant creodont from Mongolia, both drawn to the same scale. The bear's skull is 18 to 19 inches long; that of the creodont measures 34 inches in length.*

creodonts. The former, whose name means "father of cats," was a relative of *Oxyaena* that weighed no more than a black bear but had a skull almost as large as that of a lion. The lower jaws were heavy and deep, with powerful muscles that must have given great crunching power. The teeth were those of a meat-eater, but the legs were too short for active hunting. This contrast has led some paleontologists to suggest that *Patriofelis* also had otterlike habits; others think it sometimes lay in wait for prey on land but fed largely on carrion, in the manner of modern hyenas.

Dromocyon apparently was a more active hunter that resembled a short-legged wolf with an oversized head. Other creodonts were as large as grizzlies, and one from the late Eocene of Asia had a skull 34 inches long—that of the Alaska brown bear is only 18 to 19 inches. If other dimensions were in proportion, that creodont was 12 feet 6 inches long and more than 6 feet high when he stood on all fours.

Some amblypods combined bulk and essentially primitive bodies with a veneer of specialization. *Uintatherium,* of middle Eocene age, stood 5 feet high at the shoulder and weighed as much as a modern rhinoceros, which it some-

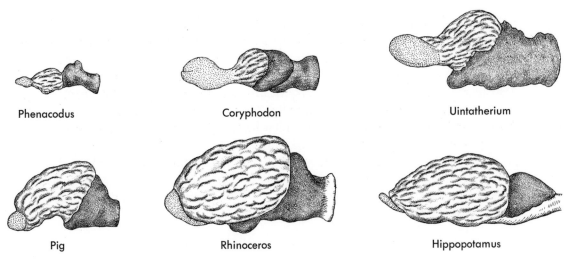

Phenacodus Coryphodon Uintatherium

Pig Rhinoceros Hippopotamus

Brains of archaic mammals (upper row) *had much smaller cerebral hemispheres than those of modern mammals* (below) *and were much less intelligent.*

what resembled. The long, low head bore three pairs of blunt bony "horns" that were covered with skin and were 2 to 10 inches in height. Males had daggerlike canine tusks on the upper jaws—tusks that could be used against large carnivores or other males during fights for mates. A successor, *Eobasileus,* was even larger, for its skull was 40 inches long against 30 for that of *Uintatherium,* its height at the back was almost 7 feet, and its tusks extended 9 inches below the upper jaws.

Three stages in the progress of uintatheres: from Bathyopsis, which stood 3 feet high, to Eobasileus, whose height was about 5 feet and whose skull was 40 inches long

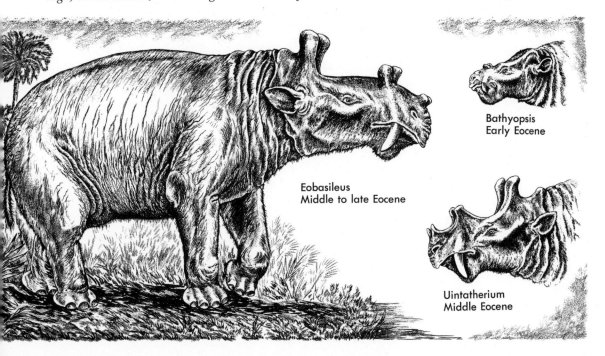

Bathyopsis
Early Eocene

Eobasileus
Middle to late Eocene

Uintatherium
Middle Eocene

With these gains in size and armament went obvious weaknesses. A big beast needed plenty of food, yet *Eobasileus* had teeth that were neither larger nor better than those of *Uintatherium.* The brain also was inadequate, at least by modern standards. Not only was the uintathere brain much smaller than that of a hippo or rhino of equal size; it also had diminutive cerebral hemispheres and achieved very limited intelligence. Uintatheres were able to think, but so dimly that instinct and reflex must have governed their lives almost as fully as they governed the lives of big dinosaurs.

This statement, in fact, applies to all "archaic" mammals—amblypods, condylarths, and creodonts. With clumsy bodies controlled by poor brains, they were ill prepared to meet competition as new and more able beasts invaded North America.

THE GREAT EOCENE INVASION

That invasion was not sudden, nor was it continuous. It began near the end of the Paleocene epoch and continued for several million years, while a strip of low, temperate land joined Siberia to Alaska. When the strip was submerged, migration halted, to be resumed on a greater scale during late Eocene times.

Results of the first influx may be traced in fossils of the Bighorn Basin, Wyoming, through which human travelers hasten to Yellowstone National Park. Now a region of badlands and ranches, the basin was a broad early Eocene valley in which *Phenacodus* ranged sedge-covered uplands, *Oxyaena* crouched in thickets, and *Coryphodon* splashed in shallow lakes or the backwaters of streams. They also sheltered small crocodiles and *Champsosaurus,* a 5-foot reptile with slender jaws resembling those of some phytosaurs.

Hoofed Mammals with Odd and Even Toes. Intruders into this mountain-rimmed Eden were scarcely superior to the natives, but they did include two new orders. One of these, the perissodactyls, contained beasts with five or three toes on each foot—numbers that might later be reduced to one. Artiodactyls, in contrast, had four toes or two. Both groups appeared almost simultaneously in Europe and North America, thus suggesting that they originated in Asia. For a while the even-toed newcomers were rare, but perissodactyls promptly became abundant and included ancestral members of the horses, tapirs, rhinoceroses, and other important groups. In the Bighorn Basin these invaders mingled with the native *Phenacodus* on uplands and were stalked by creodonts.

During middle Eocene times the Alaskan land bridge was submerged and immigration halted. There also were no striking changes among the mammals, many of which left remains in southwestern Wyoming, where lowlands surrounded a Green River lake. Green and brown muds that settled on those lowlands may now be seen in the badlands east of Lyman, Wyoming.

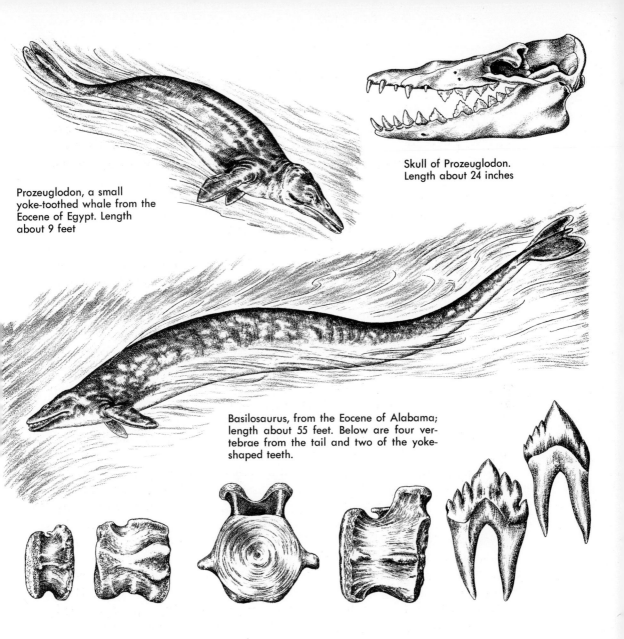

Prozeuglodon, a small yoke-toothed whale from the Eocene of Egypt. Length about 9 feet

Skull of Prozeuglodon. Length about 24 inches

Basilosaurus, from the Eocene of Alabama; length about 55 feet. Below are four vertebrae from the tail and two of the yoke-shaped teeth.

A primitive and an advanced archaeocete, or yoke-toothed whale.

The land bridge emerged again during late Eocene times, and migration from Asia was renewed. Most of the archaic American herbivores died out, though the huge uintatheres survived and the meat-eating creodonts still prospered. There were many kinds of perissodactyls, and varied artiodactyls appeared in the waves of immigrants from Asia. They gave rise to ancestral camels not much larger than foxes, "giant pigs" of modest size, and herbivores called oreodonts, whose descendants became enormously abundant during a later epoch.

Indeed, the phrase "whose descendants became" is the most revealing one we can apply to most of these late Eocene beasts. They were neither large, intelligent, nor especially novel; though they lived while archaic types died out, they could not have survived really vigorous competition. But they did have whatever was needed to produce descendants more able than themselves. They therefore were first-rate ancestors, which means that we now must examine their offspring, many generations removed.

MAMMALS TO THE SEA

We have found that reptiles, which evolved on land, soon sent invaders into the water. Early mammals did the same, in the form of whalelike beasts known as archaeocetes, zeuglodonts, or yoke-toothed whales.

The oldest known archaeocetes come from middle Eocene strata of northern Africa and North America. Skulls suggest that their ancestors were creodonts that presumably fed upon fish and spent more and more time in the water. But the stages through which the creatures evolved are unknown, for Eocene archaeocetes were fully aquatic. We see this in the pointed muzzle, elongate body, flipperlike forelegs, and hind legs so tiny that they were hidden under flesh. The serrate cheek teeth had double roots, but teeth at the front of the mouth were pointed or peglike. Nostrils had moved to the top of the head, about halfway between the muzzle and eyes.

Archaeocetes culminated in *Basilosaurus,* also known as *Zeuglodon* ("yoke-tooth"), whose remains are found in late Eocene deposits near the southern Atlantic coast. *Basilosaurus* reached lengths of 55 to 70 feet, with a relatively short head and a very long tail whose vertebrae were larger than those of the short slim body. Tail vertebrae of this and other archaeocetes are frequently found in the southeastern United States.

A few small, short-bodied archaeocetes lived on into Oligocene and earliest Miocene times, but large ones died out at the end of the Eocene epoch. Their place in the sea was taken by true whales, which probably were descended from unspecialized archaeocetes. Early whales had short, stocky bodies, and their nostrils formed a single blowhole that lay between or even behind the eyes. Some genera possessed triangular teeth much like those of sharks, though their bodies resembled porpoises. During Miocene and later times, however, the group divided into true porpoises, beaked whales, sperm whales, and whalebone whales. The first three of these retained their teeth and even increased their number to several times the original forty-four. Whalebone whales, however, became toothless and began to capture small animals in plates of "whalebone"—really specialized skin—hanging down from the roof of the mouth. Whalebone whales also have become the largest of all animals, either living or extinct. The modern blue whale, for example, reaches lengths exceeding 90 feet and weights greater than 120 tons. This living mammal, therefore, is two to two and a half times as heavy as the largest dinosaurs.

CHAPTER XXXI

More and Better Mammals

M AKO SIKA—*land* that is *bad* for camping, hunting, or travel. Thus the old-time Sioux referred to a wilderness of ridges, cliffs, bare flats, and box canyons lying eastward from the Black Hills in South Dakota. The term is now applied to any barren, much-dissected region in which the rocks are chiefly clay.

EARLY BEASTS OF THE BADLANDS

Clays of Mako Sika, the Big Badlands, make up the White River series, which is divided into a lower formation, called the Chadron, and an upper one, the Brulé. They once formed a continuous sheet, but erosion has reduced them to isolated outcrops extending from northeastern Colorado to southwestern Saskatchewan. These outcrops provide our best record of life during the first two thirds of the Oligocene epoch and some of the world's richest collecting grounds for remains of Tertiary mammals.

Because of its fine-grained clay and thin, even layers, the White River series was once supposed to have settled on the bottom of a wide, shallow lake. We now know that it was deposited on low, almost level prairies to the east of rolling hills and rounded mountains which were all that remained of ranges built during the Laramide revolution. These remnants may be seen along State Highway 220 between Muddy Gap and Casper, Wyoming. One hill, called Independence Rock, is famous both for the names of pioneers hacked into its granite and for scratches worn into it by a pre-Oligocene glacier. Grassy ground around the rock is underlain by White River clays.

The climate of the White River prairie must have been mild and fairly moist, and meandering streams overflowed after long-continued rains. Ponds and reedy lakes were plentiful, and so were groves of hackberries, oaks, and other

View from U. S. Highway 16 near the Pinnacles, Badlands National Monument, South Dakota. The Chadron formation makes up flat-topped hills in the foreground; the Brulé appears in distant cliffs.

broad-leafed trees. Redwoods, however, were restricted to forests west of the present Great Plains, in what now are the Rocky Mountains.

The Massive Titanotheres. The largest denizens of Chadron prairies were titanotheres, which reached lengths of 12 to 14 feet, heights of 7 to 8 feet 4 inches, and weights of 4 to 5 tons. In shape they resembled modern rhinos, with broad, deep bodies and massive legs. Their stubby feet had three hoof-bearing toes behind but only four in front. The head was long, low, and concave; two broad, blunt, bony "horns" grew side by side on the nose and were larger in males than in females. Though covered only with skin, the horns were dangerous weapons when backed by their owners' weight. The bulls used them to batter predators and rivals, some of which carried away broken ribs as souvenirs of battle.

Ancestral titanotheres had come from Asia during one of the early Eocene migrations. They were plump beasts 12 to 20 inches in height, with skulls that bore no trace of horns. Evolution first led to larger bodies; horns began as low knobs above the eyes of middle Eocene genera some 40 inches tall, and developed along with increase in size during late Eocene times. One of the earliest Oligocene species was 10 feet long and 5 feet tall, or as large as a good-sized rhinoceros. The real giants, which appeared somewhat later, were mas-

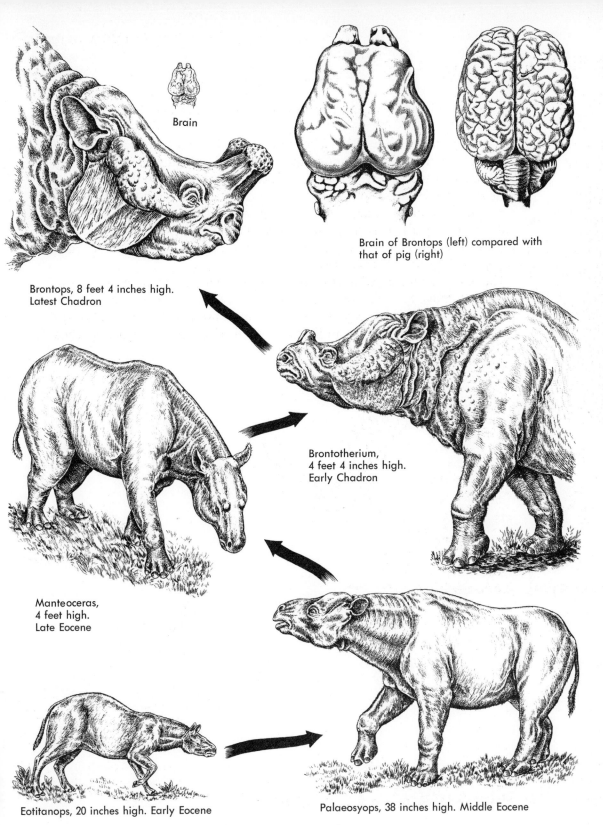

Brain

Brain of Brontops (left) compared with
that of pig (right)

Brontops, 8 feet 4 inches high.
Latest Chadron

Brontotherium,
4 feet 4 inches high.
Early Chadron

Manteoceras,
4 feet high.
Late Eocene

Eotitanops, 20 inches high. Early Eocene

Palaeosyops, 38 inches high. Middle Eocene

Evolution of the titanotheres

sive beasts with big horns and low, broad skulls that matched the bulk of their bodies.

All titanotheres seem to have been browsers, though the smallest species fed on plants that were little more than herbs. Giants, such as *Brontops* and *Brontotherium,* pulled leaves from tall shrubs and low trees with their lips, since their incisor teeth were too small for use or had disappeared. Molars, however, had grown into large crushing and grinding teeth which were twice as wide in the upper jaw as they were below. Their size shows that they could dispose of coarse food, though they were neither long enough nor hard enough to cope with gritty, siliceous grasses.

The brain had increased in size until it rivaled that of a modern rhinoceros. It seems to have been less intelligent, however, for it had fewer folds in the cerebellum, whose forward parts were not much swollen. The brain also was *relatively* small; in a 4-ton titanothere it was little larger than a man's clenched

Brontotherium platyceras, one of the largest titanotheres. The one female is smaller th

fists. A rhinoceros with a brain of similar size weighs little more than 2 tons. Some theorists have suggested that poor brains plus teeth that could not chew grass explain why titanotheres died out at the end of the early Oligocene subepoch.

BEASTS OF THE BRULÉ

The change from Chadron to Brulé formation is marked by a shift from gray clays to buff and pink deposits. Sediments also contain increasing amounts of white volcanic ash, which probably erupted from craters north and west of the present Black Hills. In many places this ash has been dissolved and redeposited as veins of low-grade opal filling crevices in the clay.

e males and has shorter horns. The male skull lying on the ground is about 45 inches long.

Metamynodon (above), *a swamp-dwelling rhinoceros of the Brulé formation; length 8 to 14 feet. At the right is Hyracodon, a swift-running rhinoceros about 5 feet long. It must have lived on dry uplands.*

Brulé prairies were inhabited by a vast variety of mammals. The herds of great titanotheres had vanished, but their places were taken by tapirs, three-toed horses, and rhinoceroses. Some of these were hornless browsers; others were small, with slender legs which suggest that they ran upon dry uplands. *Metamynodon*, however, was a barrel-bodied beast 8 to 14 feet long that suggests an overgrown version of the modern pigmy hippopotamus. *Metamynodon* undoubtedly spent most of its time in rivers and swampy lakes, where its large size protected it from prowling crocodiles.

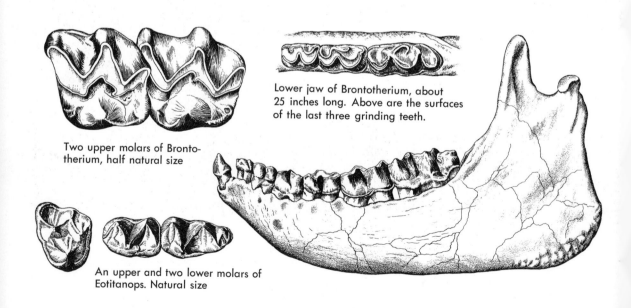

Lower jaw of Brontotherium, about 25 inches long. Above are the surfaces of the last three grinding teeth.

Two upper molars of Brontotherium, half natural size

An upper and two lower molars of Eotitanops. Natural size

(Left) *Agriochoerus, a climbing oreodont 4 to 5 feet long. Merycoidodon* (right), *an abundant White River oreodont, 16 inches high at the shoulder. In the water is Leptauchenia, swimming with its body concealed.*

Dinictis (left), *a false saber-tooth, 40 inches long from nose to base of tail. Hoplophoneus* (below) *was a true saber-tooth of slightly larger size and heavier build. Both are found in the White River formation.*

H. mustelinus, length 6.5 inches

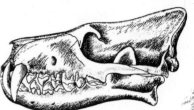

H. horridus, length 12 inches

Hyaenodon horridus, a White River creodont, its skull, and the skull of a smaller species

Artiodactyls included piglike beasts of several types, primitive camels, and many species of oreodonts. Those variously called *Oreodon* or *Merycoidodon* were short-legged, blunt-headed herbivores that still had five toes on each front foot. The first toe was very small, however, and the hind foot had an even number—four. *Merycoidodon* probably lived in great herds, for its bones, teeth, and well-preserved skulls are among the commonest mammalian fossils in the Badlands. One skeleton is that of a female with the bones of unborn twins near what was her abdomen.

Leptauchenia had still shorter legs, a stubby tail, and tiny hoofs. They, plus raised eyes and nostrils on top of the muzzle, indicate that this mammal spent much of its time in the water, where it could swim with its body concealed. *Agriochoerus,* on the other hand, had a very long tail, clawed feet, and looked like some creodonts. It could climb trees to escape enemies but may have used its claws chiefly to dig roots and bulbs, since its teeth were those of a plant-eater. It certainly did not prey on other oreodonts, whose principal enemies were cats. These had already divided into two groups, the true and false saber-tooths. The former possessed high skulls and knifelike canine teeth that were partly sheathed by flanges of bone on the lower jaws. Those jaws could open at right angles to the skull, allowing the canines to be used to stab rather than to bite the prey. False saber-tooths had longer and relatively lower skulls and at first the animals possessed much shorter canines. The lower jaws, which were deeper, did not open so widely as those of the true saber-tooths.

Small dogs also were common, though some of them resembled the modern Old World civets. The largest carnivores were creodonts, some of which had become bulky, long-headed beasts with teeth resembling those of present-day hyenas. Those teeth, plus legs that were not built for speed, suggest that the ancient animals also fed on carrion.

Stump, cone, and vegetation of Sequoia affinis Lesquereux; Oligocene near Florissant, Colorado. The stump has been called Sequoioxylon pearsalli Andrews. The pine
stumps (Pityoxylon) below stand on Specimen Ridge, a cliff of Oligocene volcanic
agglomerate in Yellowstone National Park. At the left is a piece of Pityoxylon wood.

Zelkova drymeja (Lesquereux) Brown.
Oligocene to Miocene, western United States

Alnus carpinoides Lesquereux.
Eocene to Miocene, western U.S.A.

Populus americana (Lesq.) LaMotte.
Oligocene to Miocene, Colorado
and California

Porana, a flower.
Oligocene (John Day),
central Oregon

Platanus (a sycamore).
Eocene, central California

Juglans magnifica Knowlton.
Oligocene, Florissant, Colorado

Clathropteris walkeri Daugherty, a fern.
Triassic (Chinle), Petrified Forest,
Arizona

Metasequoia occidentalis (Newberry) Chaney.
Paleocene to Miocene, western North America

Some typical Tertiary plants and a Triassic fern

OLIGOCENE PLANTS

Though fossil plants are found in the White River Badlands, they have not been well described. The best example of an early to middle Oligocene flora comes from shales composed largely of volcanic ash and exposed near the town of Florissant, on U. S. Highway 24, in central Colorado. They tell of a rolling area perhaps 3,000 feet high dotted with smaller volcanoes and larger ones that approached 8,000 feet in height. The resulting scenery must have been much like that around present-day Lake Pátzcuaro, in west-central Mexico, except for streams that flowed lazily into basins. The water accumulated in lakes, most of which were less than 50 feet deep. The climate was warm-temperate, with mild winters, hot summers, and rainfall amounting to about 20 inches per year. Most of it fell in thunderstorms during late spring and early summer.

Plants suggest those of northeastern Mexico today, with overtones of California. Groves of redwoods grew beside lakes and streams; south of Florissant many large stumps stand in beds of coarse ash. Cedars, beeches, and willows mingled with redwoods; maples, elms, hornbeams, and sumacs grew in openings. Valley sides were the home of breadfruit trees and *Euphorbia,* which looked like a branched cactus. High ground between streams was covered with pines, dwarf and mostly evergreen oaks, and scrubby chaparral. Firs, spruces, and maples grew on the mountains, so far from the lakes that their leaves seldom became fossils. But insects were preserved in abundance, and fish were common in some layers of sediment.

BEASTS OF THE FAR WEST AND ASIA

Though most Oligocene fossils come from the Great Plains, important discoveries have been made in other regions and formations. Among the latter are the Sespe formation of California, which contains bones of creodonts, titanotheres, opossums, and deep-jawed oreodonts much like those of the latest White River beds.

John Day Plants and Mammals. Central Oregon is covered by thick lava flows of the great Columbia Plateau and is not a good collecting ground for fossils. Between the villages of Mitchell and Mount Vernon, however, the John Day River and its tributaries have cut through the lavas, exposing a 2,000-foot deposit of ash and other volcanic debris. Some strata abound in imprints of ginkgos, figs, magnolias, walnuts, and maples, as well as the last dawn redwoods found in North America. Other beds contain teeth and bones of false saber-tooths, wild dogs, three-toed horses, rhinoceroses, and humpless camels. There were several types of oreodonts, including squat, piglike beasts

Baluchitherium, an Oligocene rhinoceros, was 18 feet high at the shoulder. At the left, its femur is compared with a 6-foot man.

that seem to have had long, muscular snouts. The John Day fauna, like that of the Sespe, apparently lived after the last White River strata had been deposited. Indeed, some authorities say the John Day beds and fossils date from early Miocene times.

Baluchitherium. In 1911 a British scientist working in the hills of Baluchistan, in northwestern India, found a few bones of a creature that seemed to be a rhinoceros but was larger than any known elephant. He called it *Baluchitherium* ("beast of Baluchistan") and hoped that more adequate fossils would be discovered.

That hope was fulfilled in 1922 by Walter Granger, an American working in Mongolia. There he found three partial skeletons of *Baluchitherium,* one of which included the skull. Its 365 fragments were removed and shipped to New York, where a skilled preparator and his assistants spent three months putting pieces together. In the end they had the world's biggest rhinoceros and the largest mammal known to have lived on land.

In an age when a hippopotamus is big and the elephant a giant, *Baluchitherium* seems almost unreal. His head was about 5 feet long, yet it was absurdly small upon his gigantic body, which stood 18 feet high at the shoulder and was very deep. *Baluchitherium* was a browser that lived in small herds; by raising his head and neck he could easily nibble twigs and leaves 20 feet above the ground. Unlike many Oligocene mammals, this genus lived on into the next epoch.

A slab from the Miocene bone bed at Agate Springs, Nebraska. It contains about 4,300 bones and skulls. (Photograph from the American Museum of Natural History)

MAMMALS OF THE MIOCENE

As the Miocene epoch dawned, the land bridge that had often joined Alaska to Asia apparently was under water. Mountains had almost vanished from the West; climates, though cooling and drying, were mild. Palms and figs grew in central Europe, while evergreens covered northern Greenland and grasses took possession of the Great Plains.

Still, conditions were not wholly lush and peaceful, especially in the West. Volcanoes erupted in many places, and vast sheets of lava poured from fissures in Washington and Oregon. Dry plains were often swept by dust storms that smothered piglike oreodonts that had huddled together for shelter. Streams turned into floods after sudden rains, drowning many animals and sweeping away the carcasses of others that had died and lay on the ground. These remains were then deposited in sandbanks that became veritable bone beds, crowded from bottom to top with remains of early Miocene mammals.

Beasts of the Agate Bone Beds. The greatest of those bone beds was found in 1877 by Captain James Cook, a pioneer scout and ranchman. The stratum lies in two flat-topped hills east of the post office of Agate, about 23 miles south and east of Harrison, Nebraska, filling the channel of a Miocene stream that roughly paralleled the present Niobrara River. No one knows how many bones the deposit once contained, since all except the two small hills has been worn away. But there are 4,300 skulls and separate bones in one slab of gray-buff sandstone with an area of 44 square feet; at that rate, one of the two hills contains 3,400,000 skulls and bones belonging to 17,000 skeletons. Enough to meet the needs of museums for all time to come!

Of those 17,000 skeletons, at least 16,000 represent a rhinoceros named *Diceratherium.* It weighed no more than a smallish hog, though its legs were longer and thicker. Males had two small horns side by side on the nose, but

Diceratherium (left), *the Miocene rhinoceros whose remains are abundant in the Agate bone beds. Height at the shoulder about 3 feet 4 inches. The two small horns were side by side.* Promerycochoerus *(right),* a piglike oreodont of Miocene age. About 5 feet 6 inches long

the female was hornless. *Diceratherium* must have ranged the early Miocene plains in herds as great as those of the modern bison, which numbered about 60,000,000 before the white man came.

A second beast of the Agate bone bed is an entelodont, *Dinohyus,* whose size at last justified the popular name of "giant pig." *Dinohyus* was 10 feet 6 inches long and more than 7 feet tall at the hump between his shoulders. Unlike true swine, he was very stupid, for his massive skull contained a small and simple brain. *Dinohyus* probably was as dull-witted as any titanothere and had a worse temper, since broken bones indicate that the beasts often quarreled.

A third mammal of the Agate bone bed is *Moropus,* largest member of the perissodactyl group known as chalicotheres. This grotesque creature had a horselike head, the thick body and stubby tail of a tapir, the stocky forelegs of a rhino, hind legs suggesting those of a bear, and heavy claws on three-toed feet that seemingly should have borne hoofs. Both canines and upper incisors were missing; the cheek teeth were broad and low. Since they must have chewed soft food, one theory makes *Moropus* a browser that sat up and pulled down branches with his powerful forelegs. Another theory, which is more convincing, says that *Moropus* dined largely on roots and bulbs and therefore used

(Left) *Dinohyus, a "giant pig" of the Agate Springs bone bed. Height at shoulder 7 feet.* (Right) *Moropus, the herbivore whose hoofs had become claws*

his claws for digging. They also became weapons when he was attacked or when *Dinohyus* tried to seize his food.

The Agate bone bed is early Miocene in age; late Miocene deposits are scattered over the Great Plains region from Montana to northern Mexico. Their fossils include a variety of primitive horses and more or less specialized rhinos, as well as several of the proboscideans discussed in Chapter XXXII. The largest rhinoceros was an aquatic beast about 12 feet long. Unlike *Metamynodon*, this late Miocene rhino had a stubby horn on the nose, and his legs were so short that his belly almost touched the ground when he ventured on land.

Artiodactyls were abundant, but creodonts had declined in numbers and variety. There were herds of peccaries and small deerlike beasts and several long-legged but humpless camels. Carnivores included dogs that looked and perhaps lived like hyenas and others as large as grizzly bears, with long, heavy tails. Both true and false saber-tooths were widespread. The former may have begun the habit of feeding on proboscideans, a habit which they apparently followed until the Ice Age closed.

PRODUCTS OF ISOLATION

During Miocene times a low strip of land connected Siberia and Alaska. Across this strip countless mammals wandered, those from the New World going to Asia, while Old World types came to North America. In the Pliocene epoch this land bridge sank, and mammals of the two hemispheres followed their separate ways. As a result, Eurasia (and probably Africa) developed an abundance of hyenas, of varied rhinoceroses and proboscideans, and of true deer and antelopes. North America, on the other hand, was dominated by such native groups as pronghorns, camels, and horses. The last oreodonts were short-legged, piglike beasts. Rhinos, though common, were closely related to late Miocene genera.

A much longer period of isolation allowed South America to develop a unique Tertiary fauna. The Isthmus of Panama permitted early Eocene beasts to travel southward, but it vanished under salt water as the middle Eocene closed. For the next 35,000,000 years, or until the late Pliocene, submergence after submergence left southern mammals free to develop with little interference from the North. The result was a wealth of fine and often bizarre examples of adaptive radiation in which beasts derived from simple, old-fashioned ancestors invaded a variety of habitats and lived in many different ways. In doing so, they took on forms assumed by very different mammals in other parts of the earth.

The Notoungulates. We see this clearly in the notoungulates, a group of hoof-bearing herbivores that came from Asia by way of Alaska. Though scarce and unsuccessful elsewhere, notoungulates that reached South America became common and as large as modern elephants. Those called *Toxodon* had deep heads, thick bodies, and three-toed feet that seemed too small to support their great bulk. *Toxodon* may have been semi-aquatic, or he may have been a browser in the manner of titanotheres. Other notoungulates lived like and even resembled creodonts and modern rabbits.

Snouts, Toes, and Gigantic Rodents. Litopterns probably began as descendants of primitive hoofed mammals much like *Phenacodus*. In later times some became queer long-snouted creatures, while others were more horselike than contemporary horses.

That statement sounds like a paradox, but it makes anatomical sense. To

Macrauchenia (left) *and Toxodon* (right), *two Pleistocene beasts of South America. The former stood 5 feet high at the shoulder; Toxodon was more than 4 feet.*

us the word *horse* means a mammal that has one large toe on each foot, covered by a hoof. Miocene and Pliocene horses had three toes; though the beasts might walk on only one, the other two were there and bore hoofs. But such litopterns as *Thoatherium* had one-toed feet with only two very small splint bones to show where other toes had been. With a light body and long, slender legs, this animal probably ran as swiftly as modern antelopes.

The second family of litopterns reached its zenith in *Macrauchenia,* of Pliocene and Pleistocene age. The best-known species had a broad body about 5 feet high with thick legs and three-toed, hoofed feet. Neck and head resembled those of a camel, or would have done so except for a short muscular trunk.

Rodents that reached South America in early Eocene times looked and apparently acted much like squirrels, but as ages passed they evolved into guinea pigs, capybaras, water "rats," and porcupines. One extinct type had a skull 24 inches long and a body as large as that of the wild boar. It was three times as big as the capybara, the largest of living rodents.

Edentates, Not Quite Toothless. The modern armadillo has a pointed nose, a body covered with jointed armor made of bony plates set in skin, and peg-shaped molar teeth, all others having been lost. Food consists chiefly of spiders, centipedes, scorpions, adult insects, and grubs and worms. Most of these are caught with the long, sticky tongue.

Armadillos belong to the edentates (literally "toothless ones"), an order that appeared during the Paleocene epoch. Early types were small, long-tailed beasts that lacked armor and reached lengths of 15 to 18 inches. Their American descendants evolved into five distinct types divided among armored and "naked" suborders. The former includes armadillos and glyptodonts. The latter contains anteaters, tree sloths, and ground sloths.

Armadillos have been briefly described; their shells never become rigid, but include several bony rings that allow the body to bend. The largest living species is about 3 feet long, but the Pleistocene *Chlamydotherium* became as large as a rhinoceros and weighed about 4,000 pounds.

Glyptodonts are named for their teeth, which show patterns that look as if they were carved. The really distinctive features of the group, however, are very deep heads, solid "shells" made of bony plates cemented together, and tails encased in rings or solid sheaths of bone. Miocene genera were barely 36 inches long, but those of Pleistocene age measured 6, 8, and even 12 feet. *Glyptodon* itself had a tail surrounded by movable, overlapping rings set with spikes; in *Sclerocalyptus* the hinder rings were fused, and in *Dædicurus* the tail ended in a club set with massive spikes. Powerful muscles swung the tail from side to side, delivering blows that could crush the bones of any carnivore. Glyptodonts were specially common on the Argentinian pampas during the Pleistocene.

Tree sloths are sluggish animals that hang bottom side up from branches; their remains have not been found as fossils, and those of anteaters are rare.

(Left) *Glyptodon, about 9 feet long. This armored beast came to North America during the Pleistocene epoch.* (Right) *The club-tailed Doedicurus did not leave South America. Length 12 to 15 feet*

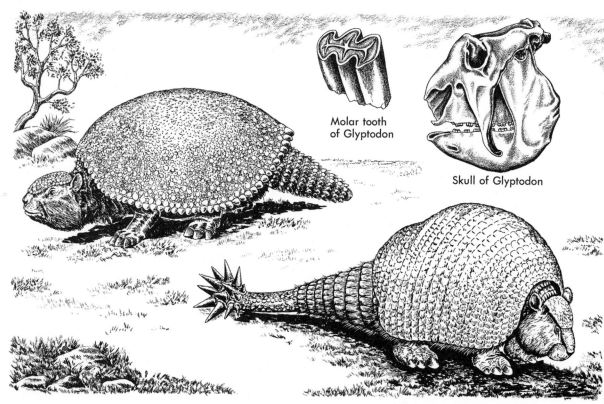

Molar tooth of Glyptodon

Skull of Glyptodon

Skull of Mylodon

Bones of Mylodon's right hind foot

Megatherium, the largest ground sloth, about 20 feet long, and the skull and hind foot of Mylodon, 10 feet 3 inches in length.

Ground sloths were plentiful, however, and became quite as specialized. Beginning with Oligocene beasts barely 3 feet long, they evolved into a variety of browsers and grazers. Though none became completely toothless, their teeth degenerated into pegs that were supplemented by bony cropping plates.

Oligocene ground sloths are not well known, but the Miocene *Hapalops* was a primitive genus about 4 feet long, including the tail. There were five toes on each foot, all bearing claws; wrists and ankles were twisted so much that the beast walked on the outer knuckles of its forefeet and on outer sides of the hind. The skull was low and relatively long, with a spoutlike projection at the front of the lower jaws. This projection bore plates with which the beast pulled leaves from bushes.

Nothrotherium was a Pleistocene descendant of *Hapalops*, about 7 feet 6 inches long. The hind legs and feet were massive; one toe had disappeared and two were clawless rudiments. The forefeet still had five toes, but the first and fifth were too small to bear claws. Though *Nothrotherium* evolved in Argentina, it later crossed the Isthmus of Panama and ranged northward to Shasta County, California. It apparently preferred dry, mountainous regions, where it fed on the leaves of yucca and other hardy plants. A skeleton preserving dry skin and tendons was found near Aden, New Mexico, and dung, hair, claws, and bones—some scraped by stone knives—were discovered in Gypsum Cave, east of Las Vegas, Nevada. These remains, which are 8,500 to about 11,000 years old, show that *Nothrotherium* lived into the present geologic epoch and was eaten by ancient Americans.

Megatherium also evolved in South America but ranged northward to Ohio and the Carolinas during the Pleistocene epoch. When fully grown, this animal reached a length of 20 feet and a weight exceeding 10,000 pounds. The skull was relatively small, with deep lower jaws that ended in a spoutlike projection that was used in pulling leaves from trees. A broad flange projected below each eye, which was completely encircled by bone. The neck was short, but the body

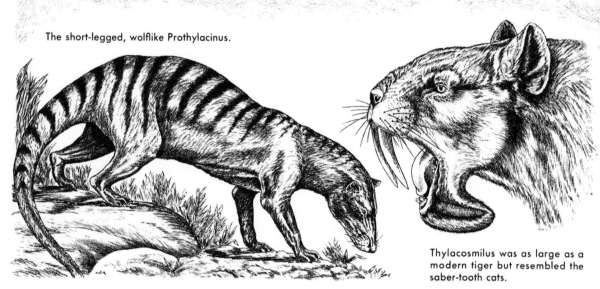

The short-legged, wolflike Prothylacinus.

Thylacosmilus was as large as a modern tiger but resembled the saber-tooth cats.

Two South American marsupials that resembled carnivores

was long and thick, and so was the tail. The hip girdle had two bones that extended forward and spread out like shovels, an adaptation that supported the internal organs when *Megatherium* sat upright. Bones of the hind legs and feet were massive, but the forelegs were not so heavy. Each forefoot had four claws, but the hind foot bore only one. The first two toes had disappeared, and the last two were degenerate. The heel bone was very large, since it and the stubby toes bore most of the animal's weight.

Mylodon and its close relatives were grazers 10 to 13 feet long and probably weighed little more than a ton. They had short, wide heads with broad muzzles and shallow lower jaws. All four legs were massive; the forefeet had five toes with claws on the first three, but the four-toed hind foot bore claws only on toes two and three. As in *Megatherium,* the heel bone was very large. A closely related genus was penned in a cave by early Patagonians. They apparently fed the captive until they were ready to eat it.

We often picture ground sloths as timid, awkward creatures that were defenseless victims of saber-tooths, lions, jaguars, and huge bears. But this conception overlooks their claws and the evidence of powerful muscles in their forelegs. Those muscles may have been used chiefly to pull down trees or break off branches, but it is hard to believe that they did not also batter enemies. Sitting up and swinging its forelimbs freely, *Megatherium* or *Mylodon* must have been far more formidable than any living bear.

Meat-eating Marsupials. No true carnivores preyed on these varied planteaters as they evolved, for South America was isolated before even creodonts

Notharctus, an Eocene beast that looked like a lemur, and its skull, 3 inches long. At right is the head of Tetonius, a tiny Eocene tarsioid from Wyoming.

could reach it. Their place was taken by marsupials, which assumed the forms as well as the habits of weasels, martens, foxes, wolves, and even saber-tooths. The last had a skull 9 inches long, with daggerlike canine teeth and an enormous bony sheath on the lower jaw. Until true saber-tooths and great cats arrived in the Pleistocene epoch, this marsupial was the most dangerous meat-eater in South America.

NEW WORLD PRIMATES

We seldom regard South American monkeys as unique. Actually, they differ more widely from Old World monkeys than the latter do from apes or man. Like edentates, they are products of isolation after early Eocene times.

The story of New World primates begins with small creatures that reached North America during the Paleocene epoch or even in Cretaceous times.

Though squirrel-like in habit, the animals stood about halfway between tree shrews and long-tailed lemurs, which now survive on Madagascar. We picture them as furry, nocturnal beasts with foxlike muzzles, eyes that looked side-wise, and feet on which the thumb and big toe were separated from other digits. The big toe, at least, had a flat nail, though the other toes probably carried claws.

This picture is largely inference, but it was realized in *Notharctus,* of mid-Eocene Wyoming, which resembled modern lemurs. A more progressive group, the so-called tarsioids, had short faces and very large eyes that were beginning to turn forward. Their nearest living relative may be *Tarsius,* which now lives in Borneo, the Celebes, and the Philippine Islands.

American tarsioids survived into Oligocene times, but lemuroids seemingly died out during the Eocene. Before doing so, however, some of them wandered into South America, where their descendants evolved into monkeys whose nostrils are far apart and open sidewise instead of lying close to one another and opening forward, as they do in Old World monkeys. Most South American genera also have thirty-six teeth and prehensile tails, which are endlessly useful in climbing. Even marmosets, which have thirty-two teeth, are unique. They have lost the last four molars ("wisdom teeth") but retain four premolars that have been lost by Old World primates.

A few monkeys have been found in Miocene and Pliocene deposits of South America, but many more come from Pleistocene cave deposits of Brazil. Although spider monkeys now range northward to Mexico, no fossil monkey is known from Central or North America.

CHAPTER XXXII

Ancient Families

As *Oxyaena* crouched in Eocene thickets, it sometimes saw ancestral horses. Titanotheres snorted at primitive camels whose relationships were shown by their teeth, not their shapes. Elephantine beasts appeared in Nebraska not long after skulls and skeletons mingled in the Agate bone bed.

These animals introduce us to three of the oldest, sturdiest groups in the mammalian world. They have prospered for ages and still exist; they have progressed instead of merely living, like the common but primitive opossum. Though horses and camels remained families, the elephants and their kin developed such great variety that they are recognized as an order.

HORSES OF MANY KINDS

The earliest ancestral horse was discovered twice, with attendant complication in names. The first discovery, made in Europe, was called *Hyracotherium* because of a superficial resemblance to the Old World cony, or hyrax. American fossils were better interpreted and became *Eohippus,* or "dawn-horse"—a name that must be abandoned in technical works because *Hyracotherium* has priority. Since eohippus is familiar and well established, however, we may keep it in nontechnical usage without the capital *E*.

The Ancestral Dawn-horse. Like most really promising ancestors, eohippus was small and unspecialized. Some species were 10 inches high at the shoulder, weighed 8 or 9 pounds, and compared with an alley cat in bulk. Others were 20 inches high and weighed about four times as much. All had arched, flexible backs and high hindquarters, which gave the beasts an almost rabbitlike appearance. We are tempted to say they would have made fine pets.

This idea vanishes when we examine eohippus' brain. It was small and primitive, with no more intelligence than that of *Phenacodus*. The skull resem-

417

Forefoot

Hind foot

Hyracotherium, or eohippus, the
oldest known ancestor of horses

*The "dawn-horse" eohippus of early Eocene age. This particular species was about
18 inches long and 9 inches high at the shoulder.*

bled that of a condylarth, too, with eyes placed near the middle and sockets,
or orbits, that were open behind. There were forty-four teeth—the primitive
number—with small gaps between incisors and canines, and then between
canines and premolars. The grinding teeth, which had low crowns, were fit
only for eating soft leaves and pulpy fruits. The front feet had four toes, each
with a hoof; the hind feet possessed only three, and so showed eohippus to be
a perissodactyl. Most of the weight was carried by doglike pads on the soles
of the feet, not by the hoofs.

Branching of the Family Tree. Eohippus disappeared from Europe during the
mid-Eocene. Before doing so, however, it produced descendants called palaeotheres, which had large bodies, short legs, long necks, and large heads with
tapirlike snouts. Hoofs were well developed, and some species acquired high
grinding teeth with cement on the crowns. Discovered during the early 1800's
in gypsum quarries near Paris, palaeotheres ranged into western Asia and survived until early Oligocene times. The latest species were as large as some
modern rhinoceroses and twice as heavy as any modern horse.

In North America, eohippus survived to the end of the Eocene epoch. Some
of its middle and late Eocene descendants lost the splint bones from their hind
feet, while their premolar teeth began to resemble molars. These variants have
been dignified by two names, *Orohippus* and *Epihippus,* but only experts can
distinguish them from the original genus.

Two Primitive Three-toed Horses. Greater progress was made by *Mesohippus,*
of the Oligocene. Though different species varied in size, the typical *Mesohippus* was about 20 inches high and 40 inches long, or about as large as a
collie dog. The skull was slender and rather deep, with a horselike muzzle but

shallow lower jaws. The eyes were farther back than those of eohippus, the orbits were still open behind, and the brain was surprisingly large for that of an Oligocene mammal. The gap, or diastema, between canines and premolars was much larger than it had been in eohippus. The grinders still had low crowns, showing that *Mesohippus* browsed on leaves and perhaps ate pulpy fruits.

Progressive and old-fashioned characters also mingled in the feet of *Meso-hippus*. Each forefoot had lost one toe, whose only remnant was a splint hidden under the skin. The middle toe of each foot was the largest, but all three had usable hoofs. Still, most of the weight rested on doglike pads, much as it did in eohippus. The back also was arched, and the hind legs still were longer than the forelegs. *Mesohippus* apparently ran with deerlike leaps.

Mesohippus was followed by *Miohippus*, a larger and somewhat more horse-like beast, whose descendants split into four principal groups. Two of these kept low browsing teeth and three usable toes on which some species crossed a land bridge to Asia and finally wandered into Europe. At home, other species apparently became as large as an African rhinoceros, which is 5 feet tall, 11 to 12 feet long, and weighs about 4,000 pounds. Appropriately named *Mega-hippus* ("big horse") these giants contrast with a third American group, *Arch-aeohippus*. Its members evolved into pigmies no larger than a good-sized eohippus.

Progressive Merychippus. Fourth among the descendants of *Miohippus* was a group which we call progressive merely because it led toward modern

Mesohippus, a three-toed horse of Oligocene age, from the White River Badlands of South Dakota. Length about 40 inches

Forefoot

Hind foot

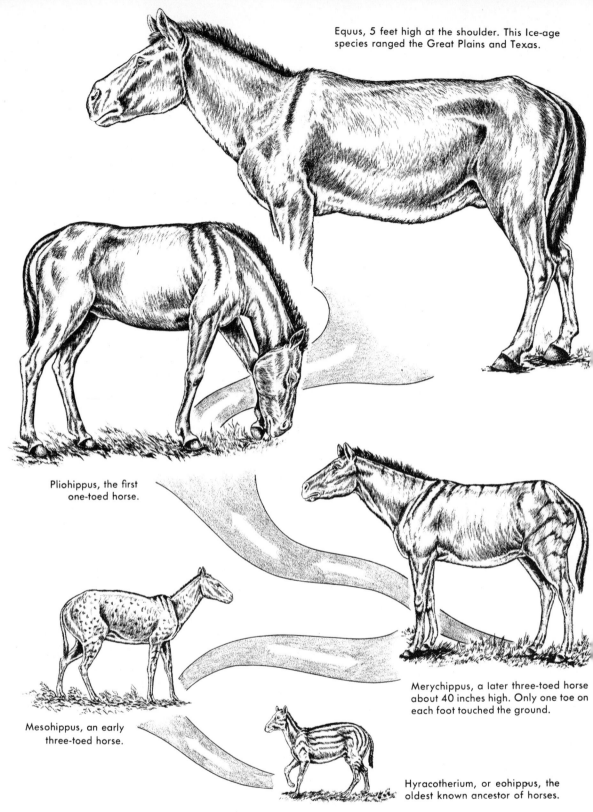

Equus, 5 feet high at the shoulder. This Ice-age species ranged the Great Plains and Texas.

Pliohippus, the first one-toed horse.

Merychippus, a later three-toed horse about 40 inches high. Only one toe on each foot touched the ground.

Mesohippus, an early three-toed horse.

Hyracotherium, or eohippus, the oldest known ancestor of horses.

The "dawn-horse," and some of its descendants

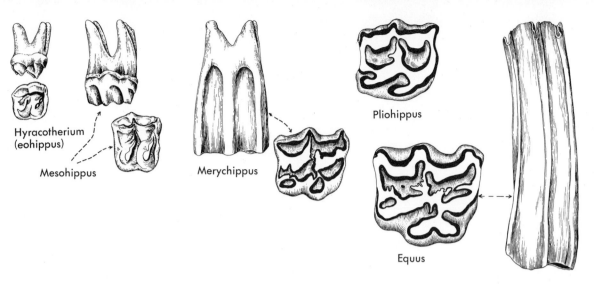

Hyracotherium (eohippus)

Mesohippus

Merychippus

Pliohippus

Equus

As horses evolved, their molars, or grinding teeth, grew larger and the enamel (shown in black) *was folded into more and more complex patterns.*

horses. Its most important member, *Merychippus,* appeared in the middle Miocene and lived on through early Pliocene times. Contrasting *Merychippus* with earlier genera, we notice these horselike traits:

Size. About as large as a Shetland pony. Height at the shoulders 40 inches, which a horseman would have called 10 "hands."

Build. Horselike, with an almost straight back. Some stocky species were slow runners; others were slender and swift.

Eyes. Far back on the head, as in modern horses. Each orbit was closed behind the eye by a bar of bone.

Legs. Bones of the foreleg were fused. Part of one bone (fibula) in the hind leg had disappeared, leaving only a spike.

How skulls changed in the horse family

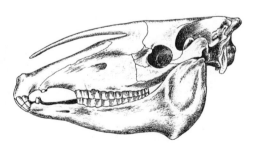

Hippidion, a South American horse of Pleistocene age

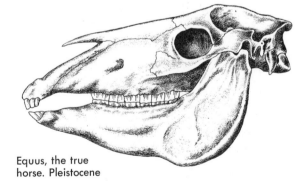

Equus, the true horse. Pleistocene

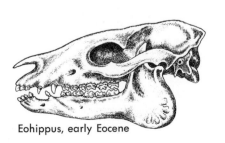

Eohippus, early Eocene

Mesohippus, Oligocene

Feet. The middle toe of each foot was large, with a broad hoof that carried the weight. The second and fourth toes were very short.

Teeth. Though *Merychippus* was born with low-crowned teeth, they were replaced by high-crowned premolars and molars whose enamel was deeply folded and crumpled and was set in bonelike cement. These teeth grew throughout most of the animal's life, presenting rough grinding surfaces as they were worn down. Roots finally formed and growth was halted at the onset of old age. The jaws worked with a side-to-side grinding motion as well as up and down.

(Left) *Palaeotherium, a relative of horses. Height about 4 feet.* (Right) *Thoatherium, a "false horse" 17 inches high, from the Miocene of South America, and the bones of one hind foot*

High-crowned teeth that kept growing while they were used enabled *Merychippus* to give up browsing and feed upon grass, which contains abrasive silica. Grass spread widely during Miocene times, allowing the new three-toed grazers to take up life on prairies and plains, where their long legs and running feet provided escape from carnivores. Descendants of *Merychippus* ranged through North and South America, Asia, Europe, and Africa during the latest Miocene and Pliocene epochs. One African form lived on through much of the Pleistocene.

From Three Toes to One. Further progress was made by *Pliohippus,* of early to middle Pliocene age. In some of its species the small toes became vestigial; in others they were reduced to tiny *splint bones* below the hock and "knee." *Pliohippus* also developed a deep body and grinding teeth that grew higher and higher, while canines became small and the gap behind them widened. As the Pliocene closed, these changes turned certain North American descendants of *Pliohippus* into *Equus,* the modern horse. In South America, another branch of *Pliohippus* gave rise to short-legged horses of the genus *Hippidion*, whose skull had amazingly long nasal bones supported by a ridge of cartilage that is not preserved in fossils. Some of these beasts ranged the open, level pampas, but others apparently lived on eastern slopes of the Andes.

Though *Equus* arose in North America, it soon spread to other continents and evolved into varied subgenera and a large number of species. Those that remained in their homeland included animals 40 inches in height and others as large as the modern Belgian draft horse, which stands 5 feet 5 inches high

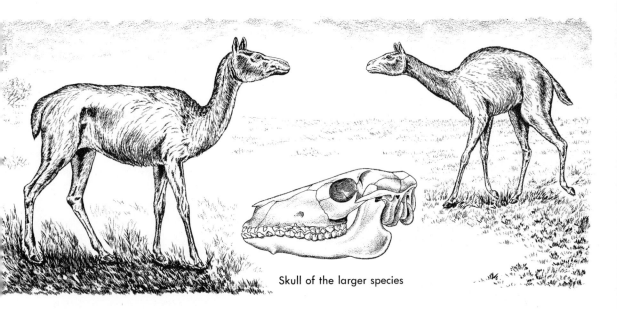

Skull of the larger species

Two species of Poëbrotherium, the large one 26 inches high at the shoulder. Both are from the Oligocene of the Great Plains.

at the shoulder and weighs as much as a ton. An abundant species of the Great Plains was not quite as large as the modern quarter horse, now ridden by many ranchers. Another Pleistocene species was about the size of a zebra but was less gracefully built.

The Decline of Wild Horses. Enormous herds of horses lived in Europe, Asia, and Africa during the Pleistocene epoch; in the Americas they ranged from Alaska to the Strait of Magellan. Then they died out in the New World, became scarce and finally vanished from Europe, and remained abundant only on the plains of Africa and—for a while—in Asia. Survivors include the African ass, three species of zebras, the Asiatic onager, and another Asiatic species that may survive only in zoos. Domestic breeds are descended from extinct Asiatic horses and the ass of Africa.

This widespread extinction of horses is a puzzle. True, man has destroyed some modern species and others have suffered from crossing with domestic breeds. But these factors seem inadequate to explain the decline that took place during late Pleistocene and early Recent times. We also find no evidence that glaciation, disappearance of pastures, predatory carnivores, epidemics, or competition with other grazers was responsible. The mystery is deepened by the fact that domestic horses from the Old World ran wild and became plentiful in both North and South America after they were introduced by man.

THE STORY OF CAMELS

Horses are odd-toed perissodactyls; even eohippus and its close kin combined four toes on each front foot with three behind. But members of the camel family had four toes or two, with nothing between, and therefore were artiodactyls. Despite this contrast, the story of camels parallels that of horses. Both groups presumably reached North America as ancestral immigrants and made most of their evolutionary progress in the New World. Both also wandered to other continents, where they still prosper, although their relatives have vanished from North America.

Protylopus, a Primitive Camel. The first known member of the camel family appeared late in the Eocene epoch, millions of years after eohippus reached Wyoming. This patriarch, *Protylopus,* was a short-legged beast not much larger than a jack rabbit, with an elongate skull and orbits partly closed by bony projections instead of continuous bars. The jaws contained forty-four teeth,

Protylopus, the oldest known member of the camel family, and Stenomylus, of the early Miocene. Stenomylus stood 27 inches high at the shoulder.

of which the canines resembled incisors while the grinders had very low crowns. There were four toes in front and two behind, with splint bones as vestiges of two additional toes. The hoofs were pointed like those of a deer, showing that the toes were not padded as are those of modern camels. Since hind legs were longer than forelegs, the animals leaped as they ran.

Poëbrotherium. Descendants of *Protylopus* ranged the West in abundant herds during the Oligocene epoch. Most characteristic was *Poëbrotherium,* whose bones are found in the South Dakota Badlands and other regions underlain by middle beds of the White River formation. *Poëbrotherium* looked like a llama about 26 inches high at the back, and it weighed less than most sheep. Its teeth resembled those of *Protylopus,* but the forefeet had only two toes, and splints had disappeared from the hind feet. The tail, though short, was longer than that of the living llama.

We sometimes assume that all ancient animals with one generic name looked alike, so that a description fitting one applies to all related species. Actually our description of *Poëbrotherium* fits only the species *labiatum;* another, *P. wilsoni,* had longer and much more slender legs, a shorter head, and a strongly arched back. Curvature did not come after death, for the vertebrae could not have straighted out when the animal was alive.

The Delicate Gazelle-camels. Three groups of Miocene camels evolved in separate ways. One led to the pad-footed, hump-backed beasts of today and may be regarded as the trunk of the family tree. The other two groups were branches that prospered briefly and died.

Stenomylus typifies a branch whose small bodies and slender legs account for the descriptive name, "gazelle-camel." *Stenomylus* was 2 feet 3 inches high at the shoulder, with a thin neck and lower jaws that seemed to have ten incisor teeth. There actually were six—three on each side—but the canines and two premolars had assumed the shape of incisors and were used to nip off food.

Most fossils of *Stenomylus* have come from the lower Miocene of Agate Springs Ranch, in western Nebraska. The quarry seems to be part of an ancient "bed ground," where a huge herd of gazelle-camels spent the night, as herds of modern guanacos sleep on the plains of Patagonia. Before morning the sick and the aged died and were covered by wind-blown sand. One night's death might account for the hundred or more bodies whose bones have been found.

Camels as Tall as Giraffes. Though *Stenomylus* resembled a gazelle, its neighbor, *Oxydactylus*—the name means "long-toe"—belonged to a branch whose lengthening legs and necks remind us of giraffes. *Oxydactylus* itself was a rather small browser that stood 4 feet 6 inches high at the shoulder, though by stretching his neck he could reach leaves 8 feet above the ground. Each foot had two toes with pointed hoofs but no trace of pads.

This group culminated in *Alticamelus* ("tall camel") of the middle Miocene and early Pliocene epochs. Large species rivaled modern giraffes in height, but their bodies did not slope toward the tail. The low-crowned teeth still were

Head and skull of Procamelus, a
Miocene ancestor of modern camels
and guanacos

(Left) *Oxydactylus, a long-necked Miocene camel 4 feet 6 inches at the shoulder.*
(Right) *Alticamelus, a Miocene beast with such long legs and neck that it has been
nicknamed the "giraffe camel"*

adapted to browsing, and the feet had nail-shaped hoofs as well as pads
which carried them over sandy ground.

From Procamelus to Modern Camels. During mid-Miocene and early Pliocene
times the main line of camel development was typified by *Procamelus*, which
looked like *Poëbrotherium* but had a longer neck and was 4 feet high at the
shoulder. The head was long and low; teeth vanished from the front of the
upper jaw, forcing the beast to graze by catching grass between its hard upper
gums and the lower incisors. The bony arch behind each orbit was complete,
and the feet (like those of *Alticamelus*) had both pads and hoofs.

Descendants of *Procamelus* were great travelers. Some went to Mexico and southeastward, crossing to South America as soon as marine barriers were removed late in the Pliocene epoch. These migrants gave rise to several forms with well-developed pads on the toes, including the modern guanaco and vicuña. The former, a humpless beast fitted to life among mountains as well as on plains, was tamed by prehistoric Indians. Its domestic descendants are the llama, a beast of burden, and the alpaca, which is bred for its wool.

Camels also reached Asia in Pliocene times, evolving into two genera, *Camelus* and *Paracamelus,* which ranged from China to Europe and northern Africa during the Pleistocene. The latter is now extinct, but the former survives in two fully domesticated species. The one-humped dromedary, which may be native to Africa, is a big animal 10 to 11 feet long and 6 to 7 feet high at the shoulder. Two-humped Bactrian camels of central Asia are not so large, have longer hair, and can endure colder climates than their one-humped relatives.

No one knows when or where humps evolved, for these fat-filled structures leave no mark on the skeleton. Many authorities assume that humps appeared in the Old World; others put them on camels of Pleistocene North America. Some of these camels were as large as dromedaries, but others were 15 feet tall and were much more heavily built than the earlier giraffe-camels. At least one genus, *Camelops,* survived into the Recent epoch, for its skull, with shreds of dry flesh, has been found in a cave near Fillmore, Utah.

(Left) *Camelops, an American camel 7 feet high at the shoulders. An Ice Age animal, it survived into Recent times.* (Right) *The guanaco, a humpless camel of modern South America. It lives on both mountains and plains.*

Palaeomastodon (right), *of Oligocene age, ranged from 3 to 6 feet in height. It had developed a short trunk and tusks, and its grinding teeth were becoming large. Moeritherium* (left), *about 2 feet high at the shoulder. The oldest known ancestor of elephants, it lived in swampy regions of northern Egypt during Eocene and early Oligocene times.*

PROBOSCIDEANS: LONG NOSES AND TUSKS

Unlike horses and camels, proboscideans did not evolve in North America. Their story is one of repeated migrations, with evolutionary changes that turned small, undistinguished beasts into tusked, trunk-bearing giants that weighed 5 to perhaps 7 tons.

Ancestors and Aberrant Tuskers. The oldest known proboscidean is called *Moeritherium* because its remains are found near ancient Lake Moeris, whose bed is now a fertile valley in the Egyptian province of Fayum. *Moeritherium* was about 5 feet long and 25 inches high at the shoulder, with a thick round body, sturdy legs, and short five-toed feet. The skull was low, wide, and blunt, the eyes were far forward, and the high-placed nostrils suggest a tapirlike snout. The grinding teeth were low-crowned, but four incisors were large enough to show that the growth of tusks had begun.

Moeritherium was no wanderer but remained in its northern Egyptian lowland during the late Eocene and early Oligocene epochs. There it produced at least three divergent groups of descendants.

Dinotherium was most aberrant of these; a beast of elephantine build and bulk that still was not an elephant. One Miocene species had a low-browed skull about 48 inches long, with a square jaw and projecting bones in the nose, which certainly was a trunk. Grinding teeth were low-crowned and primitive; the upper jaw was short and lacked incisors, but the chin extended outward and downward and carried two short, curved tusks. *Dinotherium* became common in eastern Europe and western Asia during the Miocene and early Pliocene epochs. It then died out in those regions but survived well into the Pleistocene in tropical Africa. There is no hint that it ever reached the Americas.

A Variety of Mastodonts. A second group that sprang from the moeritheres began with *Palaeomastodon*, found in early Oligocene rocks of Egypt. Some species were tapirlike beasts 3 to 4 feet high, but others reached a height of 6 feet and weighed a couple of tons. All had thick legs, blunt feet, skulls that were high at the back, and short trunks instead of snouts. Both upper and lower jaws bore tusks, but those of the upper jaw were longer and curved downward. The grinding teeth had low crowns with blunt-tipped crests and ended in several roots.

During the next 5,000,000 years, descendants of *Palaeomastodon* reached Europe and crossed Asia to North America but left few if any fossils along their routes of travel. As the animals wandered they also evolved, becoming elephantine in bulk and shape but retaining their low-crowned, crested teeth. Some also kept four tusks, but others lost those of the lower jaw.

The American mastodon, 7 to 9 feet 6 inches in height, and one of its molar teeth

Skull of Gomphotherium, or Trilophodon, about 36 inches long

Phiomia (right), *about 4 feet 5 inches high, was an Oligocene relative of mastodons. It lived in Egypt, but its descendant,* Gomphotherium (left), *wandered into Europe, Asia, and North America. It reached 8 feet in height and had a very long lower jaw.*

The term *Mastodon* was once applied to a long series of these animals that lived during Miocene and later epochs. The Miocene and Pliocene beasts then received other names, restricting *Mastodon* to two species of Pleistocene and early Recent age. Then an older name, *Mammut,* was found, and rules required that it be used for technical purposes. Mastodon thus became a general word, like eohippus, and is not to be capitalized.

So much for names and their changes. *Mammut* itself, which knew nothing of nomenclature, was an elephantine beast whose teeth (which are often found as fossils) still had separate roots and blunt crests. There were two good-sized tusks on the upper jaw, but the lower tusks had disappeared or were mere vestiges. The body was covered with rusty brown hair; though each foot had five toes, most of the weight was carried by a springy pad. Heights ranged from 7 feet in females to 9 feet 6 inches in big bulls.

This description fits *Mammut americanum;* another species found only in the West differed in details. The American mastodon ranged from New England and Florida to Mexico, California, and Alaska; fossil teeth indicate that it also crossed northern Asia and reached the eastern plains of Europe. In North America, *M. americanum* lived beyond the end of the Ice Age and was hunted by early man. An animal whose remains were found in Ohio died 8,000 to 9,000 years ago.

The Rise of Gomphotheres. Though mastodons had tusks and long trunks, they did not give rise to true elephants. The latter beasts are descendants of gomphotheres, a complex family whose teeth are so much like those of mastodonts that the two are sometimes confused.

The founder of this family was *Phiomia,* another descendant of *Moeritherium. Phiomia,* which lived in Egypt during the Oligocene epoch, was 4 feet 5 inches in height, with a snoutlike trunk, long lower jaws, and very short tusks. Its grinding teeth were distinctive, for they had divided crests and additional cusps, or blunt points. Except for their size, they resemble the molars of a pig.

Phiomia remained in Egypt, producing offspring that are variously known as *Gomphotherium* and *Trilophodon.* Again, names are not very important; what counts are changes in teeth and lower jaws. The former were increasingly complex; the latter became longer and longer, until some measured as much as 6 feet. The upper jaws were relatively short, but the tusks they bore were longer than those of *Phiomia.* Some species were only 6 feet high, but others reached 8 feet and so equaled many circus elephants.

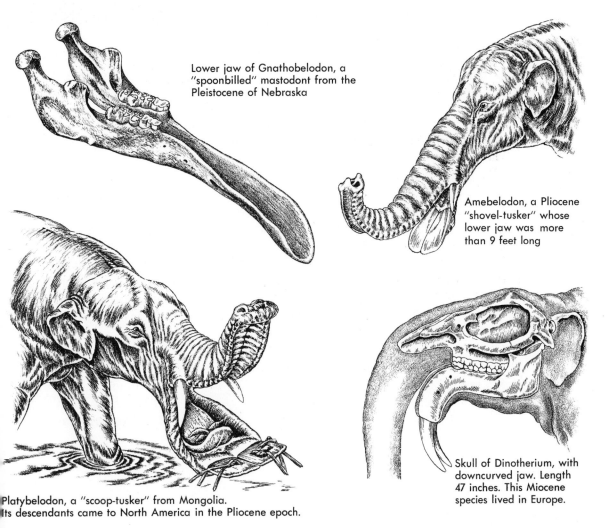

Lower jaw of Gnathobelodon, a "spoonbilled" mastodont from the Pleistocene of Nebraska

Amebelodon, a Pliocene "shovel-tusker" whose lower jaw was more than 9 feet long

Platybelodon, a "scoop-tusker" from Mongolia. Its descendants came to North America in the Pliocene epoch.

Skull of Dinotherium, with downcurved jaw. Length 47 inches. This Miocene species lived in Europe.

Aberrant Mud-grubbers. *Gomphotherium* apparently evolved in Africa but soon spread to Europe, Asia, and North America. With it came a related genus called *Platybelodon,* which had lost its upper tusks. The lower jaws narrowed in front of the cheek teeth but then flared out to accommodate two broad, flat tusks that formed a broad scoop with which *Platybelodon* dug roots from swamps. A short trunk kept the roots on the shovel, while a striplike tongue separated food from muck and passed the former back for chewing.

Scoop-tuskers were discovered in the Caucasus and made news in the early 1920's, when they were found in Mongolia. Then both jaws and skulls came to light in northwestern Nebraska, along with other mastodonts termed shovel-tuskers and spoonbills. The former had tremendously long lower jaws bearing flat tusks that were longer but narrower than those of *Platybelodon.* Spoonbills had lost their lower tusks, but their lower jaws formed concave, thin-edged "spoons" that were excellent for grubbing.

Stegodon and True Elephants. The ancestor of true elephants probably was an early *Gomphotherium.* Somewhere—perhaps in central Asia—it produced descendants whose skulls became short but high and whose lower jaws also were shortened. Their premolars became small, too, but the molars increased in size and developed ridgelike crosswise crests of enamel partly covered by cement. New teeth began to advance obliquely instead of growing straight upward or downward, and only eight could be used at one time.

The first result of these changes was *Stegodon,* a very primitive elephant that evolved in early Pliocene Asia but reached Africa during the Pleistocene, or Ice Age. Meanwhile it gave rise to three other groups that ranged through Asia, Europe, Africa, and North America. Including species that survive today, we divide these true elephants as follows:

Loxodonts. This group, which appeared in the Pliocene, includes modern African elephants (*Loxodonta*) and their fossil relatives, one of which lived in Europe after man reached that continent. The loxodont skull is not much higher than that of *Stegodon,* and its grinding teeth are relatively low, with irregularly lozenge-shaped cross plates that rarely number more than ten. In *Loxodonta* itself the tusks are long but not deeply curved, the back is depressed behind the shoulders and slopes abruptly to the tail, and the ears are very large. The forelegs are longer than the hind, and there are four nail-shaped hoofs on each forefoot but only three behind.

Some loxodonts are very large; the big African species reaches a height of 11 feet 6 inches at the shoulder, and *Loxodonta antiqua* of the Ice Age is said to have reached 14 feet. On the other hand, species that inhabited Malta and other Mediterranean islands were pigmies, the smallest being a little more than 3 feet high and weighing no more than a good-sized hog. They were much smaller than the forest-dwelling pigmy elephant of modern Africa, which reaches a height of about 6 feet.

Mammoths. These extinct elephants of the Pleistocene, or Ice Age, and early postglacial times have been given several names but now are placed in the genus *Mammuthus,* which must not be confused with *Mammut.* The skull is pointed at the back and was carried higher than that of *Loxodonta.* The tusks grew downward at first and then arched forward, becoming very large. In old males they often curved so far that they crossed and turned back toward the body. In some primitive European and Asiatic species, such as the southern mammoth (*Mammuthus meridionalis*), the molars contain only ten to twelve plates, but in progressive American types plates of the third molars number twenty-six to thirty. There were four hoofs on each hind foot, but it is not clear whether the forefoot had four hoofs or five. If the number was five, one hoof was very small.

The largest American mammoth, appropriately called *imperator,* lived in the South and Southwest and is one of the two tar-pit species described in Chapter XXXIII. The other, generally called *columbi,* ranged northward through temperate regions. With allied species or subspecies, it reached heights of 10 feet 6 inches at the shoulder in contrast to 13 feet 6 inches for big bulls of *imperator.*

A woolly mammoth (Mammuthus primigenius Blumenbach). This species ranged across Europe, Asia, and North America.

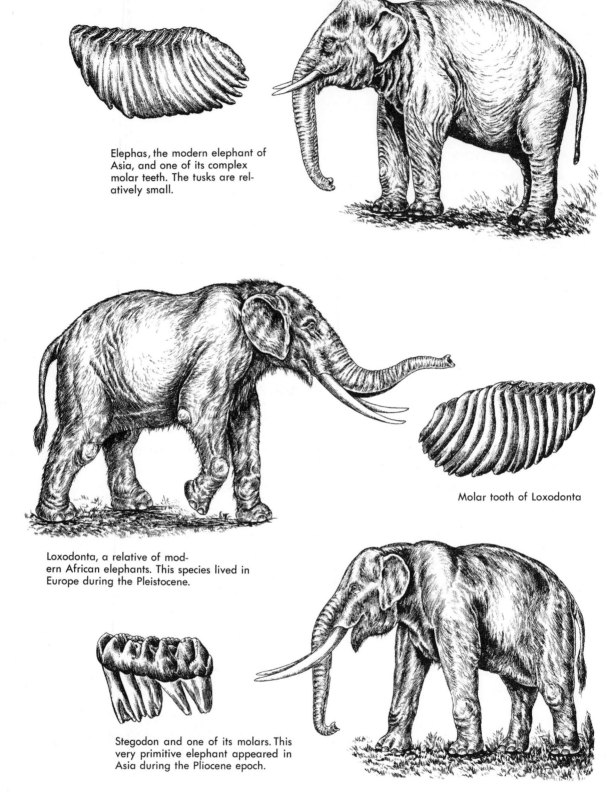

Elephas, the modern elephant of Asia, and one of its complex molar teeth. The tusks are relatively small.

Molar tooth of Loxodonta

Loxodonta, a relative of modern African elephants. This species lived in Europe during the Pleistocene.

Stegodon and one of its molars. This very primitive elephant appeared in Asia during the Pliocene epoch.

Three stages in the evolution of elephants. They show the increasing size and complexity of molar teeth and the reduction of tusks in the modern Elephas.

Though fossils of the Columbian mammoth and its kin outnumber those of other American species, the animals are less widely known than *Mammuthus primigenius*. This is the woolly mammoth, which ranged from western Europe across Asia and North America to New England. In spite of its name it was not very large; a big bull stood 9 feet high at the shoulder, though its head was 8 to 12 inches higher. The tusks were large and deeply curved; those of one specimen measure 16 feet in length. The forelegs were long and the hind legs short, making the back slope steeply toward the tail. The skin bore a coat of gray wool covered by long, coarse, reddish-brown hair. This protection against rain, snow, and cold explains why the mammoth was able to live in comfort only a few miles from the ice.

The woolly mammoth is one of those rare fossils whose soft parts are known, since frozen bodies complete with hair, skin, and dried blood have been found in Alaska and Siberia. It also appears in paintings and statuettes made by cave men of Europe, who trapped the beast in pits and killed it with stone mauls attached to rawhide ropes. These were thrown across overhanging branches, allowing the hammers to be pulled up and then dropped on the victims' backs or heads.

Asiatic Elephants (Elephas). These presumably are descendants of early mammoths; today, as in Pleistocene times, they inhabit southeastern Asia and the East Indies but are familiar in zoos and circuses. The skull is very short and deep and is rounded on top, often with a bulging "forehead." The tusks are directed downward and seem to be disappearing, since they never are very large. Many females, indeed, lack them, and so do some males. The molars are high and broad, and the last ones to appear have twenty-four closely folded cross plates. The back is arched behind the shoulders; the feet are short and blunt, with five toes and pads of elastic tissue that receive most of the weight, since they touch the ground before the toes do. There are five hoofs on each forefoot and four behind, though the hoof of each fifth toe may be very small. The brain, which weighs 10 to 11 pounds, seems to be superior to that of *Loxodonta*. The height of full-grown males reaches 8 to 10 feet at the shoulder, and the weight is 8,000 to 10,000 pounds.

CHAPTER XXXIII

Beasts and Birds of the Ice Age

"Near the Pueblo de los Angeles there are more than twenty springs of liquid petroleum, pitch, etc. Farther to the west of the said town, in the middle of a great plain of more than fifteen leagues' circumference, there is a great lake of pitch, with many pools in which bubbles or blisters are continually forming and exploding. . . . In hot weather animals have been seen to sink into it, and when they tried to escape they could not do so because their feet were stuck, and the lake swallowed them. After many years their bones come through the holes, as if petrified. I brought away several specimens."

Thus a Spanish explorer, José Longinos Martinez, wrote of the Rancho La Brea tar pools, which he saw in 1792. But contemporaries ignored Martinez' bones that looked "as if petrified," and so did explorers, ranchmen, and geologists who saw the tar pools during the century that followed. Not till 1906 were excavations begun by paleontologists. Within ten years they took out hundreds of thousands of bones—the greatest and most comprehensive array of Pleistocene, or Ice Age, fossils found anywhere on the globe. Other thousands of bones remain in the tar under what is now Hancock Park, in western Los Angeles.

THE PLEISTOCENE ICE AGE

Before going further we must clarify that deceptively simple term, Ice Age. The earth has passed through several "ages"—actually epochs—during which climates grew cool and glaciers spread widely in one part of the world or another. The first of these epochs came during Huronian times, at least 1,600,000,000 years ago. There were others near the end of the Eozoic and Paleozoic eras, but the last one began less than 1,000,000 years ago and has not quite come to an end in Greenland. Termed the Pleistocene, or "most recent"

436

of geologic epochs, it is the one whose results are most often seen and most easily recognized. We frequently call it *the* Ice Age, forgetting that others lasted longer and that their glaciers sometimes covered more ground.

Condensed summaries often make the Pleistocene seem like an age-long winter, followed by catastrophic floods as ice sheets melted. That picture, however, is too simple. Over much of North America and Europe there were four major glacial advances and a minor fifth. Between them came intervals of warmth and melting, in which climates sometimes were warmer than they are today. Interglacial deposits near Toronto, for example, contain trees that now grow in the central Mississippi Valley, Ohio, and Pennsylvania.

When the tar-pool fossils were first studied they seemed to be early Pleistocene. That error has been corrected, and the remains are now assigned to the time of the last, or Wisconsin, glaciation. It began about 100,000 years ago

A male southern, or Columbian, mammoth; height at shoulder about 10 feet 6 inches. Found at many places in the Southwest, this one is shown east of San Gorgonio Pass, California.

Scene at the Rancho La Brea tar pits in late Pleistocene times, perhaps 20,000 years ago, showing typical mammals and birds. **1.** *The great vulture, Teratornis, with a wingspread of 10 to 12 feet.* **2.** *Small pronghorned antelope (Breameryx), 20 inches high.* **3.** *Ground sloth (Nothrotherium), 3 feet 3 inches high at back.* **4.** *Stork about 4 feet high as it stands here.*

and ended in southern California about 10,000 B.C. An estimate of 20,000 years will do for the age of Rancho La Brea's fossils.

LIFE ON THE ANCIENT LOS ANGELES PLAIN

So much for geologic background. Let us now examine the record of Ice Age life and conditions preserved in the tar pools.

The country itself provides no surprises, for the nearest glaciers were in the Sierra Nevada, 150 miles away. Then, as now, the region of Los Angeles was

More mammals of the Brea tar pits, in what is now Hancock Park, Los Angeles.
5. *Giant short-faced bear, 4 feet 2 inches high.* **6.** *The Brea lion, 4 feet 2 inches at the shoulder.* **7.** *Two imperial mammoths, 10 to 13 feet in height.* **8.** *Camelops, 7 feet at shoulder.* **9.** *Bison skull.* **10.** *Horse skull.*

a plain rimmed by the Santa Monica, San Gabriel, and Santa Ana Mountains. Creeks flowed to an early version of the Los Angeles River that ran southward to what is now San Pedro Bay. Grassy flats were dotted with chaparral thickets and groves of live oak, juniper, cypress, and Bishop pine. Small mammals were much like those of the present, for they included mice, ground squirrels, kangaroo rats, cottontails, and jack rabbits, but plants suggest that the climate was warm and less influenced by the ocean than it is today. Seasons of moderate rainfall alternated with summer and autumn droughts.

Hoofed and Clawed Herbivores. Though small mammals were familiar, most of the large ones seem strange. Bison were plentiful, for example; not the modern "buffalo," but a species more than 7 feet tall at its hump. Big bulls had skulls 27 to 32 inches wide between the horns, which curved less than those of the present-day bison.

Wild horses were less abundant than bison, but they roamed the plain in small bands or herds. All belonged to one species, *Equus occidentalis,* which stood 4 feet 10 inches high between the shoulders, with a bulging forehead, a thick body, and relatively short legs. Although not so tall as the modern quarter horse (a favorite "cow pony" in the West), it was more heavily built.

Camels of the tar pits also were large, standing 7 feet at the highest part of the back. The skull suggests that of a llama, but bones of the body resemble those of the modern two-humped Asiatic species. There were great herds of

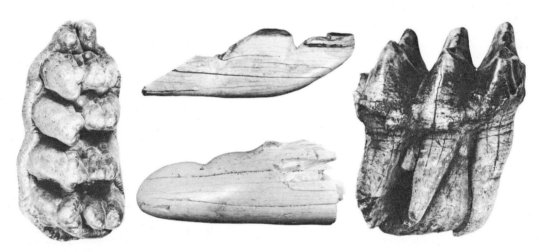

Upper molar of Serridentius, a mastodont from Florida

Tips of two American mastodon tusks. They show grooves that were worn by roots which the animal dug from the ground.

Second left lower molar of the American mastodon. It shows the high cusps, two of which are slightly worn.

Breameryx, a pronghorned "antelope" 19 inches in height at the shoulder. Its horns were divided into two straight spikes, one of which was much larger than the other. Teeth indicate a diet of grass, which the pronghorn eats today.

The largest mammals found in the tar pools were mastodons and mammoths. The former was *Mammut americanum;* the latter included two species, *Mammuthus imperator* and *M. columbi.* None reached the maximum size of its species and none was plentiful. A mastodon skeleton in the Los Angeles Museum is only 7 feet 3 inches in height.

The commonest edentate of Rancho La Brea is the ground sloth called *Mylodon* or *Paramylodon,* which ranged from Patagonia to southern Oregon and eastward as far as Nebraska. *Nothrotherium* wandered down from nearby mountains, where it probably was common. A third genus, *Megalonyx,* also lived among mountains but sometimes visited the plain and was trapped in tar. The La Brea fossils belong to a subspecies that ranged eastward to the Atlantic coast. It was described in 1797 by Thomas Jefferson, who mistook its claw-bearing toe bones for those of an enormous lion. Jefferson carried the fossils with him when he rode to Philadelphia to become President. His description, published in 1799, was entitled *A Memoir on the Discovery of Certain Bones of a Quadruped of the Clawed Kind in the Western Parts of Virginia.*

Varied Carnivores. Where plant-eating animals were common, carnivores were sure to come. They included weasels, skunks, badgers, foxes, coyotes, bobcats, and bears, all belonging to modern species or closely related forms. With them was the dire wolf, *Canis dirus,* a heavy-headed beast not quite so

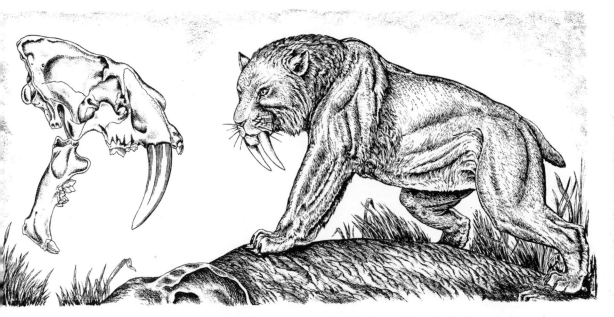

Smilodon, last of the saber-tooths, about 40 inches high. The skull shows how widely the beast could open its jaws, freeing the canine teeth for use as daggers.

large as the timber wolf of today. It was common and probably hunted in packs, but ate carrion as well as freshly killed food.

Cats included three species of puma, or mountain lions, as well as *Felis* (or *Panthera*) *atrox.* This was a powerful lionlike creature that ranged from Alaska to Mississippi and the valley in which Mexico City now stands. Males were one fourth larger than the biggest tiger, though females were about the size of a jaguar. This "Brea lion" was an active hunter that preyed on horses, camels, bison, and other herbivores.

Smilodon, last of the saber-tooths, was a short-tailed beast, much more heavily built than the modern lion. Its body was massive, its legs were heavy, and its brain was smaller than that of the Brea lion and puma. Its canine teeth, like those of all other saber-tooths, were curved, knifelike weapons used for slashing or stabbing—not biting—large animals such as mastodons and ground sloths. *Smilodon* did not run his prey down, since his legs were not built for speed. We picture him as a beast that lay in wait near groves or water holes, pouncing upon ground sloths and other victims. Strong forelegs and claws gripped the victim's back, while the teeth slashed downward again and again, inflicting jagged wounds that deepened as the gaping jaws partly closed. High-placed nostrils enabled *Smilodon* to breathe, even when his muzzle was buried in the long, coarse hair of a ground sloth.

But did *Smilodon* always hunt? We doubt it, in view of his clumsy build and the number of skeletons buried in Rancho La Brea tar pools. Like dire wolves, the saber-tooth probably ate carrion when he could find it and often devoured animals trapped in the sticky tar. In so doing, he himself might become mired—but the smilodont brain was too dull to weigh the chance of future disaster against an immediate and visible meal.

Largest of all tar-pool carnivores was *Tremarctotherium,* a gigantic short-faced bear that ranged from the Yukon to Pennsylvania and Texas. The California species stood 4 feet 2 inches high at the curve of the back and was 7 feet 6 inches long. Corresponding dimensions for a large grizzly are a height of 3 feet 4 inches and a length of 5 feet 10 inches. If the Pleistocene giants had the habits of other bears, as they probably did, neither grizzlies nor black bears had much chance to succeed on the ancient Los Angeles plain. The remains of both are much less common than those of tremarctotheres.

Insects and Birds. Unlike many another fossil fauna, that of Rancho La Brea includes large numbers of insects and birds. Among the former are many carrion beetles, which fed upon and even lived in decaying carcasses. Birds ranged from geese and a stork more than 4 feet high to woodpeckers, waxwings, and little chipping sparrows. More than half of them, however, represented the order of vultures, eagles, and hawks.

Many hawks belonged to modern species, and so did bald and golden eagles. Others were related to species now found in Central America. The walking eagle was a ground-dweller with legs almost as long as those of our great blue heron. Instead of soaring in search of prey, this eagle ran down small rodents and captured them with its claws.

Eight or more species of vultures fed at and were trapped in the tar pools. One was much like the modern California condor but belonged to an extinct species that ranged from the southern Cascade Mountains to Florida and Mexico. Another was more closely related to condors of South America but had a longer beak. Both seemed small beside *Teratornis,* which ranged from California to Texas, Florida, and northern Mexico. *Teratornis* stood 30 inches high as it perched, weighed about 50 pounds, and had a wingspread of 12 feet. The openings for its nostrils were very large, suggesting that it hunted by smell rather than sight.

WHY AND HOW DID THEY DIE?

Examining these varied creatures, we wonder why they are found in the tar pools. What brought them there in the first place? How did they get into a substance which they should have done their best to avoid?

The answers appear when we look at the tar pools as they were in late Pleistocene time. Most of them filled low spots on the plain, and their asphalt was covered with water. The pools therefore provided homes for snails, water beetles, and water bugs, as well as resting places for geese, ducks, and grebes. Herons, cranes, and shore birds waded in shallows, and toads came to lay their strings of gelatinous eggs. Now and then herds of bison, antelope, or horses paused at the pools to drink.

This picture fits the moist season; in the dry one, which lasted from late spring until autumn, the river shrank, creeks ran dry, and tar pools became almost the only source of water. Herbivores traveled miles to reach it; some stood on the banks to drink and were safe, but others waded out and were caught as they sank into the asphalt. So were meat-eaters that came to feed upon the dying herbivores.

(Left) *Preptoceras, which resembled a muskox, lived in California. True muskoxen ranged widely near the front of continental glaciers.* (Right) *Cervalces, the elk-moose, ranged from New Jersey to Iowa.*

There was, in fact, an orderly sequence of mammals, birds, and insects. First came a thirsty herbivore, which might be anything from a rabbit to an imperial mammoth. Going too far in its haste to drink, it found itself mired in the tar. Struggling to escape, the beast sank more and more deeply, at the same time attracting attention from prowling carnivores. They made an easy kill—but unless they were both careful and lucky, they too were trapped in the tar. So were carrion-eating dire wolves, which snarled and snapped at each other on the torn carcasses.

Hawks, eagles, and vultures watched these struggles or caught the odor of dead meat. Some came down, ate their fill, and left, but when several attacked one body, fights were sure to result. The birds pushed and beat each other with their wings, and those that lost their balance often fell into the tar. The final stage came when blowflies laid eggs in the carrion and beetles fed upon it. Many of these insects either fell into the tar or were buried with carcasses as they sank.

Sinking took place more slowly than we might suppose. Many bones in the tar pools are deeply weathered; others were gnawed by mice after carnivores had finished with them. Such bones must have lain at the surface for weeks or months, perhaps in such large, tangled piles that they could not sink rapidly. Thus they attracted still more mammals and served as perches for the small birds whose remains also are found in the tar.

ANIMALS OF THE ICE FRONT

Though the tar-pool animals lived in the Ice Age, none of them ever saw a glacier or experienced a snowstorm. From Montana to New England, however, other mammals lived within a few miles of the shifting ice, moving northward when the glaciers melted and southward when the ice advanced again.

One of these hardy beasts was the musk ox, an animal now restricted to arctic America. During the Pleistocene it ranged from the middle Atlantic states across Asia and Europe to England. A stocky animal 3 feet 6 inches to 4 feet high, its long hair stopped rain and snow while a woolly undercoat kept it warm. The modern musk ox actually seems to prefer cold, blustery weather. Related animals that lived in California may have chosen less rigorous climates, but others apparently lived near the edge of the ice.

Caribou, or American reindeer, also are animals of Arctic "barren grounds" that lived near the front of the ice during Pleistocene times. There they often met woolly mammoths and mastodons, though the latter also ranged far south of the ice front, even to Florida. They apparently preferred swampy woodlands, where they often waded in search of food and sometimes were mired in mud. Moose also were swamp-feeders, but mountain goats (really

Figgins' bison (right) *was killed by ancient men; it was closely related to the species found at Rancho La Brea. Bison latifrons,* (left) *was a large species with a very high hump and horns that spread more than 6 feet.*

antelopes that were late migrants from Asia) preferred dry barrens where the weather ranged from cool to cold.

The majority of Pleistocene mammals lived in less exposed regions during interglacial times. The Great Plains and plateaus swarmed with horses, which also ranged across prairies and among forests of the East. The commonest western species was about the size of a modern cow pony, but *Equus giganteus* of Texas was bigger than the largest draft horse, while *E. tau* of Mexico was as small as a Shetland pony.

Tapirs, which had lived in North America since middle Oligocene times, were common east of the Mississippi River until glaciers made their last great advance. Rhinoceroses, however, had vanished at the end of the Pliocene epoch, though a species with two long horns survived until the close of the Ice Age in Europe, where it lived near the woolly mammoth. Like that animal, it had a woolly undercoat covered with long, coarse hair that was yellowish-red in color. In spite of its habits and appearance, this northern rhino was related to a small hairy species that now lives in southeastern Asia, Sumatra, and Borneo.

Artiodactyls included most of the species now living in North America, as well as a bulbous-nosed saiga antelope and another large animal that closely resembled the African eland. *Cervalces,* the elk-moose, was a large beast with divided antlers and very large hoofs that lived in forests from Iowa to New Jersey. It was very different from the so-called Irish elk of northwestern

Europe. The latter species, which survived until about A.D. 1400, really was a gigantic fallow deer whose antlers spread 7 to 10 feet. Skeletons, which have been found in peat bogs, seem much too delicate to have supported those enormous antlers.

Several species of bison ranged the Great Plains and prairies but were less abundant in the well-wooded East. *Bison latifrons,* which apparently ranged from Florida to Oregon, was an enormous creature with spreading, slightly curved horns 5 to more than 6 feet in width. The animal commonly called *Bison taylori,* of the southwestern plains, apparently should be called Figgins' bison. It was closely related to the high-humped species (*B. antiquus*) of the tar pits and was about as large. Figgins' bison was one of those killed and eaten by prehistoric Americans some 11,000 years ago. Flint spear points were found among the bones of this extinct "buffalo" in 1926, near the town of Folsom, New Mexico. The skeletons lacked tails, suggesting that they had been cut off when the animals were skinned. Similar finds have been made in other regions, where "Folsom men" killed camels, horses, and mammoths as well as bison.

(Left) *The giant deer of Europe, Megaceros. Height at shoulder about 6 feet.* (Right) *The woolly rhinoceros (Dicerorhinus) lived in both Europe and northern Asia. Like the giant deer, it survived the end of the Ice Age.*

Ice Age beavers belonged to the living species and ranged through a large part of the United States and northern Mexico. Giant beavers (*Castoroides*) were northern animals that inhabited lakes from New York to Nebraska. They were about as large as black bears and measured 8 feet from nose to tip of tail. Though their gnawing teeth were large, the animals may have fed on water plants in preference to bark. There is nothing to show whether or not they built houses and dams, as beavers do today.

Porcupines, which now are animals of mountains and northern forests, emigrated from South America and spread over the whole United States and into Canada. With these prickly rodents came the ground sloths *Mylodon, Nothrotherium,* and *Megatherium.* We have seen the first two among mammals of the tar pits, but *Megatherium* ranged eastward to Florida and South Carolina. It must have frequently encountered *Megalonyx,* which had arrived during the Pliocene.

This condensed summary ignores two factors of great significance. The first of these is the repeated migration that took place as ice sheets and mountain glaciers spread and then melted away during interglacial stages. As a result, animals that lived in Kentucky and even Florida during cold subepochs ranged northward into Canada when the climate grew warm. The same thing happened in nearby seas, where walruses sometimes swam off the coast of New Jersey but retreated to the Arctic when sea cows, or manatees, were able to live in bays and rivers of New Jersey.

The second factor is a steady diminution in both numbers and variety of mammals. When the Ice Age opened, North America had one of the world's richest mammalian faunas, with virtually all existing species plus mastodons, mammoths, tapirs, horses, several species of bison, ground sloths, and glyptodonts, saber-tooths, lions, and huge short-faced bears. Several of these vanished before the epoch closed; others survived only in favorable regions such as Florida. Even animals such as Figgins' bison, camels, horses, small ground sloths, and plains-dwelling races of the imperial mammoth, all of which survived the coming of man, died out within a few thousand years after the Ice Age ended. They left the continent "zoologically impoverished," even though a few species such as the elk, caribou, and modern bison ranged widely and in great herds. When white hunters and settlers destroyed these, they merely continued a process that had been going on for almost a half million years, since the glaciers began their second advance.

CHAPTER XXXIV

Read, See, and Collect

WE have surveyed the story of fossils from very ancient times to the end of the Pleistocene ice age. This survey, with its illustrations, will answer the questions of many readers. Others, whose imaginations have been stirred or who collect fossils, will want more information. This chapter tells where to get it, and offers suggestions for making and keeping a collection.

Information about fossils must come mostly from museums and books. Here we think first of the United States National Museum in Washington, the American Museum of Natural History in New York, the Carnegie Museum in Pittsburgh, and the Chicago Museum of Natural History. The National Museum has immense collections of invertebrate fossils and plants, as well as many vertebrates; exhibits are being modernized as this book goes to press. The American Museum of Natural History contains superb exhibits of fossil fish, amphibians, reptiles, and mammals, with a large number of dinosaurs. The Carnegie Museum displays both invertebrates and vertebrates, including large herbivorous dinosaurs. The Chicago Museum has few dinosaurs, but its other fossils are varied and its dioramas are excellent. Life-size restorations of a coal forest and beasts of the South Dakota Badlands are specially notable.

The Peabody Museum of Natural History at Yale University, New Haven, Conn., contains a superb *Apatosaurus* and a mounted *Camarasaurus,* as well as many other vertebrates and invertebrates, and excellent cycads. The Museum of Comparative Zoology at Harvard University, Cambridge, Mass., displays fine Permian vertebrates and aquatic reptiles. The Academy of Natural Sciences in Philadelphia, Pa., has compact, instructive exhibits that include fine ichthyosaurs and plesiosaurs and the first dinosaur discovered in North America. The Milwaukee [Wisconsin] Public Museum also has exhibits of both vertebrate and invertebrate fossils. The Exhibit Museum of the University of Michigan, Ann Arbor, contains several excellent dioramas as well as general exhibits that include vertebrates from Permian and Triassic formations.

Outstanding Canadian museums include the National Museum in Ottawa and the Royal Ontario Museum in Toronto. The latter contains a superb series of Cretaceous dinosaurs from Alberta, as well as invertebrates and dioramas. The Redpath Museum of McGill University, Montreal, is a small general museum that contains Dawson's specimens of *Eozoon* and other fossils.

North America's outstanding regional museum is that of the state of New York, in the Education Building at Albany. Its paleontologic section includes fossils, dioramas (one a natural-size restoration of the Devonian forest at Gilboa, N.Y.), and a full-scale restoration of a mastodon. The following list mentions several other regional museums and comments briefly on their exhibits:

New Jersey State Museum, Trenton. Fossils of New Jersey, including a restoration of the duckbilled dinosaur whose bones are in Philadelphia.

Rochester [New York] Museum of Arts and Sciences. Fossils of western New York; dioramas.

Buffalo [New York] Museum of Science. Fossils of western New York; dioramas.

Alabama Museum of Natural History, University. Alabama fossils.

Cleveland [Ohio] Museum of Natural History. Fish of the Cleveland region.

Nebraska State Museum, Lincoln; part of the State University. Fossils of Nebraska, the mammals being especially important.

Museum of Natural History, University of Kansas, Lawrence. Kansas fossils, especially mosasaurs. Restorations of fish.

Museum, South Dakota School of Mines, Rapid City. Typical fossils from the Great Plains, with some especially fine specimens from the nearby White River Badlands.

Denver [Colorado] Museum of Natural History. Fossils of Colorado and nearby states, including excellent dinosaurs and mammals.

University Museum, University of Oklahoma, Norman. Fossils from Oklahoma and other southwestern states.

Texas Memorial Museum, Austin. Invertebrates and vertebrates of Texas, including animals associated with ancient man.

Arizona State Museum at the State University, Tucson. This is a museum of archaeology, but the Ventana Cave exhibit shows a diorama of Ice Age mammals associated with man.

Museum of Northern Arizona, Flagstaff. Small but excellent collection of fossils from northeastern Arizona.

Museum of Natural History, University of Oregon, Eugene. Fossils of this northwestern state.

California Academy of Sciences, San Francisco. Small display of California fossils and very large study collection of invertebrates.

Santa Barbara [California] Museum of Natural History. Fossils of southern California and offshore islands, including a very large toothed bird.

San Diego [California] Museum of Natural History. Fossils of southern California.

Los Angeles [California] County Museum. The best display of fossils from the famous tar pits. The museum also maintains an exhibit in and among the pits themselves, with life-size restorations of some mammals. For this, go to Hancock Park.

Many colleges and universities that do not maintain public museums still have exhibits that are very much worth seeing. Thus the geological museum of Princeton University has many fine fossil vertebrates, including the elk-moose, *Cervalces*. This museum also displays plants and animals from the Devonian river deposit on Beartooth Butte, Wyoming. The Museum of Paleontology of the University of California, Berkeley, has extensive collections of Triassic vertebrates, Tertiary plants, and invertebrates from the West. In general, collectors who want to visit such museums may inquire for the department of geology and there ask about exhibits or study collections.

Fossils are exhibited in the museums and trailside displays of many state and national parks and national monuments. Especially noteworthy are the dinosaur bones in rock at the Dinosaur National Monument, near Jensen, Utah. A small state museum in Vernal also contains fossils.

BOOKS AND MAGAZINES

Books about fossils are many, but most of them were written for specialists. The following lists include titles of general value for beginners as well as for readers who make the study of fossils a hobby.

History and Geologic Background

Giants of Geology, by C. L. Fenton and M. A. Fenton (Doubleday, 1952). Surveys the development of geology and related sciences through biographies of their leaders. Chapters 2, 7, 10, 13, 16, and 17 deal with fossils and such paleontologists as Hall and Hugh Miller.

Historical Geology, by C. O. Dunbar (Wiley, 1949). A popular and admirably illustrated book on earth history. Written for college students, but not very technical.

An Introduction to Geology, vol. 2, *Historical Geology,* by W. B. Scott (Macmillan, third edition, 1932). Old but excellent and well illustrated.

Introduction to Historical Geology, by R. C. Moore (McGraw-Hill, 1949). A beginning college text, excellently illustrated, with much about fossils. Maps showing the distribution of formations are very useful.

Man, Time, and Fossils, by Ruth Moore (Knopf, 1953). The evolutionary story of fossils, traced through the lives and work of outstanding paleontologists.

The Old Red Sandstone, by Hugh Miller (various editions and dates). Hugh Miller's most famous book. Dealing primarily with the Old Red and its fossil fish, it shows how much an amateur can accomplish in paleontology.

Record of the Rocks, by H. G. Richards (Ronald Press, 1953). A survey of geologic history with emphasis on rock formations and their fossils.

The Rock Book, by C. L. Fenton and M. A. Fenton (Doubleday, 1940). Pages 145–252 discuss sedimentary rocks, with many illustrations.

The World in the Past, by B. W. Smith (Frederick Warne, 1953). A popular survey of earth history by a British author. Frequently refers to North America.

Textbooks and Reference Works

Animals without Backbones, by R. Buchsbaum (University of Chicago Press, second edition, 1948). An interesting, simple textbook of invertebrate zoology, very well illustrated.

Evolution of the Vertebrates, by E. H. Colbert (Wiley, 1955). A readable textbook of vertebrate paleontology. The simple illustrations are not numerous.

Foraminifera, Their Classification and Economic Use, by J. A. Cushman (Harvard University, fourth edition, 1948). A technical book of value in identification.

Index Fossils of North America, by H. W. Shimer and R. R. Shrock (Wiley, 1944). Describes and illustrates a vast number of typical invertebrate fossils. The best single volume for identification.

An Introduction to Paleobotany, by C. A. Arnold (McGraw-Hill, 1947). A modern American book, not too technical for general use.

An Introduction to the Study of Fossil Plants, by J. Walton (London: Black, 1953). A British textbook, less detailed than that by Arnold.

Invertebrate Fossils, by R. C. Moore, C. G. Lalicker, and A. G. Fischer (McGraw-Hill, 1952). An excellent modern textbook of great value to the serious collector.

Man and the Vertebrates, by A. S. Romer (University of Chicago Press, third edition, 1941). An introduction to vertebrate zoology, including both fossil and Recent forms. Richly illustrated.

Manual of the Foraminifera, by J. J. Galloway (Principia Press, 1933). Valuable in identification.

Outlines of Paleontology, by H. H. Swinnerton (London: Arnold, 1947). An introductory British text.

Plant Life through the Ages, by A. C. Seward (Cambridge: University Press, 1931). Technical work by a British paleobotanist. Traces the history of plants by periods.

Principles of Micropaleontology, by M. F. Glaessner (Wiley, 1947). An advanced textbook, useful in identification.

Stratigraphical Paleontology, by E. Neaverson (Oxford University Press, second edition, 1955). A technical guide to index fossils, especially of Europe.

Textbook of Paleontology, by K. A. von Zittel (London: Macmillan and Co., several editions). An old but common and useful textbook.

Treatise on Invertebrate Paleontology, edited by R. C. Moore (University of Kansas and Geological Society of America). A technical reference work in many parts. For the specialist only, though the illustrations are useful and interesting.

Treatise on Marine Ecology and Paleoecology, edited by H. S. Ladd (Geological Society of America Memoir 67, vol. 2, 1957). Chapters 1 and 2 provide an excellent and readable introduction to the study of fossils and the rocks in which they are found.

Vertebrate Paleontology, by A. S. Romer (University of Chicago Press, second edition, 1945). A comprehensive textbook; technical but with abundant illustrations.

General and Nontechnical Books

Ancient Plants and the World They Lived In, by H. N. Andrews (Comstock, 1947). A popular survey of paleobotany.

Animal Evolution, by G. S. Carter (London: Sidgwick & Jackson, (1951). A semi-technical survey of modern theories of evolution, about which little is said in this book.

Animals of the Past, by F. A. Lucas (American Museum of Natural History, sixth edition, 1922). An old book about vertebrate fossils, well written and illustrated.

Before the Dawn of History, by C. R. Knight (McGraw-Hill, 1935). Many large and excellent illustrations, mostly from paintings in the Chicago Museum of Natural History.

Canadian Dinosaurs, by C. M. Sternberg (National Museum of Canada, 1946). An introductory pamphlet.

Cold Blooded Vertebrates, by S. F. Hildebrand, C. W. Gilmore, and D. M. Cochran (Smithsonian Scientific Series, vol. 8, 1930). Part 2, Chapter 1, and Part 3, Chapters 1–6, deal with fossil amphibians and reptiles. Comprehensive and readable.

The Dinosaur Book, by E. H. Colbert (McGraw-Hill, second edition, 1951). A well-written, authoritative, and superbly illustrated book about fossil reptiles in general.

Dinosaurs, by E. H. Colbert (American Museum of Natural History, 1957). An introductory booklet, very well illustrated.

The Dinosaurs, by W. E. Swinton (London: Murby, 1934). A general book about dinosaurs, including European forms neglected by most American authors.

Earth Song, by C. L. Camp (University of California Press, 1952). Simple and well illustrated; deals chiefly with western vertebrates.

Evolution in Outline, by T. N. George (London: Thrift Books, 1951). A modern popular outline that emphasizes fossils.

A History of Fishes, by J. R. Norman (Stokes, 1931). An excellent general book about fish; Chapter 17 is devoted to fossils.

A History of Land Mammals in the Western Hemisphere, by W. B. Scott (Macmillan, revised edition, 1937). A semitechnical book, richly illustrated.

History of the Primates, by W. E. L. Clark (British Museum [Natural History], second edition, 1950). A modern introduction to a subject not treated in this book.

Horses, by G. G. Simpson (Oxford University Press, 1951). A comprehensive, semitechnical account of modern horses and the evolution of the group. Well illustrated.

Life of the Past, by G. G. Simpson (Yale University Press, 1953). A discussion of paleontologic principles. Not well illustrated, but the text is very much worth while.

Prehistoric Animals, by J. Augusta and Z. Burian, translated by G. Horn (London: Spring Books, 1956). A large and handsome volume with sumptuous illustrations in gravure and color; written and published in Europe.

Search beneath the Sea, by J. L. B. Smith (Holt, 1956). An account of the discovery of living coelacanths, by the man who first described them.

Shelled Invertebrates of the Past and Present, by R. S. Bassler, C. E. Resser, W. L. Schmitt, and Paul Bartsch (Smithsonian Scientific Series, vol. 10, 1934). Part I deals with earth history and fossils.

The Succession of Life through Geological Time, by K. P. Oakley and H. M. Muir-Wood (British Museum [Natural History], second edition, 1949). An excellent booklet on British fossils.

Water Reptiles of the Past and Present, by S. W. Williston (University of Chicago Press, 1914). An old but interesting book.

Man

Ancient Man in North America, by H. M. Wormington (Denver Museum of Natural History, third edition, 1949). A concise survey, with good bibliography.

Apes, Giants and Man, by F. Weidenrich (University of Chicago Press, 1946). Important discoveries in southeastern Asia.

Art in the Ice Age, by J. Maringer and H.-G. Bandi (Praeger, 1953). Superb illustrations, many in color.

The Eagle, the Jaguar, and the Serpent, by M. Covarrubias (Knopf, 1954). Pages 9–72 deal with the origin of American Indians.

Early Man in America, by E. H. Sellards (University of Texas, 1952). A detailed summary by an outstanding geologist who has studied fossil man.

Mankind So Far, by W. H. Howells (Doubleday, 1944). A good and simple general book.

Men of the Old Stone Age, by H. F. Osborn (Scribners, third edition, 1919). An old book that is without rival in its survey of the Ice Age mammals associated with ancient man. Well illustrated.

Up from the Ape, by Earnest Hooton (Macmillan, 1931). Old but excellent.

Children's Books

All about Dinosaurs, by R. C. Andrews (Random House, 1953). Much, but by no means all, about these reptiles.

Animals of Yesterday, by B. M. Parker (Row, Peterson, 1941). A simple paperbound book with colored illustrations.

Dinosaurs, by H. S. Zim (Morrow, 1954). A simple book for readers under 12.

The First Mammals, by W. L. Scheele (World Publishing Co., 1955). A sumptuous book for readers over 12 or 14.

First Book of Prehistoric Animals, by A. Dickerson (Watts, 1954). A simple introduction for children of 12 years and under.

Life Long Ago, by C. L. Fenton (John Day, 1937). A comprehensive book for readers of 10–12 and older. Treats both plants and animals; many illustrations.

Prehistoric Animals, by W. L. Scheele (World Publishing Co., 1954). For readers of 12 and older. Many large illustrations.

Prehistoric World, by C. L. Fenton (John Day, 1954. London: Dobson Books, Ltd., 1957). Stories about important fossil animals, followed by discussions. The British edition contains some material not in the American but lacks the colored illustrations.

Stories Read from the Rocks, by B. M. Parker (Row, Peterson, 1941). An introduction to geology, with several pages about fossils. Colored illustrations.

Guides for Collectors and Museum Visitors

Ancient Landscapes of the Grand Canyon, by E. D. McKee (McKee, 1931). This booklet summarizes the geology of the canyon and discusses fossils.

Common Fossils of Missouri, by A. G. Unklesbay (University of Missouri, Handbook 4, 1955). Guide to identification.

A Forest of the Coal Age, by B. E. Dahlgren (Chicago Museum of Natural History, 1933). Discussion of plants in the Coal Age diorama in the museum. Well illustrated.

Fossil Birds, by H. Howard (Los Angeles County Museum, 1955). A booklet about birds of the Rancho La Brea tar pits.

Fossil Mammals, by H. C. Markman (Denver Museum of Natural History, 1952). A well-illustrated booklet dealing primarily with fossils in the Denver Museum.

Fossils, by H. C. Markman (Denver Museum of Natural History, third edition, 1954). This booklet surveys fossils, especially those in the Denver Museum. Well illustrated.

Geologic Guidebook of the San Francisco Bay Counties, edited by O. P. Jenkins (California Division of Mines, Bull. 154, 1951). Pages 177–202 deal with fossils. Well illustrated.

Guide for Beginning Fossil Hunters, by C. W. Collinson (Illinois Geological Survey).

Guide to the Fossil Mammals in the British Museum (Natural History), (British Museum [Natural History], 1934). A well-illustrated booklet.

Guide to Fossil Plants in the British Museum (Natural History), (British Museum [Natural History], second edition, 1935). A useful booklet; many European plants had close relatives in North America.

Handbook of Paleontology for Beginners and Amateurs, by W. Goldring (New York State Museum Handbooks 9 and 10, 1929 and 1931). Handbook 9 is a guide to the identification of New York fossils; 10 discusses formations.

An Illustrated Guide to Fossil Collecting, by R. Casanova (San Mateo, Cal.; Naturegraph Co., 1957). A classification of fossil animals and plants. Collecting localities on pages 72–78.

Methods in Paleontology, by C. L. Camp and G. D. Hanna (University of California Press, 1937). The standard guide to methods of collecting and preparing fossils.

Ohio Fossils, by A. LaRocque and M. F. Marple (Ohio Division of Geological Survey, Bull. 54, 1955). A beginner's guide.

Rancho La Brea, by Chester Stock (Los Angeles County Museum, fourth edition, 1949). A guide to fossil mammals of the tar pits.

Nontechnical Magazines

Excellent articles on fossils occasionally appear in *Life,* the *National Geographic Magazine, Arizona Highways,* and other publications; the best way to find such articles is to consult the *Readers Guide* in a college or public library. Articles also may be found in the following magazines:

Desert Magazine (Palm Desert, Cal.). Carries occasional articles on fossils as well as on rocks and minerals.

Natural History (American Museum of Natural History, New York 24, N.Y.). This well-illustrated monthly magazine contains articles on fossils by members of the museum's staff.

Pacific Discovery (California Academy of Sciences, Golden Gate State Park, San Francisco). An excellent magazine that contains occasional articles on fossils.

Rocks and Minerals (Box 29, Peekskill, N.Y.). This bimonthly collector's magazine carries occasional articles on fossils and collecting localities. The latter are always up to date and reliable.

TECHNICAL PUBLICATIONS

Technical books and articles on fossils are published by geological surveys, museums, universities, scientific societies, and research institutions such as the Carnegie Institution of Washington. University libraries have these publications, and so do large public libraries. Small ones may own a few technical books that deal with subjects of general interest or with fossils of the areas in which libraries are located.

Some of these publications may be found by looking under headings such as *Fossils, Dinosaurs, Trilobites,* and so on, in library catalogues. A still better course is to consult bibliographies published by the United States Geological Survey and various state surveys. The former are elaborately indexed, and with a little practice one can easily "run down" publications on the fossils of a given region, age, or biologic group. Selected bibliographies also appear in many textbooks and reference works such as *Index Fossils of North America*.

Many readers and collectors, however, live beyond reach of libraries that have these bibliographies or the books and magazines listed in them. When these persons really want information they may write to their state geological surveys, to the departments of geology in their state universities, or to the U. S. Geological Survey, Washington 25, D.C. Inquiries should be as clear and specific as possible.

WHERE CAN FOSSILS BE COLLECTED?

One of the commonest questions is "Where can I find fossils?" Several important regions and localities have been mentioned in this book: others are noted in Casanova's *Illustrated Guide to Fossil Collecting*. Still others may be found by inquiry, by reading museum labels, or by consulting technical books. Many of these tell just where and in what stratum fossils may be found.

So much for specific localities; now for some general rules. The first one tells us to search in sedimentary rocks, since only a few igneous deposits contain fossils. Exceptions include agglomerates and tuff covering petrified forests and borderline formations such as the Florissant shales, which consist chiefly of volcanic dust that settled in lakes.

A second rule reminds us to avoid very coarse sediment, such as conglomerate, and rocks that have been metamorphosed. Coarse sediment grinds shells and other remains to pieces, and few fossils survive the processes that turn rocks into slate or contorted marble. Very fine-grained, or lithographic, limestone also is likely to be barren, and fossils in chert are hard to secure unless the rock is thoroughly weathered.

These limitations leave fine sandstone, ordinary limestone (including chalk and marl), dolomite, shale, and clay as likely rocks in which to find fossils. We seek them in hillsides, in quarries, cuts and banks, gullies, or stream beds, and on dumps from clay pits and coal mines. Fresh diggings may produce good specimens, but old and weathered exposures are likely to be better. Much of our own most successful collecting has been done on weathered, rain-washed heaps of clay stripped from a pit in one of the Iowa hills described in Chapter I.

The collector should try to determine the exact bed or horizon from which his specimens come. This is easy on level surfaces or those with very gentle slopes. In quarries and on cliffs one may trace slabs to the bed from which they came or may pry them from beds still in position. But both slabs and individual fossils slide down steep, eroded slopes. Here one does well to collect along the slope rather than uphill or downhill, separating one's finds at levels where new types of fossils appear. Sooner or later a gully may reveal the actual section, or digging may be done to determine the level at which certain fossils are found.

MOST COLLECTING EQUIPMENT IS SIMPLE

In a day when many hobbies require complex equipment, that for collecting fossils remains simple. The following essentials will suffice for all except the most detailed work or the collecting of large vertebrates.

Maps. Ordinary road maps suffice to show general localities and the best way to reach them. For precision, add topographic maps published by the U. S. Geological Survey, Washington 25, D.C., by the Geological Survey of Canada, Ottawa, and by state and provincial surveys. These maps show roads, houses, streams, and details of the land surface. Geologic maps, published by the same agencies, show the distribution of formations.

Tools. These begin with a geologist's hammer. There are several makes; many collectors prefer the one-piece Estwing with leather-covered handle and chisel end. Cold chisels of two or three widths (up to one inch) are essential for splitting hard rocks; a butcher knife may be used to divide fissile shale. A GI or larger shovel is often needed to remove topsoil and rubbish or to take up samples of clay and other loose deposits. A 24-inch wrecking bar may be required to move large slabs of rock.

Containers. Strong paper bags of moderate size may be used double to hold small specimens. Large ones may be wrapped in newspaper or paper towels. Cigar boxes or small cardboard boxes will hold fragile finds after they are wrapped in tissue paper or cotton. These materials may be moved about in a sturdy basket or small box with a carrying handle.

Bags and specimens wrapped individually should be labeled. Sturdy paper and pencil should be used, the paper being folded once or twice with the writing inside.

Cloth bags are best for samples of clay, sand, etc., from which fossils are to be freed by washing.

Notebook. A loose-leaf notebook of moderate size is useful for notes and sketches. They may be made with a pencil that is not soft enough to smudge or a ball-point pen.

Pocket Magnifier. This will enable one to examine details of specimens or to see small specimens such as foraminifers.

Steel Tape. Five or 6 feet long, for measuring sections and strata.

Knapsack. The box or basket suggested above is designed only to move materials as one works. If equipment and collections must be carried some distance, they should be carefully placed in a knapsack. The type that is fastened to a frame or packboard keeps rough specimens from hurting the back.

CLEANING AND PREPARING FOSSILS

Specimens should not be cleaned on the spot; to do so wastes time and invites damage. Take your finds home before you clean them and remove undesirable rock.

The time-honored methods of cleaning are two. Specimens in hard rock may be trimmed down with hammer and chisel or, if necessary, with a hacksaw. Fossils found in clay, marl, or other soft sediment may be washed, and sediment that still clings to them may be removed with a brush or a needle whose blunt end has been set into a piece of wood. Such work should be done under a strong magnifying glass mounted upon a stand.

Many specimens in soft, earthy limestone may be cleaned with a knife or small chisel ground to a thin, sharp edge. Many of the crinoids illustrated in Chapter X were prepared in this way and finished with a needle.

Fossils preserved in silica may be freed from rock by dissolving it in acid. Other fossils must be boiled in water to which chemicals are added. Still others are cast in plaster, rubber, or commercial compounds. Such methods are not for the beginner, and the advanced collector who uses them wants more information than can be given here. He will find it in *Methods in Paleontology*, by Camp and Hanna, or in circulars provided by dealers such as Ward's Natural Science Establishment, 3000 Ridge Road East, Rochester 9, N.Y.

CABINETS AND LABELS

Fossils, like rocks, are easily kept, for dust and pests do not destroy them. Many collections are kept in shirt and cigar boxes or on shelves; larger ones are housed in drawers, with small specimens being placed in cardboard trays and vials. Directions for making a cabinet of drawers and trays to go in them are given on pages 340–343 of *The Rock Book* by Fenton and Fenton.

Labels may be typed or written on good white paper cut to fit the trays. Each label should contain a number that has been given the specimen or set of specimens, the name, the formation, and the locality. Specimens from different formations or horizons should be given different numbers. Many collectors like to put a minimum of information on the label and the rest on a card 3 by 5 inches or larger. Such cards may be filed alphabetically or by number for ready reference.

Collectors are often advised to paint numbers on their specimens. A simpler method is to apply them with a fine pen and India ink in places where they will not be too conspicuous. Such numbers are not hard to make, and they serve the purpose of keeping each specimen with its label.

Glossary

This glossary includes terms that are repeatedly used but which, with a few exceptions, are not the names of groups. The latter, and terms that apply to limited groups of organisms, may be found by means of the index. The plurals of a few words are given in parentheses.

Abdomen. In arthropods, the main division of the body behind the thorax; in crayfish and lobsters it is often miscalled the tail. The mammalian abdomen lies behind the diaphragm and contains the liver, stomach, and intestines.

Abdominal ribs. Bony supports developed in the flesh that encloses the thorax and abdomen, especially of reptiles.

Adaptation. Any structure or function, including instinct, that fits an organism to its surroundings and way of living.

Agnaths. Jawless vertebrates that do not have true paired limbs.

Ambulacral areas. Double rows of ambulacral plates found in echinoids. Some ambulacral areas are narrow and almost straight; others are petal-shaped.

Ambulacrum (ambulacra). A radial band of porous plates in the test, or shell, of echinoderms. During life the ambulacra contain tube feet. In crinoids and other relatively primitive echinoderms the ambulacra are grooves along which cilia take food to the mouth.

Antenna. A sensory organ extending from the head, especially in arthropods. It is not concerned with sight or the perception of light.

Appendage. A movable, projecting part of the animal body—leg, antenna, and so on.

Archosaurs. The group of reptiles that includes thecodonts, crocodilians, flying reptiles, and dinosaurs.

Artiodactyls. Hoofed mammals that typically have two or four toes on each foot. The first toe is almost always absent.

Asexual reproduction. Reproduction by budding or any other method that does not depend on the union of male and female cells.

Auricle. The outer part of the ear in mammals; also any earlike projection, even on shells.

Beak. The rounded or pointed extremity of a pelecypod or brachiopod shell, at which it began to grow. Horny growth on the jaws of birds and some reptiles. The horny jaws of cephalopods also are sometimes called beaks.

Body cavity. The open space between the body wall and the internal organs of an animal. It is lined with mesoderm and is often called the coelom.

Bone. One of the parts in the vertebrate skeleton. Also a hard material containing irregular, branched cells and relatively large blood vessels.

Brachia. The organs of a brachiopod which bear cilia that set up currents of water that carry food to the mouth. In brachiopods, same as lophophore.

Brachial valve. In brachiopods, the valve to which the brachia, or lophophore, is attached. Also called the dorsal valve.

Braincase. A boxlike structure of cartilage or bone that encloses the brain and is attached to the backbone. It forms the essential part of the skull.

Byssus. A cluster of threads which some pelecypods secrete, attaching themselves to other shells or to rocks.

Calcite. Limy material that is found in corals, shells, etc. It is softer than a knife and bubbles when weak acid is dropped on it. Calcite also forms beds of limestone.

Calyx. The depression, or cup, at the top of a coral skeleton. Also the structure of plates enclosing the body of a crinoid or similar echinoderm.

Canine teeth. Teeth between the incisors and premolars of mammals. The canines generally are sharp and may be very long.

Carapace. The hard shell that covers the head and part or all of the abdominal region of an arthropod. Also the bony shell of a tortoise, turtle, or glyptodont.

Carbonization. A process of incomplete decay which destroys volatile substances but leaves carbon. Carbonization has been especially important in the preservation of ancient plants.

Cardinal area. A flat or curved surface between the beak and hinge line of a pelecypod or brachiopod. The cardinal area of brachiopods is also termed the interarea.

Cartilage. Relatively soft, translucent material containing rounded cells; it is found in the vertebrate skeleton. Cartilage may be strengthened by limy material or it may be replaced by bone.

Cell. A small lump or mass of living material; one of the units of which living things are composed.

Cell wall. A covering, generally hard or woody, which a cell forms around itself. Wood is made up of cell walls.

Cement. A layer of bony material that covers the roots and often the crowns of teeth. Most conspicuous in the teeth of horses and proboscideans.

Cephalothorax. A body division that combines head and thorax. Best seen in arthropods (crustaceans, merostomes, arachnids).

Character. Any distinguishing feature or trait of an organism. Most characters are inherited, but some are determined by environmental factors such as food, temperature, or chemicals in water.

Cheek teeth. The molars and premolars.

Chelicerae. The first, or front, pair of appendages in spiders, eurypterids, etc.; one is a chelicera. These organs generally are used to cut or tear food.

Chitin. Stiff material forming the outer skeletons of arthropods and some other animals. There are many types of chitin, which differ in chemical composition.

Chordate. Any animal that has a notochord at some stage in its life history. Many books put all chordates in one phylum.

Cilia. Soft, hairlike structures developed by many cells. They are shorter and more numerous than flagella.

Coelom. Same as body cavity.

Colonial. Living together. Most colonial organisms build up complex exoskeletons that support many individuals.

Column. The jointed stalklike structure to which the bodies of crinoids and many other echinoderms are attached. Each section of a column is a columnal.

Condyle. An enlarged, rounded surface of bone forming part of a movable joint; especially the occipital condyle.

Conifers. Cone-bearing shrubs and trees that produce sexual reproductive cells, not spores. The leaves generally are needles or scales. Lycopods have cones but bear spores.

Corallite. The skeleton built up by one coral animal, or polyp, whether solitary or part of a colony.

Correlation. In geology, the process of linking beds and formations of similar age.

Costa (costae). A ridge on the surface of a coral or shell. The costae of shells are radial ridges produced by thickening.

Craniate. An animal with a braincase of bone or cartilage. Same as vertebrate.

Cranium. Same as braincase. This term is also used for the whole skull.

Cycads. Palmlike trees and shrubs that became very abundant during the Mesozoic era. The modern sago "palm" is a cycad.

Dentary. A tooth-bearing bone that forms the whole lower jaw of mammals.

Diaphragm. A membrane, especially the muscular one that divides the thoracic and abdominal regions of mammals.

Dolomite. A rock resembling limestone but consisting largely of another mineral less readily attacked by acids. Many stromatolite deposits are dolomite.

Dorsal valve. The brachial valve of a brachiopod.

Ectoderm. The outer body-layer of animals.

Egg. The female sex cell. It often contains a supply of food for the organism that is to develop.

Embryo. A newly forming organism. The animal embryo comes before hatching or birth.

Enamel. Dense material covering the scales of some fish and the teeth of vertebrates in general. It is the hardest substance produced by animal bodies.

Endoderm. The inner body layer of animals.

Environment. The surroundings of any organism, including other living things.

Exoskeleton. An outer skeleton; an external structure that supports the body. Commonly called a shell.

Femur. The upper bone of the hind limb or leg. Commonly called the thigh bone.

Finfold. A lengthwise fold of skin which, in theory, divided into fins.

Flagellum. A long lashlike or threadlike extension of a cell, able to beat to and fro.

Flora. The group of plants living in one region or at a particular time. Thus we speak of the John Day flora, or the flora of the Painted Desert in Triassic times.

Foramen. An opening through a bone or shell. A round opening at or near the beak of a brachiopod, accommodating the pedicle. Other types of openings have other names.

Formation. A series of beds that are essentially uniform in character and formed during a limited part of geologic time.

Fossils. In everyday terms, "prehistoric" organisms. Technically, the remains or traces of organisms that lived during ancient geologic times and were buried in rocks of the earth's crust.

Ganglion. A group or cluster of nerve cells that acts as a center of nervous influence.

Ganoine. Enamel-like material on the scales of fish. Ganoid scales have thick layers of ganoine forming their outer surface.

Gastrolith. A stone swallowed by a bird or reptile and used to help grind food in the stomach. Popularly called gizzard stone.

Genus (genera). A group of related species.

Gills. Organs for breathing in water. They developed in various ways in the various phyla of animals.

Grinding teeth. Broad, rough-crowned molars and premolars adapted to grinding food.

Habitat. The kind of place in which an organism lives. Swamps were the habitat of large herbivorous dinosaurs.

Hinge line. The edge of any bivalve shell along which its two parts are held together.

Humerus. The upper bone of the forelimb, often called the upper arm bone.

Ice Age. When capitalized, this term refers to the last, or Pleistocene, glacial epoch. It involved several glacial advances and retreats in the Northern Hemisphere. There were several earlier ice ages.

Igneous rocks. Rocks that once were hot and molten. Some cooled and hardened underground, others at the earth's surface. Few contain fossils.

Ilium. The uppermost of the three bones on each side of the pelvic girdle.

Incisors. Teeth at the front of the mammalian jaw. They generally are adapted to biting, but those of elephants are tusks.

Index fossil. One that indicates the geologic age of the rocks in which it is found.

Instinct. An inherited pattern of action. Nest-building or digging is an instinct.

Interarea. See cardinal area.

Invertebrate. An animal without a skull or braincase. The term is generally applied to any creature that lacks a notochord.

Ischium. The hinder of the three bones on each side of the pelvic girdle.

Jaw. One of the structures forming the framework of the mouth in vertebrates, or a similar structure among invertebrates. Vertebrate paleontologists often use the term for one half of the lower jaw. Each half consists of one or several bones and is joined to its counterpart at the midline.

Laminae. Thin layers of solid material—bone, enamel, or sediment.

Larva. An early stage of an animal, between embryo and adult or fully formed juvenile. Larvae generally move about freely and feed but differ anatomically from adults. Reptiles and mammals lack larvae.

Ligament. A band or sheet of compact tissue that fastens one vertebrate structure to another. Ligaments that bound the vertebrae of bird-hipped dinosaurs together were often stiffened with limy material and are found in fossils.

Lophophore. A ring or similar structure bearing tentacles and cilia. See brachia.

Mantle. In brachiopods and mollusks, a sheet of flesh that secretes the shell.

Mesoderm. The middle body-layer in animals. It becomes thicker than the other layers, forming muscles, bones, and other organs.

Metamorphic rocks. Rocks that have been greatly modified by heat, pressure, and water, or all three in combination. Seldom contain fossils.

Metamorphosis. A pronounced change in form from one growth stage to another, as the metamorphosis of a soft larval mollusk into one with a shell.

Micropaleontology. The study of microscopic fossils, especially Foraminifera.

Molars. The rear teeth of mammals. Most molars are adapted to grinding or crushing.

Muscle. An organ made up of fibers that contract and produce movements. The muscles of most fossils are traced by impressions made upon bones or shells.

Muzzle. The projecting jaws and nose of an animal, especially a mammal.

Naris (nares). An opening in the skull that contains one or both nostrils. The external nares are at the surface; the internal nares are in the hard palate.

Nostrils. Openings in the top of the head, the muzzle, or the nose. In most fish they let water into the organs of smell, but in some fish and in higher vertebrates they are used in breathing. See naris.

Notochord. An elastic, rodlike structure running lengthwise of the body and supporting it. Found in at least the embryonic stages of all animal phyla that are sometimes grouped together as chordates.

Nucleus (nuclei). A special structure within the cell of all organisms except monerans. It seems to control the life of the cell and determines heredity.

Occipital condyle. The rounded knob of bone by which the skull is attached to the first vertebra.

Orbit. The bony socket of the eye.

Organ. A group of cells or tissues that function as a unit—the eye, heart, etc.

Organism. A living thing; one cell or a complex of many cells that exist and function as one complete unit.

Palate. In fossils, the bony roof of the mouth.

Pectoral. Pertaining to the anterior or upper thoracic region, as the pectoral fins of a fish.

Pelvis. The bony girdle to which the hind limbs are attached. Often called the hip girdle.

Perissodactyls. Hoofed mammals that have an odd number of toes on the hind feet and generally on the forefeet.

Pineal body. A small, conical organ above or between the opposite halves of the brain. Some pineal bodies apparently served as crude eyes.

Placenta. A soft organ that develops in the uterus of most mammals. In it the mother's blood comes so close to that of the young that food and wastes can be exchanged.

Plication. A small fold or corrugation that affects the whole shell and is not a thickening of it. Contrast with costa.

Polyp. A soft-bodied animal, especially a hydroid, coral, or sea anemone.

Precambrian. Before the Cambrian period or older than the Cambrian system of formations.

Premolars. Teeth between the canines and molars of mammals. Premolars may be adapted to grinding, shearing, or crushing.

Protoplasm. Living material; the semifluid material of cells.

Pseudopod. An extension of the cell's protoplasm, used in moving or feeding.

Pubis, or pubic bone. The anterior of the three bones in each side of the pelvic girdle. In "bird-hipped" dinosaurs the pubis also has a long backward projection or becomes almost vestigial.

Radula. A rasplike organ, or "tongue," in the mouth of a snail.

Reflex. An automatic action in response to some stimulus.

Revolution, geologic. The changes that brought one era to an end and led to another.

Sclerotic plates. Bony plates in the eyes of certain reptiles and birds. The plates in each eye form a ring.

Scute. A thin plate or large scale.

Sedimentary rocks. Rocks formed of sand, mud, and other materials that settled in layers or beds. Often called "stratified rocks." Most fossils are found in sedimentary rocks.

Segment. A part of the body that is marked off or separated from other parts, especially if they are in series. Segments of the eurypterid body are good examples.

Septum. A dividing wall or partition between two cavities or structures.

Shell. Any hard covering of an animal body. Shells develop in various ways.

Silica. Glassy material found in many sponges. It also replaces wood, shells, and other material in many petrified fossils.

Siphon. A tubelike organ that takes water into the body or carries it out. Found in mollusks.

Siphuncle. A tube that leads from the living chamber of a cephalopod to the tip of the shell.

Sperms. Male sex cells. Also called spermatozoa.

Spiracle. In blastoids, one of five openings that allow water to flow out of the body. In insects, an opening that lets air into tubes that run through the body. In fish, the first gill slit, modified into a tube. In amphibians, the spiracle becomes the eustachian tube of the ear. This is kept by reptiles, birds, and mammals.

Spore. A special reproductive cell that can develop into a new organism without being fertilized.

Suture. The line along which two hard structures join. Cephalopod sutures are formed where septa meet the cell wall. Sutures between bones of the skull close with age.

Tabula (tabulae). In corals, an almost horizontal plate across the center of the corallite.

Temporal opening. An opening between bones of the skull. Temporal openings determine the classification of reptiles.

Tentacle. An elongate flexible (not jointed) appendage, usually near the mouth. Corals capture food with their tentacles.

Test. A hard covering or supporting structure; a shell.

Thorax. The main division of the body behind the head. In amphibians and most higher animals, it is the part enclosed by ribs.

Tuff. A rock formed of cemented volcanic dust and ash.

Tusk. A long pointed tooth that protrudes from the mouth. A boar's tusk is a long canine; the elephant's tusk is an incisor.

Umbo. The strongly convex part of a brachiopod or pelecypod shell, next to the beak. Also called umbone.

Valve. One half of a bivalve shell, either brachiopod or molluscan. Also any fleshy structure that closes or partly closes an opening.

Ventral valve (of a brachiopod). Same as pedicle valve.

Vertebra. One of the bones or sets of bones forming the vertebral column, or backbone.

Vestigial organ or structure. One that has been greatly reduced during the course of evolution. The side toes of horses became vestigial.

Index

Pronunciations of many names and technical terms are given in parentheses. Though the name or term may be plural, the pronunciation almost always is singular, thus: Acanthodians (ak" an tho' di an). For some terms, the plural is given after or instead of the pronunciation, as in Naris (nay' ris), *pl.* nares.

Heavy type indicates pages on which black-and-white illustrations appear, or pages faced by color illustrations. In references that include several pages, illustrations are indicated only if they appear on one of the pages actually listed. Thus the discussion of ammonoids extends from page 191 to page 200, but references to illustrations will be found under the names of genera and species.